A MISS'SIPPI R

The *Road Leads* to *Yond*

BILLY RAY GRIFFIN

Wasteland Press
www.wastelandpress.net
Shelbyville, KY USA

The Road Leads to Yond:
A Miss'sippi Recollection
by Billy Ray Griffin

First Printing – April 2021
Paperback ISBN: 978-1-68111-408-8
Hardback ISBN: 978-1-68111-409-5

Printed in the U.S.A.

0 1 2 3 4 5

INTRODUCTION

Just a few inches beneath the crusty alluvial topsoil…enfolded in the composted floodplain dirt…in a place called the Yazoo Valley…in a time seemingly far removed from current time…there sprouted a soul that inched its way out of nothingness…and embodied itself in the sanctuary of a family that dwelled inside a sharecropper's house not far from the Quiver River Divide.

In the after years we always called it Frank and Mary's old house. The inhabitants had been an aged yet adored Negro couple who lived there without charge because they were too old for steady work and the white landowner felt indebted to keep a roof over their ancient heads until they passed into eternity.

Though I have no memory of living in the house as a baby, my parents invariably pointed out the place as the site of the first and third sons birth.

The place took root in my memory only as an abstraction inasmuch as the old house eventually deteriorated from age and neglect...the only tangible remains left at that time of note was a large fireplace whose chimney had fallen into a massive mound of moldy mortar and time worn crumbly bricks. As a general rule, I remember very little of the house but I do remember the general location of its set and as related earlier, the site was out in the country near the convergence of the Quiver and Sunflower Rivers in the Mississippi Yazoo Delta.

In furtherance...to say the Mississippi Yazoo Delta expands a large flat area in northwestern Mississippi containing some of the most fertile soil in the world underscores its real impact, at least in reference to the richness of its soil. For all I know it may have the richest earth in the entire world...I would not be surprised. But looking at the folks arising from the rich soil, one would have thought that affluence would have been the dominant social condition. But, on the contrary, the small farmers of which there were many...hardly broke even; much less prospered at the end of a growing season. My forbears knew that condition quite well in 1940, but the ones still living didn't bemoan the fact. The land provided a foundation for a livelihood. All that was required of the landsitters, including the women and their children was a hardy exertion of labor at no direct cost to the final product which was cotton. Cheap labor was the key to keeping a family's head above water and food on the table. That was the way it was.

Sitting contentedly, smack dab in the middle of the Yazoo Delta was a little town commonly known as Moorhead,

Mississippi, where "The Southern crosses the Yellow Dog". It's not surprising to the uninformed that that unusual calling card might confuse the first time reader but it simply meant that two discrete railroads crossed on the same level within the city limits of this small crossroads.

Moorhead, the place of my birth in 1940, was a small but bustling agricultural town right smack dab in the middle of the Yazoo Delta. Inhabited by roughly 2500 people in the days of this book's setting…the population was probably split half and half between white and black. A majority of all trade and commerce revolved around cotton farming and a Junior college located in the southern part of town.

Seeing as the jumping off point of this narrative begins in 1955… it seemed proper from a launching standpoint, that certain details should be introduced to the reader to set the stage for a better table setting of the story that proceeds in Chapter one.

Reflecting back to 1955, the timeframe of this penning ushers in with an assumption the reader knows the backgrounds of the central characters and their forebears. The reason for that assumption relates to the development of my writing progression. My initial effort was a Christmas story set in 1948 which took place in the calendar year 1948. That initial effort contained sufficient background information relative to the main players from the 1948 story to generally set the stage, so to speak, for this 1955 edition.

As such, it must be acknowledged, the story presented in this issue, starting with Chapter 1contains no rescripting of a story called "*A Yazoo Delta Christmas Remembrance*" which without reference creates a void in the resulting version. And the reader is right...that's not good...and it's not an intelligent move to confuse the reader before he or she gets started in Chapter one. It would be a shame to let the reader's attention wander errantly so early in the browsing phase of this introduction.

In spirit, the main thrust of the book's theme is not to cast light on the characters per se, although the characters themselves add to the flavor of the story...the real theme of the book desires to portray a Mississippi farm boy seen through three cuts of life set in his sleepy hometown stretching in time from his adolescence through early manhood in the late 1950s.

Neither the family...nor the main character of this offering purports to have had a celebrated standing that would make a reader sit up and take notice. Instead, the reader is left to his or her own faculties to decide if these true to life scenarios are worthy of their reading time. Unless the reader is a native of the Yazoo Delta, in all likelihood he or she has never heard of the characters, the area or the culture. But hopefully some enjoyment can be squeezed from the many humbling and laughable situations that spring forth along the road of this particular boy's journey from peach fuzz kid to late term teenager.

The general tone of the story is meant to be non-serious...in fact, please accept the tenor of the presentation as humorous, witty and warmhearted in the main, especially when the writer refers to self. The family is revered and any mocking of those members is not intentional. Any appearance of mockery of my family in an attempt at humor is not meant to belittle. As a family, we always felt comfortable in our skins and never hesitated to laugh at ourselves if a humble situation presented itself.

Amusingly, to support that claim of flippancy, the term "sodbusting" was used a couple of times in the accounting of these hazy remembrances from six decades past. It is not intended to be disparaging in its use...as a matter of modesty its use is taken lightly to mean a "son of the soil", one who possesses a relationship with the good earth to the extent that he reverently remembers his young working days in the endless cotton fields. He remembers the days when dampened black loam squished up between the toes making little angular extrusions resembling mud curlicues. He remembers it felt good to have that cool mushy earth oozing around the barefoot toes, tickling sensitive nerves that carried a message to the brain that soothed the tedium of the hoe or the pull of the tar bottomed cotton sack.

Or better said in homespun language...*sodbusting*...now obsolete in its usage...was what one would have called "a sweet nothing" for a person not afraid of hard backbreaking work. In a similar vein, he who savored the sensations of tilling moistened cotton rows in bare feet thought the activity bore a badge of pride and credit, to be worn on the shirtless sun-baked chest in non-observance. It wasn't necessary to shout to the heavens that we were sodbusters but we didn't deny it either.

Without further qualification, the charge of this Introduction is to step back in time and establish a foundation for the story at hand that springs to life in 1955. The following excerpts are drawn directly from a Christmas short story, its purpose being, is to furnish a bridge to the time and events occurring before the opening of this book:

The story in Chapter One actually starts here, a generation before my time.

My parents, Troy Griffin and Josephine Moore were married in 1936 by a Justice of Peace in Indianola, Mississippi. Troy was 18 and Jo was only 17 years old. Within a year, they had their first son, Stan, in two years Maxwell Gene (Bud) came along and Bill came into an unsettled world in 1940. The Great Depression was lingering and a World War was looming on the horizon as Hitler's name became a byword. Benny the fourth son was born as the War was coming to a close in 1945.

Not too long after the marriage Jo and Troy took the plunge and set up housekeeping in an old three-room shack on patriarch Edgar Griffin's property. As can be seen, the entrenched sharecropping lifestyle was forever being propagated, generation to generation.

But Troy dreamed of owning his own land, so with help from his father, aided by an ad in the Greenville, Mississippi newspaper that advertised forested land in northeast Louisiana for sale at very attractive prices, he contemplated a new beginning for himself and Jo and his incipient family. There was one catch, however. The land contained hardwood forest and would take tremendous effort to clear cut and de-stump the fertile land before it would be fit for cotton cultivation.

After critical analysis of the objective at hand, he signed on the dotted line and purchased 40 acres. Likewise, his father decided to purchase an additional and adjacent 20 acres as an investment.

It took the two of them about three days to make the trip to the Louisiana outback, but their venture into the unknown was just beginning. Edgar Griffin, in his early sixties was too old to be of much help doing manual work, but he took on the job of pulling up small tree stumps using chains and the team of horses for locomotion. Troy, along with a hired man, used a two man cross cut saw to cut down trees as fast as they could, ending the process by igniting the stumps. The stumps would smolder for weeks before they eventually burned up leaving a fertile ash residue that could be plowed through. It was a slow process.

In that first year, the winter of 1937 to the winter of 1938, the objective was to clear some of the land and build a house and small barn and that was done by commuting from Moorhead and living a pioneer's life in Louisiana for the involved men folk. Troy's brother Grady helped during the non-farming season as did Jo's father and younger brother Eugene. This meager crew was able to clear enough land to plant a small cotton crop beginning in 1938.

And so it was. The hardships were manifest but the dream of ownership and being one's own master was intoxicating for this youthful couple. Despite the austerity, they were on their way to making an enterprising start in life after a year of unrewarding sharecropping on Edgar's land near Quiver River.

With these sad accommodations in hand, it was time for Troy's wife, Jo and her baby, Stan, to move to North Louisiana and they came in a car but they couldn't get it close to the house because the road was dirt. This turn of events, necessitated parking the car on a main gravel road about a half mile from the house and shuttling the family back and forth via horse drawn wagon. This shuttle method of transport became standard procedure in rainy weather, however, sometimes in dry weather, the car, an early 1930's mud caked Chevrolet Sedan, would be driven to the front yard of the house, but if rain intervened during the night, the horses were hooked up to the car via trace chains / singletree and towed back up to the main road for safekeeping, away from the boggy turning row of a road that accessed the house.

As the little farm struggled to support the small family, the cultivable acreage gradually grew bit by bit, but prosperity for the family was not in the offing. The more the principals of this endeavor worked, the more the family got behind financially, owing to having to meet land payments and other never ending expenses.

The outlook was bleak but the couple remained optimistic to a fault. Years of toil continued for another five years and there was little to show for the effort other than the fact that they didn't starve.

Sorry to say, but the pioneer experiment in North Louisiana didn't have the permanency that one would expect. Between deaths in the older Griffin's family and family commitments to help the living spouse, brought Troy back to Moorhead in 1944 to caretake for his mother and farm her 40 acres of bequeathed land. But the Louisiana dream didn't die, it was merely put on hold as Troy didn't relinquish ownership of his farm in the outback, instead he found an older couple to sharecrop his land. This setup became status quo until the land in the sticks was sold in the early 1950's.

Moving back to the Delta in 1944 from Louisiana was like moving from Abe Lincoln's birthplace to Chicago. We were overjoyed to be back in a civilization that had some amenities and some boys and girls to socialize with. In Good Will, I don't remember many children being around.

So the saga of the outback was finally reaching its finale in 1944. With the family bearing a headcount of five, they settled in with Adeline Griffin and daughter Nell at the old Griffin Homestead on Quiver River right smack dab in the middle of the Yazoo Delta.

Shortly after the 1944 Christmas, the family moved again to a 60-acre farm south of Moorhead where Troy agreed to work on halves for the owner, Mr. Ferguson. To this day I'm not sure what precipitated that move because we returned to Grandmother Griffin's house after a two-year hiatus spent at the Ferguson Place. Once again we were in a house that had no electrical power and it felt like we were going backwards...it was almost like being in Louisiana again. On a positive note, the big frame house had a large wraparound porch which served the three boys wonderfully as a rain proof playground.

There were two notable events that occurred in those two years at the Ferguson Place and those were the birth of **Benny** in February 1945 and my starting first grade at Moorhead Grammar School in 1946.

A severe stroke felled grandmother Griffin in 1946 resulting in her transfer from the Old Griffin Homestead to one of her daughter's home for convalescence. It was déjà vu all over again---before one could shake a stick, we were moving back into the old clapboard house that seemingly we had just left two years before. But this was only the beginning of a continual disruption of our lives. Grandmother never recovered and died in 1947. By 1948, Troy Griffin and family had once again been supplanted from the Old Griffin Homestead due to an ownership change. Uncle Hugh Matthews had bought the old Griffin place and this is when Troy opted to occupy the 1949 tenant house so eminently mentioned in this collection of memories.

In the year 1949, there were at least eight family homes with lots of kids. Twenty-eight youngsters lived in eight frame houses that stretched from farm to farm along a two mile strip on a gravel road that intersected another road that ran about ½ mile to the old Edgar Griffin Homestead situated on Quiver River.

As one could imagine, this settlement of families and children fostered an interesting environment of hard work and firm values and it also fostered hard play and good times. The place just outside Moorhead, Mississippi is now referred to as the Sheffield Road corridor. In our day, we didn't call it anything...it was just a place we called home.

The following narrative is a group of interrelated stories within three storylines. They cover the years 1950 thru 1959.

CHAPTER ONE

Part One

The Christmas of 1949 ended memorably and the year 1950 seemingly hovered too long as the Troy Griffin family once again, disoriented to some extent, packed up and moved up Sheffield Road to a new/old renovated house situated on our 56 acre **home place.** The year 1951, a special time in my past would have to be considered a period of major adjustment, as we settled into the new living quarters and adapted to routines that came with the new place. In the next three years, 1952, 1953, and 1954, life normalized and the pace of change slowed like the big ole Mississippi River in a summertime drought, slowly moving its billions of gallons of muddy and polluted waters southward to the river's terminus near the Jetties where the water flow was so slow and spread out that its ripples become barely visible to the naked eye.

And that was the way our life was in late 1954...slow and even. Then the year of our Lord 1955 emerges and here we are stranded and bored in the summer's dreary hot season of this heretofore uneventful year. Even though, the years above are passed over quickly, they were eventful years from which many incidents can be drawn for future engagement but for the sake of not getting sidetracked from the central story at hand, the underlying details between 1949 and 1955 will remain temporarily extinct.

In 1949, my age was nine and my physique was medium schoolboy but now in 1955 I had grown to six feet tall and was fifteen years old. However, there was not much bulk to my tall frame...maybe 135 pounds and there was very little testosterone aided facial hair but on the flip side, undesirably, there was a smattering of acne on my young face. Speaking of hormones, I have always contended that the pace of time (how fast time appears to go by) is a function of how much testosterone the male of the species has embedded in his body chemistry. The more testosterone the male possesses, the more, one can expect the pace of life to quicken, although now that I'm old with no hint of that hormone fluxing through my body, the strength of that contention has to be weighed against the facts. Simply stated, that deduction just mentioned is a theory shot full of holes owing to the fact that in old age, time actually increases to the speed of light.

One strange observation at age fifteen that I found befuddling was the sprouting of a coin size patch of stiff black hair on my jutting chin. Just that one spot...there were no other similar spots on my body, so one can see how silly I must of looked shaving every other day to remove a quarter sized bit of stubble. Nature certainly produces its quirks.

My freshman year of High School had concluded in May and I would soon be a sophomore in the fall. I had my eye on a couple of cute girls but couldn't mount enough courage to meet them at the Picture Show much less hold hands (actually that statement is an untruth). Being a late bloomer, I didn't drive a car mainly due to the fact that I was very low on the family's pecking order of motor carriage importance. At best, I was a *persona incognito* who could handle a hoe and milk a cow but it was always understood that I … "shouldn't even think about the mention of gassing up the old car for a night on the town". Incidentally, what a night on the town in Moorhead would entail was and still is a puzzle to me. My parents took it that two teenage boys driving the family car was all their central nervous systems could stand.

Older brothers, Stan and Bud did drive and dated occasionally, but they also had to provide gas for our two tone green 1952 Chevrolet Deluxe sedan.

That year of purchase, it had been a gift from heaven when my father drove into the driveway in the brand new shiny two shades of green car. Who would have dreamed the Troy Griffin family would be so affluent as to own a new car? Without any forethought of status, I always took it for granted that we were destined to drive nothing better than a 1940's rattletrap. "Proud" wasn't nearly accurate enough of an adjective to describe our pride in having a new car. The next morning, walking out to catch the school bus, I could hardly take my eyes off that glowing piece of automotive finery, all ablaze in the bright morning sunlight. Its stark contrast to our old gray unpainted house was striking. I think I walked a little taller that morning knowing all the kids on the bus had their eyes trained on the new Chevy. How little did I know that "big shot" status was of little value in the real world but it took several years for me to realize that showiness, to use a metaphor, is a zero sum game?

My Dad could afford that car because he sold his much loved farm in Oak Grove, Louisiana for a trifling sum. If anyone realized the blood, sweat and tears that were exhausted on that homestead in the late 1930s and early 1940s, it would make you cry to know he squandered it all on a "Government Motors" car in the early 1950s.

Oh how sad! And to know that Bud reduced our proud car to a steer abattoir in 1956 is doubly sad. Yes, ole Bud ran over a calf in the highway and tore half the front end out of our cherished 52 Chevy. On top of the physical damage to our poor car, the impact between animal and machine produced an eruption of cow manure so broad it covered half the vehicle. In addition, due to the lengthy time it required to tow the car back home the next morning, the manure had dried and it took a herculean effort to clean the car of plasticized compost. I think the chemical effect of the residue took off a layer of paint when viewed in silhouette looked like a miniature Angus inkblot.

Oh our pretty car--- our ego boosting talisman…why did you die so young? Little did Bud know at the time that he had not only destroyed a car but he had also put the final death knell into a poor family's last trace of land ownership existing in our memories of the Louisiana frontier?

On a happy note, the flying abattoir, better known as our 1952 green Chevy Deluxe sedan was resurrected from its crumbled state by Dad and Bud, a couple of months after the accident. Bud had the good fortune to find a car grave yard in Greenwood that contained a wrecked 52 Chevy, thus a fender and other sheet metal parts were salvaged for a remake of our only road conveyance. The colors didn't match but eventually a spot paint job returned the old Chevy to its prior magnificence (I'm joking). In line with everything else the Griffins owned, the contrivance didn't look great but it was nevertheless functional.

It's notable to report that Bud's penchant for knocking the front ends out of automobiles has had a long history worth recalling. A couple of years after the "Calf" incident, Bud ran over a highway barricade on a closed road south of Jackson, Mississippi resulting in another front end going to trash heaven. What made it so gut wrenching was the fact that he had just purchased this sweet looking Pontiac Bonneville or whatever it was. True to this inborn predilection, Bud went on to periodically cave in several more car grills and fenders as time went by in the 60s, 70s and 80s. Car insurance agents loved him.

But regressing to the part where no one trusted me with the family car, my only option was to walk to town or catch a ride with my family or someone in the corridor making a trip to the bright lights of Moorhead. The main attraction in summertime was a public swimming pool in town and that's where my buddies and I spent most of our time when we were not working in the fields or attending the Picture Show. The cost for both recreational activities was only $.15, which was quite a bargain even in 1955. Katie Jean, one of my classmates since first grade always welcomed me as a participant in varying degrees of aquatic horseplay, which could hardly qualify as horseplay…it was more like treading water face to face and staring into each other's eyes. At fifteen, not only was I feeling my oats, when in truth, if one analyzed the situation closely, the oats were starting to sprout randomly, the least of which was on my chin. This little innocent aquatic activity was much safer than holding hands at the Picture Show i.e. if one could keep his hands out of sight of those aggravating and **tease** happy buddy friends. If caught in the act of consorting with a pretty girl, the abuse offered by my pals went unmitigated for days on days. I remember one time when I was a junior at Sunflower Agricultural High School, the abuse got so intense, that I broke off a relationship with a girl who I had just started going steady with. And she was a girl I had pursued for two years and for most of those two years, she wouldn't give me the time of day. I finally reeled her in and then I let those goofy buddies of mine undermine my good fortune. The biggest instigator of that inamorata jilt job was none other than my good buddy, Sonny. Now that anecdote takes the cake for all time stupidity. What made it so ironic, the girl was beautiful...one of the best-looking girls in Sunflower county.

Part Two

It was the middle of July and cotton cultivation season in the Yazoo Delta had reached its prime. Normally, a cotton crop would require three complete sweeps of hoeing starting in May and ending in early August. Troy Griffin and his boys were just starting their 3rd rotation of removing grass and weeds from around the row crop cotton plants. By now the plants had grown to small size bushes aided by a dose of double strength fertilizer (ammonium nitrate), which induced a growth spurt that augmented the production of cotton blooms and deep green bolls. As the cotton plant grows larger every day, the shaded area under the bush starves the undesirable grass and weeds from sunlight making the necessity of hoeing less required. Since this was late July… and was the third go round of hoeing…the need for more of this type hand work would be finished for the year when we finished in a couple of weeks. After a couple of days the elder of the group would generally absent himself from the group to take care of plowing the cotton crop one more time to remove grass and weeds that the hoeing process missed. After that, the cotton plant would have reached a size that the tractor wheels would start to cause damage to the cotton plant with its loaded flowers and maturing cotton bolls, spilling out into the void area between rows.

On this particular day, there were four of us practicing what we knew best but cared if we never saw a hoe handle for the rest of our lives. But it was a necessary evil to clean the cotton crop one more time before "laid by" came upon us. That in definition was a halcyon period when the crop was allowed to mature and ripen into big bolls of cotton prior to picking. The intervention called "laid by" was our nirvana, a period of bliss that we looked forward to all summer for it meant we had a few weeks of freedom from our summer labor. Today, however was not a favorable nor happy day, because we were in our second day of a twenty-day process (time it took to hoe our 30 acres of cotton). In other words, it was 18 days before that magical objective could be reached and all those long hot days stood between us and the last row that abutted the Melvin's first row. They had a farm next to our place and the six boys had also started on their last pass a few days earlier. I could see them in the distance, probably about a third of a mile away...they were hoeing away with the same aplomb that we were caught up in…the final assertion of labor before the "laid by" nirvana also referred to as "Dog Days of Summer" rolled around. When that time arrived, more than likely we would be getting together with the big family of boys to play some tag football and "Steal the bacon". But unbeknownst to me, that wouldn't happen this year, 1955. A dialogue later that day would initiate a plan that would pre-empt any consideration of meeting up with the Melvin boys in a couple of weeks for our customary frivolities.

In the field that July day, there were four of us chopping away at the weeds and grass but Bud, second oldest brother was not one of the party but Stan the oldest boy was with us but perhaps only temporarily. Bud had had good fortune and gotten a job at **Tehnet's Service Station** in Moorhead, our hometown. Dad allowed him to take the car to town for his 9-hour day pumping gas and fixing flat tires at a $.50 per hour wage rate. This rate beat the field hand wage rate of $.30/hr. Stan, a recent high school graduate and undecided on college in the fall, had also worked part time for a local crop duster who was also our well-known mail carrier but there was a short interruption in his poisoning schedule, so Stan had returned to the field to help his family out a little before the defoliation season started after the cotton opened in September. The crop dusters used the same technology for spraying defoliate (leaf removal) as they did for boll weevil poison spraying.

The day, extremely humid and hot, was commonplace for this time of the year in the Delta. The almost cloudless day...there were a few fleecy looking clouds floating overhead but nothing of any substance to give the group any relief from the blaring sun. Benny, the fourth boy was now 10 years of age and had gotten to be pretty proficient at his favorite hobby of hoeing (ha). Please notice that we never used the term **hoe in the plural form**, for obvious reasons. At this stage of development, Benny could probably be categorized as a novice hoe hand as opposed to a tenderfoot chopper. He would lag behind the group and Stan, not wanting to be part of the corny battalion would charge ahead about fifty feet so he would be out of earshot of his mundane Dad and brothers. This allowed him a little separation and privacy, which was conducive to his tendency to daydream about some of the attractive girls that had been in his senior class at Sunflower Agricultural High School in Moorhead, Mississippi. With Benny bringing up the rear... that left Dad and me hoeing at the same pace and being close together we would discuss insipid things like physics, philosophy, religion, psychology and mathematical theories, etc. Do you find that revelation shocking? Just thought I'd awaken you before you dozed off. Nope, we didn't discuss those topics, because Dad was not a deep thinker, nor was I at that stage of my life. More realistically we talked about common things like crop potential, weather, kinfolks, yesteryears, sports and geography. Actually, we didn't discuss sports, inasmuch as my Dad had absolutely zero interest in sports but he loved geography and would talk about places of the world for hours. A 1910 set of used Compton Encyclopedias that my mother bought at a "going out of business sale" several years prior, helped my father enlarge his interest in foreign countries and broaden his perspective. We would converse back and forth and for the most part, it was good natured give and take, but one day, being intellectually inquisitive, I posed the following question… "Dad, do clouds circumnavigate the earth, in other words, do the clouds that we see above us go around the world and come back?" He looked at me quizzically and brusquely replied "how the hell would I know that." Without hesitation, I recognized the untimeliness of my meteorological query and quickly down shifted my hoeing pace. Slightly crestfallen, in a couple of minutes I was about 10 feet behind him and was left to answer my own thought-provoking questions as they turned over in my head…the main one being "I think the Old Man needs a break from my esoteric meanderings." But usually he was very patient with our stupid questions, however on this particular day I guess his patience was not circumnavigating in a full circle.

As I mentioned earlier, something happened that day that put the coming month of August 1955 on a collision course with the Griffin's first real chance to experience a summer vacation. Heretofore, the word vacation meant "those trips that other people take in the summer to enjoy sights and places unseen." The reality of a vacation was not something, any of my family members thought about, much less dreamed about.

It was in the afternoon of that very hot day and I was moseying along the cotton row chopping away with an uninspired lean, when out of the blue came verbiage from my father's mouth that literally floored my sense of comprehension. What did he say??? I can't believe the words that just came out of his mouth. I shook the cobwebs out of my ears and asked him to repeat what he had just uttered. He repeated firmly "I think we may take a trip to Asheville, NC to visit Grady and his family maybe next month." Grady was a younger brother who had moved to the Carolina Mountains in 1951 to assume a job as an Analyst with the National Weather Service. I was stunned…I couldn't believe it… but thinking it too good to be true, I immediately started asking questions.

When in August? Time is running out?

He replied "middle of the month, we'll stay a week at Grady's and take in the sights of the Smoky Mountains."

"But Dad, we don't have any money to go to North Carolina…it would take at least $25.00 just in gasoline for the trip and incidental costs would contribute another $25.00 for a total of $50.00. That's more discretionary money than we spend in a routine two-month period." I didn't really say discretionary, I think I just said money.

"Well, we'll all have to chip in…Bud and Stan can contribute, they have jobs and I have some ideas on how we can make a few dollars to fund the trip." Two Moorhead Grocers … Lamb and Clyde Adams have indicated they'll buy all the butterbeans, purple hull peas and tomatoes we can furnish between now and the middle of August. You and

Benny will have to come up with a couple of ideas, so put your thinking caps on."

I was stunned but excited and immediately put the old brain in overdrive thinking about Asheville and the Smoky Mountains. I couldn't wait for the workday to come to an end, so I could get home and pull out the old Compton Encyclopedias to get some information on that remote from Moorhead area. I wasn't sure Asheville was even listed in the encyclopedia...for all I knew Asheville may not have been on the map when the old Compton's Books were printed in the early 1900's.

I then asked Dad if he had talked this over with anyone else in the family and he admitted he had not. Not even Mom knew what he was up to but I knew she would like the idea and it was a given that Stan and Bud would endorse the planning of such a trip.

As soon as the clock hit 6:00 PM and the work day ceased, I hightailed it to the house which was about a 1000 feet from the cotton field we were working in at the time. Paging through the first book of the Compton Encyclopedia set, their appeared the name Asheville, NC with a paragraph or two of facts and figures and perhaps an aerial photograph of the downtown. What an interesting place compared to Moorhead. Due to the absence of any current data, an extrapolative guess put the population at around 20,000 and as best as I could discern the ethnicity of the city was pretty close to 100% white. Of course, that fact didn't mean anything to me because Moorhead was 60% black and the races got along just fine in those days. It was western North Carolina's largest city and of course being mountainous at 2500 feet above sea level had a moderate climate and that mightily appealed to me because the summer days in Asheville and the Smoky Mts. rarely got out of the 80's (F) and the low humidity made the climate delightful unlike the Delta summer where the August miasma becomes equatorial. Oh yes, I think I like this idea of Troy Griffin's, my good father, more and more. Next Compton topic: Smoky Mountains and boy was I entranced at what I saw and read.

Not knowing whether to approach my mother or the other kids until the Old Man broke the news; I reluctantly maintained my silence and waited on him to make his pronouncement, which he did at the supper table. We were all energized and ready to get with the money-making propositions that were suggested. Bud and Stan agreed to contribute $10 apiece from their wages at the service station and crop dusting service. This left approximately $30 to be raised by the rest of us. Benny and I would collect as much scrap iron as we could in our spare time over the next three weeks and sell it to the Jewish scrap iron dealer in Moorhead. His business was close to the Southern railroad track and he paid a half penny per pound of iron, rusty or not, but mostly rusty was the standard.

A blacksmith shop located a far piece from the house, equipped with a forge and welding machine, facilitated the prefabrication and maintenance of all our farming equipment, tractor, trailers and car. Detritus from the shop was steadily accumulating and had not been cleaned up since we moved to this house in 1950…as it was, it amounted to a big pile of mostly unusable metal parts like plow remnants, drive shafts, radiators, batteries, sheet metal, you name it, it was there. This pile and some others that we knew about would be our ticket to paradise, that beautiful mountain haven in western North Carolina.

After supper with dusk rapidly descending and with my head in the mountainous clouds (no pun intended), I parked myself on the back porch in a little straight back chair that Mom always kept there next to the ringer washing machine. Yes, we were really uptown now; we had a ringer washing machine as opposed to a big black pot and a rubbing board that was the norm in the Cro-Magnon days in north Louisiana. Yep, those city folks would be charmed if they knew we were so up and coming in this modernistic world out on Sheffield Road. We were now big time. It made wash day a breeze for Mom, as she now only had to heat water in the big iron kettle to add to the tub to get the wash underway. The automatic dasher in the tub did the work and the pivotal ringer removed gross water after the clothes were rinsed in a galvanized tub placed next to the washer. Such brilliant engineering…what will they think of next? To be sure, the worst part of the modern process was the bucket transfer of hot water from the black pot to the washing machine tub…meaning that the horror of a misstep could result in a scalding splash of boiling water onto the body of the careless carrier. Because of the danger, the leading lady of the brood reserved that exercise exclusively for her own tending. She didn't have any faith in her teenage boys doing the job safely, inasmuch as they sometimes suffered from ADD. I don't think it was a lifetime congenital affliction as the acronym implies, but it was…

without a doubt a short-term lack of interest in that particular chore for the boys.

How in the world did I get sidetracked on washing machine minutia when I really just wanted to sit here in the cool evening breeze and construct in my mind, vistas of the uplands of the Blue Ridge Mountains?

Well, as a matter of fact, I did just that. The serenity of the late July evening cast a spell over me and my mind started to wander into a pristine landscape of craggy mountains, massive gray rocks and fast flowing clear streams surrounded by white barked Birch trees. Naively, unknown to me at the time, my dreaming had gotten off on the wrong erroneous foot, due to my lack of understanding and knowledge of what the Blue Ridge Mountains looked like. The image being painted in my brain was a visage of Rocky Mountain beauty conjured up from all those ubiquitous western pictures and paintings, one sees in books, libraries and public places. I assumed all mountains looked the same. Until such time that I could put my hands on some literature of the Tennessee and North Carolina Mountains my mental picture of Eastern American Highlands was a misrepresentation of the sights to be seen. But that didn't deter my thoughts that night or the next several nights. I was already on an imaginary mission that would only be brought to a correction once the Smoky Mountains were physically broached in mid-August.

After I went back inside the house, I could see that Mom was extremely excited about the prospect of going up into the Mountains to witness something that she had never seen before. It was true, she had never been out of the state of

Mississippi; furthermore she really liked Norma Ruth, Grady's wife and was overcome with the anticipation and social aspect of seeing her and her children in addition to seeing the sights of Eastern Tennessee and Western N.C. which in her case it could have easily been in Timbuktu for all she knew.

Dad's experience with Mountains was another story. As it turned out, he had experienced mountains on a couple of trips that he had made in previous years, one to Oklahoma and another one to Greensboro, N.C. That's the main reason he was so keen on going back to the mountains to do more probing and sightseeing...he had always had a hankering to go back to the highlands. I intended to find out more about his mountain junkets as we continued our march across the cotton fields in the next couple of days. Tonight, he was telling Benny and Mom what to expect at the higher elevations and the typical scenery one would see. Benny was especially taken aback by his disclosure that more than likely we would come in contact with black bears due to their plentiful numbers in the Smoky Mountain National Park.

I was somewhat disappointed in my research efforts but the old Compton book didn't satisfy my appetite for more information on the desired subject. I had thought I could make a trip to the Sunflower Junior College library in Moorhead to get more up to date literature but then I realized that the college was closed for the summer. A summer school course had just ended and those teachers involved in teaching the belated classes had closed shop and taken off on their own short lived vacations. The place was a ghost town, the old school grounds were shut up like an old cattle barn in winter time.

Well so much for that possibility, I accepted the fact that I would just have to be surprised by the prevailing *Flora and Fauna* when I got there in person, making it even more entertaining for the ignorant traveler. Besides, after gleaning my father of geographical information for the next few days in that highly acclaimed Citadel of academia (the cotton patch) I'd be well versed in all facets of accepted mountain culture and the environments that go with it. Assuredly, he would fill my ear full of it in the next few weeks because he was certainly capable. With perfect candor, my father even with his lack of formal education was very learned in geographical and botanical subjects. Never have I seen a plant or a tree in our Delta habitat that he couldn't identify on sight. Find a tree that escapes your ability to assign a name…just go ask Troy Griffin and he'll tell you the tree name without blinking an eye. The same went for shrubbery, flowers and other extraneous bushes. He was a sharp observer with pioneer insights.

Even if I couldn't get all the information I wanted on the N.C. Mountains, one might ask, what is the big deal? They say ignorance is bliss. Let it go at that. But I had this compulsive nature to know as much about a subject as I could find once my interest was piqued. It's a shame I didn't apply that same motivation to my academic pursuits. I know most people will find this an oddity but I wasn't an "A" student at the top of my class like Boyd Horton, Nan Allen, Keats Cartwright and Toby Bell. Mid-grade was the level I equilibrated at, you know, like water seeks it own level. I hate to admit it but there was a trace of lazybones encoded in my DNA.

The whole family was wild eyed that night except Stan who was off on a date with a very comely young lady who was destined to be the Sunflower Junior College Trojans head majorette once school started in September. Admittedly, old Stan had a knack for attracting beautiful distaffs, but he had a car to enhance his appeal. I didn't have the wherewithal that he had at this stage in school nor did I have a pining for romantic entanglements like him, given my lack of resources. I only had my disarming charm to get me through the rocky road of attracting the opposite sex. In my case, the charm must have been fairly weak because my batting average with the young ladies tended to fall into the sandlot category.

We all went to bed that night feeling good about what lay ahead of us come the middle of August 1955.

Instead of going straight to the cotton field that next morning, we loaded up the trailer with wash tubs and woven baskets and proceeded via tractor to the vegetable truck patch located in fertile ground about midway of the place where the tomatoes, beans and peas were growing in abundance. A water well and gasoline driven pump were used to irrigate the somewhat delicate vegetation assuring a good harvest regardless of drought and a severely hot July sun. The setup also prolonged the growing season of the vegetables, for in most instances, the crops fizzled this time of year. However this year had seen a steady series of cooling showers roll through in late evening that kept the veggies enriched with nitrogen fixing nutrients and the cool nights combined to augment the yield of tomatoes, butter beans, okra and purple hull peas like we'd never seen before. It appeared the Good Lord was on our side providing us an ample bounty of nature's best, as proof of his approval that we deserved that vacation our sights were set on.

The four of us tackled the job of harvesting the produce and ended up with a bushel of tomatoes, two bushels of purple hull peas and a bushel and half of butter bean and a bushel of okra...not a bad "catch of the day" to say the least. Lamb's Grocery would be glad to take these luscious edibles into his coolers for a quick sale. Because Moorhead was a farm area, most shoppers raised their own vegetables and didn't buy from a grocery store, but as I said, veggies in late July and early August were hard to find, so our little produce enterprise was successful. Successful, however may have been an over statement given the fact that our total sale for the day was only $2.00. But two dollars add up if repeated over time and that was the idea. Our goal was to accumulate a total of $10.00 over two weeks or until the garden played out in early August. From the truck patch, we delivered the produce to the car and placed the baskets in the trunk and on the back seat for Mom to take to Lambs Grocery a little later in the morning. The car was moved under a shade tree to make sure the veggies didn't dehydrate.

Part Three

In short order, back in the cotton patch, our hoe handles were flying and Dad was regaling us with stories of the North Carolina Mountains. Today there was no regimentation of the hoeing posse...even Stan dropped back from his customary forward position and Benny moved up from the rear to be in close proximity to the PhD of Geographical Studies, Mr. Troy

Griffin. Normally a silent man, today my Dad was in his element as storyteller and historian of past mountain trips.

In summary, account #one picked up the story of a few years back in 1951, J.D. Shurden, husband of Aunt Arlie, Dad's older sister, came to Moorhead to coax his brother-in-law, Troy, to fill a mission for him by going to Oklahoma City to drive back to the Delta, a self-propelled International Harvester Combine (an automated threshing machine) that he had recently purchased. Since it was in the middle of winter and money was tight, the little extra compensation that Jake offered him was enough to convince him the trip would be sufferable but not intolerable. So he took the proposition and shortly thereafter boarded a Greyhound Bus to Oklahoma City. Mind you, Troy is telling the story in graphic detail and we, the hoe brothers, were listening attentively without any trace of wanderlust to distract the storytelling. We were fully focused on his saga as his telling of it unfolded.

Knowing the weather would be extraordinarily frigid in the Oklahoma Plains and the Ouachita Mountains on his return to the Delta via Oklahoma City, Fort Smith, Little Rock and Greenville, Jo Griffin took over Troy's outfitting and made her husband take long handle underwear, double layers of pants and shirts, A heavy overcoat, ear muffs, face covering cap, heavy insulated gloves and a couple of quits, not to mention heavy lace up boots and thick wool socks. Too, one must realize that the IH Combine, although self-propelled, its cab was not enclosed, thus Troy would be exposed to the prevailing elements at a typical speed of 25 miles per hour. That was quite enough exposure to kill a driver if not adequately insulated against the cold. Thanks to heaven, Mother took over the planning for his return trip as its doubtful Troy would have been adequately thorough in his planning to avert freezing to death or coming down with double pneumonia.

So, on to Oklahoma City, the transient combine driver travelled, arriving on the heels of an arctic front that skirted across the Kansas and Sooner State plains like a runaway locomotive howling and blowing snow in front and leaving behind drifts as large as sand dunes. Once arrived in the big city, the International Harvester dealer came to the bus station and picked up the combine buyer's emissary, who was all too anxious to get on the road. Shaking his head in disbelief that this young man from Mississippi was embarking on a risky journey thru the Ouachita Mountains that most sane people would never attempt in summer much less in the dead of winter. But that was my Dad…he was a seasoned risk taker. At the dealership, around 13:00 hours, Troy ate some lunch and changed into his arctic gear and wrapped with the two thick quilts headed the Combine on an eastward compass point and slowly worked his way out of the big city. Fortuitously, the dealership was in the eastern suburbs of the city and before long he was rambling along on a major highway snaking through the snow covered countryside of central Oklahoma. Moving at a speed of 25 - 30 mph, on Highway 9, he made it to Eufaula, Oklahoma before nightfall and decided to spend the night at a small motel on the outskirts of the small town. From a comfort standpoint, he coped with the 30 degree weather pretty well…cold feet seemed to be his biggest concern, but the large thick quilts were a Godsend and had buffered his body from the chilling winds and blowing snow. Actually no snow was falling that evening; it was blowing unto the road from small drifts out in the fields. As mentioned before, a cold front had moved through the area the night before, dumping snow but the weather was now clear.

In the early 1950's franchised motels like we have today did not exist, so the little motel that he had pulled up to was more like one would see on Route 66 or like the Alamo Motels of the day, you know, the unitized cabins with a big circular driveway out front. Since the motel was next to a vacant lot, Troy was able to park the large farm implement fairly close to his cabin insuring him of a direct view through the cabin's back window. He was relieved that he had found such amenable accommodations in such a short time.

After warming up a bit, he asked about a restaurant and walked a short distance to a greasy spoon and had a fine Mexican supper. Dad always loved Mexican food and would partake of that cuisine at every available opportunity and tonight was no exception. He met an old man in the café and they struck up a conversation about Eufaula, and it being a small town, served as the county seat which was good luck for a traveler because the hub of the county was blessed with a motel. He also learned from the man that Eufaula had a sizeable Creek Indian population and that the Creeks came from Alabama back in the late 1800's. The poor Indians didn't come of their own accord...the US Government forced their migration to the Oklahoma Indian lands as they did the Cherokees of Georgia and the Carolinas. Muskogee, capital of the Indian nation in Oklahoma was not far north of Eufaula.

Tomorrow would be the real test of endurance, as the Ouachita Mountains stood between him and Little Rock, Arkansas. With that daunting objective rolling over in his mind, he went to bed, got a good night's sleep and hit the highway slightly before day break the next morning. With the red colored Combine aimed in the direction of Fort Smith, Arkansas, Troy became interested in finding a café where he could replenish his energy level with his typical fare of eggs, ham and biscuits. Remember, he was 6 foot 2 and weighed 230 pounds and he needed plenty of sustenance to keep the big body warm and the mind alert. He also needed to gas up the big rig and found a service station before reaching the end of the city limits. It soon became obvious the gas pump hose was too short to reach the Combine's gas tank. Fortunately, the station has a five gallon can with a spout and Troy was able to fill the tank in piecemeal fashion.

Making good time in the 25 degree weather, the weight of the machine and the large tread tires offered better traction than the cars and trucks zooming by him and he repassed several on the side of the road as the highlands rose in front of him. In about three hours, Fort Smith was in his sights and he cautiously moved through the city and out into the reaches of the Ouachita Mountain Range, the highest peaks topping out at 2500 feet in elevation, although none of these high points were in the Fort Smith vicinity.

After eating a chicken fried steak for lunch and filling his thermos with coffee, the return to Tutwiler resumed on the eastern side of the Oklahoma/Arkansas border. The snow covered mountains were very pretty but it was hard to notice their beauty in the rarefied air of so much cold. Amazing how the body quickly adapts to cold where activity is involved but not so much when a person is sitting rigidly still. But Troy said he didn't get cold and with his attention focused on staying out of the road ditches and manhandling the manual steering, it seems reasonable to assume the tussle with the steering mechanism was the key to keeping him warm and reasonably comfortable. The previous night at the Eufaula motel he had had severe cramps in his fingers, more likely caused by tense gripping of the steering wheel.

The Combine took up a lot of road space which necessitated a slowing down when approaching bridges...this in itself slowed him down but there was not a lot of traffic so his movement through the east to west mountain folds afforded good visibility and he was able to maintain a 20-25 mph clip on this second day out of Oklahoma City. His destination for the second night was Russellville, AR, a moderate sized town that sat at the crossroads of two highways and on the banks of the swollen Arkansas River. Finding a motel there would not be hard but finding one with Combine parking might pose a problem. Truck routes around towns in the early 1950's were not common, so as a result the equipment driver had to take the big Combine through the middle of these small boroughs and I'm sure he was the recipient of the ire of a lot of the townsfolk who were impeded by his 20 mph movement. But a slow pass through the towns couldn't be helped.

The audience of the story telling, specifically Benny, Stan and I, was waiting to get some details of the region's flora between Fort Smith and Conway but Dad was stingy with that part of his narrative, the reason being he didn't really know except to acknowledge that most of the forest was hardwood. Due to the winter conditions and the snow it was hard to make any definitive observations as to undergrowth, flowers and other miscellaneous plant life. Wildlife was totally absent of observation except for a couple sightings of deer just off the roadbed in a valley northwest of Ozark, AR.

During the telling, just to be funny, and trying to add a little panache to his story, I asked Dad if he encountered any hitchhiking armed convicts or perhaps some unruly hillbilly women who tried to kidnap and molest him but he chuckled and without answering went on with his story. Later on I interrupted him again and inserted a piece of hearsay that I was anxious to confirm but neither he nor any of my brothers knew the answer. The question was: "That childhood song --- S*he'll be coming round the mountain when she comes---* alluded to the Ozark Mountains did it not? That would have been up in the regions where you were travelling but maybe not...the Ozarks are in northern Arkansas and you were in the west central part of the state?" No one knew, so I made a mental note to look it up in the encyclopedia when we knocked off for lunch.

It was about dark, in his long day when he hit town. There was not much snow left on the ground in Russellville, resulting in heavier traffic but it still wasn't bad. Troy maneuvered the Combine through town via Hwy 64 and looked for a motel on the southeastern outskirts headed toward Conway. He didn't see an Inn anywhere and decided to pull over into a paved parking lot off the highway and see if he could find a policeman or resident who could direct him to a motel. He soon had directions to a motel but had to backtrack to a highway that skirted the Arkansas River to find it and secure a parking place close to his room.

After gassing up the next morning in cloudy and barely unbearable weather, he was once again tooling down Hwy 64 with his sights set on Conway, then Little Rock and finally Pine Bluff. By now he had pretty much acclimated to the exposure and was starting to enjoy the sightseeing, what little there was to see besides mountains, curves and valleys, but to him this was unseen territory and he was taking it all in albeit not in the greatest of comfort.

At Little Rock, he semi-circumnavigated the big city by taking a bypass that stayed to the east of the metropolitan area. As expected, bearing down on Pine Bluff, the terrain leveled off and evidence of alluvial soil became obvious as row crop farms began to dominate the landscape. Then it was dusk again and he spent the night in Dumas, AR where he enjoyed another Mexican meal of rice, refried beans and several enchiladas, a word he couldn't pronounce, but man, oh man were they delicious. He was getting his sate of Mexican food but he loved it almost as much as he savored Mom's gravy steaks cooked in a pressure cooker.

Later in life, when I lived in Baton Rouge, My parents came to visit and on a Sunday before they returned to Moorhead, I decided to grill some T-bone steaks as a treat for our honored guests including Bud and his wife to be. As Dad sat across the table champing on his expensive and delectable steak, I asked him "how was it?" He looked at me, his eyes full of content, he somewhat seriously retorted; "you know…

actually I would prefer a little gravy on mine" I laughed to myself and thought...he's being honest because I have no doubt in my mind that a gravy steak was more suitable to his tastes than a big T-bone steak. God bless his candor.

The story was now in its descendancy and Troy was wrapping up his yarn---no---not for an instant do I think it was a yarn...I don't think Dad was capable of spinning a yarn...he was one who always told the truth and I willingly would bet my life that this revelation of his journey through the Ouachita Mountains in arctic conditions was as honestly spoken as Moses depiction of the Burning Bush.

The final leg of the trip from Pine Bluff to the center of the Yazoo Delta was uneventful after the high blood pressure raising occurrence of crossing the mighty Mississippi River at Greenville over an ice slicked bridge. I can't imagine a human sitting high in the saddle of an Army tank sized International Harvester Combine traversing the widest river in the USA. Apparently it didn't bother Troy Griffin because he knew he had a guardian angel that roamed that bridge site and always guided him to safety whether coming from Moorhead or returning to the home place, smack dab in the middle of the Yazoo Delta. Since the mid 1930's, that Angel had taken his hand as he made countless crossings over the Mississippi River by ferry or high rise bridge. I was willing to believe Troy's guardian angel, an old gray haired black man strayed over into the middle of the Delta and looked after Troy throughout his life. My Dad had some life threatening close calls in his life but he always seemed to avert major injuries or sicknesses. Call it being looked over or call it good luck, or just fate... but I think he had an angel at his side, just like he had when he made this impossible trip in the dead of winter from Oklahoma City to Tutwiler, Mississippi in 1951.

Between Leland and Indianola, Mississippi the red Combine bowed its back a bit and the straight away road made for some big-time speed compared to the circuitous mountain ways. After four tense days of haphazard zigzagging around icy bridges and acute curves, the large mechanical road hugger pulled into the driveway of the Griffin domicile on Sheffield road just as a thousand blackbirds in flight made an awe-inspiring dart to a vacant 30 acre dormant soy bean field covered with stubble. Much like fish in an aquarium, the birds in unison observed by the human eye, formed a black venetian blind that appeared and disappeared as their bodies angled in flight and finally landed en masse in the food laden flat patch. For those not knowing, the soy bean threshers do a good job of capturing the harvested beans but some of the beans fall with the stubble and that's why the blackbirds seek out the seemingly barren fields in winter during their migration to the south.

We all shot out of the house, to see our heroic Paterfamilias pull into the home place, safe and sound, but no way could we ever come close to imagining the rigors he had endured to make the trip that paid him a paltry $30. But he enjoyed it, and if given the opportunity to duplicate the same assignment, he would have probably only hesitated for a couple of minutes before accepting the challenge for a second time. That was my father, a tough son of a gun. He was still a youthful 33 years old.

The story ended the next day in Tutwiler at the J.D. Shurden place near Parchman State Penitentiary as Troy made delivery of the big red I.H. combine without fanfare. After a short visit and lunch with his sister, Aunt Arlie, he was in Jake's pickup on his way back to the center of the Yazoo Delta. Jake was so happy to have his new Combine in hand, he pulled out a half pint of Early Times whiskey and offered Troy a swig as a celebratory gesture. Being the gentleman that he was, Troy didn't refuse Jake's token of good will.

Part Four

We broke for lunch on this very hot day in July, 1955 and due to making a mental note to check out the origins of the old time song "She'll be coming round the mountain when she comes, driving six white horses when she comes" I went straight to my Compton Encyclopedia but couldn't find any relative source of the old traditional folksong. I'd have to delay my search and maybe combine it with my library search for Smoky Mountain literature.

Rather than bore the reader with too much minutiae about part two of Dad's experiences in the mountains, I'll quickly spare the details and move on to the family's money making ideas for funding their first ever vacation.

Once we were back in the cotton field for the afternoon's resumption of work, the boys were still packed together in a group waiting to hear the report of a Carolina trip to Greensboro that Troy had taken in 1953 in concert with several other fellows from Moorhead. Uncle "Bunk" Moore was a county school bus driver for a Moorhead route for many years and became privy to information reported from the Sunflower County School System that a fleet of buses had been purchased from a North Carolina company. As it turned out, the School Board needed six men to go to Greensboro and drive the six buses back to the Delta via a route through the Blue Ridge Mountains.

Putting his name on the list of applicants, Troy was selected along with "Bunk" and Uncle Eugene Sheffield to participate in the trip to bring the brand new "Blue Bird" buses back to Indianola.

Embarking as a group on a June day, they traveled to Cherokee, NC and spent the night at a motel there in the Smoky Mountains. The men were unprepared as far as clothing, because they didn't foresee the temperature getting down into the 40"s that night in Cherokee. As they shivered their way to eastern North Carolina via Hwy 70 through Asheville and Hickory, once descended of the mountains, the atmosphere warmed up to customary temperatures. They all wished they had a coat, but every one of them had misjudged the June weather not taking into account the temperature at the higher elevations. This was excellent information to have when travelling and Dad learned his lesson well and would not make the same mistake twice. He put it in his pipe of experience and smoked it. It would serve us well in planning our trip to come in a few short weeks.

Needless to say the six guys picked up their buses in Greensboro and headed back across the Blue Ridge for the two day trip back to Indianola. Along the way they enjoyed the sights and the refreshing light air… in essence it was a free vacation with food and lodging provided by the Sunflower County School Board. They all talked about that marvelous trip for years to come and for sure my Dad was forever struck with mountain fever and couldn't wait for the opportunity to return to the area and show the picturesque Eden to his family.

My brothers and I had heard these stories before but we had not paid much attention to them…they were not as interesting as they were today owing to our elevated awareness of our impending vacation that would become real in that vastly interesting mountain theater in a few short weeks.

Part Five

With fresh details in our minds of what we would encounter on "the vacation" we started sorting out the images that would make us happiest. We trained our thoughts on the scenery, towns and cities we would pass through, the food, the National parks, the animals, the girls, the novelties and theme parks, etc. etc. and pelted Dad with questions which were answered to the best of his ability. We were so green and naïve at that time, we didn't realize that a vacation is more an illusion than it is a realization of substance. In hindsight, life experience has shown that vacations never live up to expectations.

Our hoeing alignment reverted to the day before, i.e. Stan lurched ahead to lead the pack and Benny dropped back and I lingered in between Benny and Dad. I figured the patriarch needed some rest from his story telling; besides we all needed some separation to do some deep thinking about what rich folks think about when they load up their big cars and head off for Colorado and California. It was really beyond our comprehension but we had the capacity to make our brain ganglia fire off sparks even if the nerve endings were just receiving duds.

But so much for dreamland, realistically we needed to get our feet firmly planted on the ground and get with the money making efforts. For example: Benny and I asked the elder if we could knock off the hoeing work at 4:00 PM to scout out some scrap iron sources down at Buckshot Hill and Quiver River. An observation last year when a group of us teenage boys camped out on the jungle infested Hill, indicated that probably years before; someone had discarded junk Ford T-model parts in a landfill. If I remembered correctly there were some motor parts and some Tin Lizzy sheet metal pieces that would add up to maybe a couple hundred pounds of scrap iron.

We needed to go to Buckshot Hill and see if the rusty stuff was still there. Since the summer months were in full blossom, we acknowledged the land fill close to the river would be covered with weeds and overgrowth. And, not insignificantly…the presence of water moccasins was almost a given. We would have to be very careful to prevent getting bitten by one of those pugnacious overinflated stump tail monsters. I asked permission to take the green Oliver tractor to the place just described and we were soon on our way down the gravel road to Sonny's house and past into the woods that led to Buckshot Hill. We were soon in the vicinity of the landfill but our task before us was intimidating. Yes, the site was grown up but we could make out rusty metal heaped in a pile with some other pieces scattered in a ten foot area. Well for sure the scrap was still there but we needed a trailer to be able to retrieve it, which meant another trip back. Also, the land at this site was owned by Uncle Eugene and we'd have to get his permission to recover the iron, for all we knew, he was the one who dumped it there. On top of that when we came back we would have to put on long pants, long sleeved shirts and high top shoes to protect against briars and snakes mentioned above. In addition to moccasins (cottonmouths) there were also copperheads in this river bottom, and needless to say, both species were very poisonous. We would need thick leather gloves and Dad kept a pair in his blacksmith shop for handling forged cultivator blades and the like. I started thinking to myself..."is this worth it?" But we didn't have much of a choice because our money making exploits were limited and time was running out.

I looked at Benny and he had sweat droplets covering his upper lip and there were grandma beads on his neck which would soon turn to "rust" as Mom called it. He would have to stick his head under the water faucet for a good dousing when we got home. On second thought, I needed the same treatment on my sweaty head. Indeed, my whole body needed a good scrubbing. And out of the ether, an idea popped in my brain...hey...while we are down here at the Quiver Riviera, let's make the best of a chance encounter...let's go swimming and do double duty. I drove the Oliver down the hill behind Uncle Hugh's shop where we did all that downhill wagon and barrel slalom foolishness and parked the tractor next to our adopted swimming hole and away we sprinted through a cocklebur thicket, diving headfirst into the slightly less than pristine river water. If there had been an EPA in those days, they would have had a citation in the mail to county officials.

In a little while, Sonny heard our noisy threshing and came running, lickety split, down the slope, peeling off his clothes as he neared the river bank. As one might expect, buck nakedness on a hot summer afternoon in a cool country stream was our normal *modus operandi* unless Sonny's sisters were present. Seemingly our immodesty was an anachronism to our era but swimming nude was looked upon as acceptable, and we didn't give a second thought to our unobscured exhibitionism. We were totally oblivious to prying eyes.

How we averted catching typhoid from the bad river water I'll never know.

After Benny and his older brother's successful reconnoiter, we decided then and there that we would go back to Buckshot Hill in about two weeks and collect the heap along with the other stockpiles that we had identified. Of course the biggest haul would be the one at the blacksmith shop and there was another piece or two of scrap that someone had dumped at the bottom of the Moorhead Bayou Bridge on Sheffield Road near Hwy 82. We'd hustle down there and add it to our scrap collection on the same day.

Part Six

Stan, my oldest brother at age 17 was working with the family for a few days to help with the final hoeing while his part time employer, a crop duster, was in a slack period. The spraying season was in its last days of summer, and Mr. Hobbs was only doing some spot flying and couldn't offer Stan a sustainable full day's work as an attendant. The job entailed loading bags of insecticide into a chamber in the plane from which it was discharged uniformly through a chute during its almost ground touching flight. They called it top dressing. Handling the heavy bags was back breaking work but the job paid $.50 an hour from about 4:00 AM to 11:00 AM. You see, the most advantageous time for dust application was in the morning hours while the dew was still heavy, which allowed the dust to stick to the cotton plant leaves, blooms and bolls, killing the weevils on contact.

However, Stan was not complaining and in fact had enjoyed the last few days in the fields, talking it up about the vacation and listening to the travel accounts of the group's most experienced journeyer. He had committed to go with the family to help with the driving and you could tell he was excited about the trip as much as we were. Stan's senior class had made a trip to Washington DC in May but their travel through the mountains was mostly at night, consequently he had not witnessed much outside the bus windows. In contrast, I think most of his attention was focused on the female classmates and their escapades. Gulliver would have to wait.

Everybody was really in a good upbeat mood as the days marched on into late July and several more vegetable sales were closed with Lamb and Clyde Adams. The total veggie fund was now up to $8.00 and we still had a couple more pickings before the crop started its wilt down. We expected to have $12.00 in that vacation kitty before the week expired.

In the meantime, Benny and I had met with Uncle Eugene and using some "poor mouthing" convinced him to let us have the scrap iron down on Buckshot Hill. He thought our intentions were good for the family outing and the only thing he asked from us was to replace the rip rap with a like amount of bricks and stones to prevent erosion. We went back to the scrap iron cache with the Oliver and a trailer and without getting bit by a snake, although a couple were sighted, loaded up the iron and combined the other piles at Dad's shop and at the Moorhead Bayou. As instructed and true to our word, we filled the hole at the Hill with a load of broken bricks and mortar that had been left from flue construction. Mr. Ben Himelstein, here we come...our weigh ticket from the scales showed a net weight of 1500 lbs and at a half cent a pound, our yield was $7.50. We were quite content with our little entrepreneurial venture and so were our parents. Adding up our collective dollars and change we had $19.50 and two IOU's from Stan and Bud for $20.00, making a total of $39.50. With everything considered, a shortfall of $10.50 had to be offset by August 15 to fulfill our objective of $50.00 to fund the trip. But Benny and I had a couple more tricks up our sleeve to help the cause and we had already taken steps to make it happen. We knew our Uncle A.P. who now owned Grady Griffin's old place, had a 10 acre soy bean field that was loaded and being taken over by Coffee weeds. Volunteering to do a walk-through to machete the coffee weeds for $2.50 a day each, Uncle AP accepted our offer. Now we had to get a day off from hoeing to go hack the coffee weeds. How could Dad refuse us? He didn't. As a matter of fiduciary consideration, he was very obliging.

Another $5.00 was added to the travel fund and we had had fun making like Natives in Africa clearing line for Caucasian explorers. Any departure from hoeing was always a welcome respite for the hoe brothers.

Of all my life musings, one remarkable thing that stands out in stark contrast to the odds against chance is the fact that in living18 years on the farm and its environments, none of us kids were ever bitten by a snake even though none of us ever wore shoes at the height of snake season. Talk about guardian angels, they must have hovered over us in coveys. By all rights, how could Benny and I roam through that soy bean field in waist high vegetation and not have a big copperhead slither over our bare toes. But we were absent of fear. All I can say is "thank you Lord for holding our hands and watching over us." I always figured my Angel was an elegant ghostly being with a good ole Mississippi name like Sammy Ray. Gender wouldn't matter, male or female was fine... the name would still be appropriate. Thank you very much Sammy Ray, "you did a jam up heck of a job." I hope to meet you in person one of these days...I'm sure I will... just a matter of time.

Stan was more or less abiding his time by hanging around with the Hoe brothers, for he had not made up his mind to enroll at the Junior College to further his education and possibilities. Mother and Dad weren't education advocates...they didn't encourage or discourage...their ambivalence, more or less left it to the individual son to make the decision. Certainly at 17 years of age, Stan's impulse was to get out on his own...he couldn't envision a future as a student for years to come. So, no doubt, he was planning to fly the coop and this trip to the mountains would be his last chance to be a part of the Troy Griffin family as a whole.

He had a stirring to be a pilot and thought he would aspire to be a cotton duster like his employers in the business. They made pretty good money and only worked for about half the year. However the work was dangerous and the life span of crop dusting pilots was like 40 years, which was not good. It was only a year or two ago that a good friend of his and also a person that he worked for in the summer of his sophomore year died in a cotton field south of Moorhead attributed to an accident related to a power line that he was unable to negotiate. He crashed and died at the scene.

The pilot's name was Campbell and I believe he was an itinerant crop duster from Ohio, who came south in the summer to take advantage of the peak need for flyers. I don't remember his first name, but he was probably a veteran of World War II since his age was estimated to be middle to late thirties. He was a good guy and took Stan under his wing, taking him up often and teaching him some piloting skills…enough to instill a deep interest in the possibility of flying for a vocation. He was pretty well established in the community and just about everyone knew him by name even though he always returned to his home state when the crop season ran its course.

We were all surprised and saddened when news of his death made the rounds. Out of curiosity, we rode out to see the accident scene and found the mangled plane still embedded in the ground a short distance from the power line that he never saw. The crash scene was a poignant reminder that small planes could be deadly and it seemed a lot of them went down.

Even though Stan got his pilot license years later and owned several planes in his lifetime, the death of Mr. Campbell had a significant impact on his decision not to be a crop duster.

Part Seven

To counter the notion that my act was nothing but work, work, work, let me introduce Sonny Matthews, real name Thomas, my first cousin and best friend, who was my pal'ing around buddy in high school. Sonny and I had just entered that universal age group that invariably give parents the most misery, but as I sit here reminiscing, the two of us at age 15 and 16 in all honesty, from a behavior standpoint would have to be considered at worst, benign threats to our parents inner peace. We just didn't do untoward things...we won't even think about drinking a beer. As a matter of propriety, Sonny was very critical of any person who imbibed alcohol, period. I'm sure he adopted that bit of abstemiousness from his mother, Aunt Eulah who was an absolute toe the line straight shooter when it came to the Ten Commandments and the standards it connoted.

But on second thought, let me qualify that "benign" statement with a replacement thought. As time passed, Sonny Boy and yours truly eventually adopted some behavioral patterns that didn't exactly fit the modest mold that was alluded to earlier.

Sonny had his driver's license and drove Uncle Hugh's 1950 Fleetline Chevrolet, back and forth, to and from Moorhead. Usually he would come by and pick me up and we'd go to the movies, the pool hall or maybe a sporting event at the Jr. College. Neither one of us was much of a pool player but we liked to watch the older fellows play for money. There was one old guy in particular, who loved to play the pinball machine for money and would get $5.00 bags of nickels to feed the machine. The guy would hang on and hang on, winning games occasionally but in the end he always left the premises broke. As can be seen, we rarely spent any money but we vicariously watched other people spent their wads and go home broke, but we always had the last laugh, we went into the establishment broke and walked out broke. We were way ahead of the game with no sweat wasted, just time wasted but nevertheless enjoyed.

Blue jeans, white loafers and creped nylon shirts were the rage at the time and we were always decked out in those three items without fail. Those nylon shirts were something else, for one thing they were hot as all get out and they seemed to promote sweating even though the material appeared to be 100% porous. On top of being hot, a tee shirt had to be worn under the almost transparent nylon shirt for modesty's sake. But what the heck, style was more important than comfort.

I always made sure I didn't venture out around the livestock barns and pens after dressing for an exciting evening out, because of the obvious concern of picking up some manure based shoe polish on those white suede hoofers. We weren't brand conscious at the time but became adherents of Levi blue jeans or at least I did when I reached 11th grade. I remember Sonny sticking with Khaki pants because he thought his legs were too skinny for jeans. By the way, Sonny and I were both 6-foot-tall beanpoles...but I might add, he being a year older than me was probably an inch taller. It was important for us to stay tuned to the prevailing fashion trends because everyone was conscious of wearing the right clothes and maintaining good grooming habits, however difficult it was owing to the use of hair oil and a lack of toiletry facilities in our homes. Nevertheless, even with all our drawbacks, we still managed to put forth a presentable appearance. At least in our own minds we did...maybe the cutest girls didn't but who cared...certainly not us, but wait a minute. Yep, we most certainly did care...peer pressure was an irrevocable fact of life and it was a psychological barrier that perplexed us all, especially those of us who struggled with a countrified self-image. But we all thought pretty high of ourselves; certainly we put on a good front and we were not a bunch of wallflowers.

We could Bop (yes I believe we were bopping in 1954) along with the best of the local yokels...my style of bopping put me advancing around the room making a complete encirclement of said dance floor every time "Rock around the clock" or some other "ditty" was played. Yes, ole Bill Haley was the Bebop Guru in 1954 and 1955. My self-proclaimed interpretive dancing technique wasn't too catchy but it got the job done. Oh yes, another favorite bopping stomper was "Shake, rattle and roll." As a matter of record...that standard was the Sunflower Junior College Marching Band's theme music as we all cheered on our Trojan football team that season of 1954. The Trojans were good that year and the team and band were rewarded with a trip to a bowl game in south Mississippi to play San Angelo (Texas) Junior College.

Lanky David Holder was the best dancer around...he had a slip and slide method to his bopping that no one could mimic but I could come close if I kicked off my white suede loafers and shuffled in my frictionless socks. Sonny had a little feint and prance step that he had perfected but he wasn't real convinced it caught the cute girl's eye. The unattractive ones liked his dance step but the only thing that mattered was if the cute ones liked it. If they didn't show any interest, then it was all for naught. In those infantile days of bop, we all packed into Sonny's green Fleetline and headed up to Sunflower, Mississippi for Teen Nite at the community house. The town of Sunflower had a population of about 150 people, so one could imagine the outpouring of beauties at those events. But we did alright…yes from the rural surroundings, came some nice looking fillies. One night, there was one little pretty teenager from Rome, MS who was visiting her aunt and she was the belle of the ball. Boy was she a knockout. All the boys wanted to dance with her and I made my move early in the evening and we bopped around and around the big community house dance floor. Remember, I had this unique Roger Bannister bop method that took the hand locked couple on an approximately one mile journey from start of song to finish. I noticed at the completion of our marathon, this cute femme fatale was sweating profusely and completely wore out (yes, I know it should be "worn out") but the fact of the matter was, she was absolutely shot at the conclusion of "Rock around the clock." As a result of my indefatigable virtuosity, I got shunned for the rest of the evening. Sonny had better luck with his original prance, double clutch and retreat move and since it was a one spot dance, two moves forward and two back, the same little gal was able to catch her breath. I don't think she was too taken with Sonny's style of dance but she sure liked the fact that she didn't have cover a mile like she did with me.

Indianola was another hot spot for the nomadic Moorhead nimble toed soft-shoes. When we could afford it, we generally went to Indianola to wolf down some of those delicious chili burgers at Labella's Drive-in but on occasion we went to a "Cotillion Ball" or two at the blind invitation (as in blind date) of some of the Indianola maidens. Usually it would be a double date. Unfortunately as luck would have it, more often than not, the Cotillion girls turned out to be less than the sparkling beauties we hoped for. Most of the Belles of that county seat town thought most of the rabble from Moorhead was nothing more than a bunch of sodbusters. And they were right but Indianola's effete elite were full of themselves, not all, but a good many fit that mold. In the final analysis, some of those lasses should have latched on to some of that Moorhead crowd who now in their old age are modestly hailed as healthy, wealthy and wise.

We also graduated to the big time, by making the scene at Greenwood's TAC, a teenage hangout and community center for dancing. These affairs were chaperoned by adults and I don't recall any fights occurring between outsiders and Greenwood studs. We were pretty peaceful and conducted ourselves pretty well; after all, we were highly outnumbered by the local males about 10 to 1 at any given moment.

Those days were the epitome of innocence, if only this wicked world of today could return to the values that were espoused by the mainstream youth of that day. I confess we didn't know what a recreational drug was...we hardly knew what a jigger of whiskey was. Unashamedly, we were unsophisticated, just a bunch of sober country bumpkins on the fly.

In the world of music, the years of 1954 and 1955 made some serious waves and we were there to ride the cultural tsunami called Rock and Roll into its highly visible place in history. After the dust settled, Rock & Roll, a hybrid of Country and Rockabilly music registered its rightful place in the popular musical lexicon alongside Jazz, Big band, Blues, Pop, Country and Western, Hillbilly, Scat…you name it. We were fortunate enough to be contemporaries of Rock & Roll artists like Bill Haley, Elvis Presley, Carl Perkins, Gene Vincent, Fats Domino, Roy Orbison, The Platters, Pat Boone, The Everly Brothers, and on and on. A good analogy would be like us growing up with George Washington and being his best snuff dipping buddy. We cut our Bebop teeth on those performers and they didn't disappoint us. They produced the beat for us to cut our jigs. They say the 1950's was the best time to be alive and it was but it also was a time of tumultuous change in the music world. But you know; tumultuous may be too strong of a word.

A lot of the adults thought our music was demonic but it wasn't, it was just a medium that produced a good beat, a cadence and a twangy hum to dance to. In the mid 1950's our music was not attended by wild maniacs high on drugs and alcohol…that craziness came later. Our music in those early days of Rock & Roll was just fun and energy sapping. When we finished an evening of bopping with the unattached girls we knew and some who were strangers, we went home, hit the sack and got up early to go to school or to the cotton patch.

We didn't do much dating at this time in our lives, for one thing, it was too expensive unless we met a girl at the Gayloe Theater to cozy up to and hold hands. Even that innocuous treat was a rarity.

When we were not out seeking bopping partners, there was a brassy trick we Moorhead fellows performed quite frequently if there was a good movie playing at Indianola's Drive-in Theater (its name escapes me). The trick was to pool our money and leave two ticket paying people in the car while the rest of the pack entered the car's trunk. Once entry was made and the vehicle parked next to a speaker, the culprits in the trunk would emerge, move to the back seat and enjoy a free movie. Oh yes, backing up to the sneaky entry, once the guys were snuggly cramped in the trunk, invariably, Roy would always take the opportunity to discharge a large volume (or so it seemed) of swamp gas into our oxygen starved sanctuary. We would all yell our indignation "Roy...you raunchy, uncouth son of a gun, you." We probably used stronger language but it would not be appropriate to use it in this happy nostalgic story.

Other times, we would walk across a soy bean field next to the theater grounds, find our buddies' car and settle in for the night. The second option was curtailed for good, when one of our buddies, (too bad it wasn't Roy) fell headfirst into the theater's open sewer ditch that ran underground from the concession stand but opened up at the soy bean field property line. Boy was he a mess and Sonny wouldn't let him get into Uncle Hugh's classy Fleetline for the show. The poor ole boy had to sit in a chair on the outer limits of the concession stand. I believe after the movie concluded, Sonny allowed him to seek a fetal position in the car's trunk for the ride home. What friends we were, but who in their right mind could tolerate a toilet smell as rancid as that ole boy reeked, even from the trunk. Talk about foul...wow. It was Gosh awful. Sonny had to fumigate his car's trunk for several days. Needless to say we didn't make any movie trips to the drive-in until the trunk stink was thoroughly vented.

On a milder note, I believe we all saw the movie "Rebel without a Cause" starring James Dean and Natalie Wood at the Gayloe Theater that year of 1955. It was an unforgettable movie and I remember it to this day. Another favorite of that era was "The young Stanger" with James McArthur. His character wore dungarees and a long sleeve white shirt with cuffs rolled up about 6 inches. For a while, we adopted that dress fad until our mothers got sick of laundering our single white shirt every other day. I remember Roy used to always approach Sonny with the salutation "why, if it isn't the Young Stranger, Sonny Boy Matthews." Thomas was good natured about the put down and always laughed as much as his cronies did.

Before getting back to the banalities of the "vacation," there is one more anecdote to be told and it relates to that classy light green 1950 Fleetline Chevrolet that Sonny Boy wheeled and squealed in. If Uncle Hugh only knew some of the abuse his old Fleetline took from his oldest male heir, he would have been up in arms and Sonny would have been out walking the gravel byways.

In my sophomore year, a bunch of us boys from SAHS decided to attend a basketball game up at Ruleville, MS as they were one of our most hated rivals in all sports. This was the time period before I made the basketball team so I was no jock but liked watching games. As usual, Sonny was going to be our carrier to the game and his entourage consisted of Billy T, John, Bob, Roy and yours truly. We all agreed to pony up a quarter each for gas to fund the trip. On the way up to Ruleville, about 30 miles up Hwy 49, Sonny Boy *showed out* a little and gunned the old Fleetline pretty good and he had the whole bunch of us oohing and aahing at the neck breaking acceleration the six cylinder engine seemed to possess...one could only imagine the thrust if the car wasn't so loaded down. We whizzed along and soon arrived at Ruleville and watched both our girls and boys teams lose to Ruleville that night. In a short while after telling our other standing friends goodbye, we hit the road back, but, weirdly, I had this strange gnawing premonition that the ole Fleetline was going to meet its demise before the night was over. I never told anyone about that foreboding then or after but I tell you here and now my precognition of that impending event was the real McCoy.

We were soon clustered back in the green Chevy, three in the front and three in the back seat and headed back to Moorhead. About 10 miles out of Ruleville, heading south on Hwy 49, ole Sonny Boy, still adamant in his desire to impress us with his hot car, had stiffened his right leg to apply maximum pressure to the accelerator of that scalded dog headed south. I don't know if that phrase was in common use back then but ole Sonny Boy had "his foot in the carburetor" and the six pistons were churning at a speed the engine had never seen before. If the car had had a tachometer, the dial pointer would have been bent double.

Thank God, the old car maxed out at 70 mph…that was all it was capable of doing given the fact that it was humping a cargo of about 700 pounds of Angus and 100 pounds of baby fat. Apprehensive and hunched forward, all we could hear was the cacophonous din of the engine tappets making contact with push rods and all we could see was the intermittent center line markings which had by now rolled up to a single flashing straight line. It was like a strobe light flashing and reflecting off the bewildered passengers fully dilated eyes of fear. All of us in the car were thinking out loud, somebody please holler "**Calf Rope" before Sonny Boy Matthews kills us all."**

But before any of us could put thought to words, the most hellacious racket that I had ever heard hit us like a fire hose of water. Fortunately it was a sound wave and not debris that shocked our consciousness. In an instant, as we all recovered our senses we saw Sonny holding on to the steering wheel while the vehicle decelerated of its own accord. Once under the speed limit of a German autobahn, Sonny slowly worked the silent car over to the side of the pavement. By now however, there was smoke boiling from under the hood. The passengers including Sonny all peeled out of the sedan and made a dash away from the smoking car but Sonny being in a panic lifted the hood and could see some small flames flashing from the engine. After pleading for us to return to lend help, we looked for water but had no container, so in the absence of water, we started scooping up mud with our hands and plastering the engine. I noticed Sonny was stumbling around like his right leg wasn't working right. As it turned out his leg was convulsing as a result of all the tense pressure that he had applied to the accelerator to attain top speed. By this time several cars had stopped to contribute efforts to extinguish the smoldering and smoking engine.

Once the conflagration was under control, we all had time to reflect and analyze the situation and it was apparent the overtaxed engine had slung a rod slap through the block. With the internal workings of an engine going at such a high velocity there was no way oil could be pumped fast enough through the lifters to offset the ring friction. What a shame. Uncle Hugh would be livid when the sorry news befell his ears. All his lagniappe this year would be going to Clark's Mechanic Shop to buy and install a new six cylinder engine for the Matthews family car. Although I never heard what Uncle Hugh's reaction was to his son's demolition job, I suspect, knowing his calm demeanor, he would have said "now son, how did you manage to tear that motor up...did you fail to check the oil?" It never occurred to either of Sonny Boy's parents that he was out dogging that old Chevy to its maximum endurance. Yep, ole Sonny escaped the whip, but I guess at 16 he was too old to bear a strap.

The next day at SAHS, the school was abuzz with tales of the fireball incident that had occurred the night before up north of Doddsville and Blaine. Ole Sonny Boy became a one day cult hero as the post mortem became full knowledge to everyone in the student body. It seems the story got out that the old Green Chevy had exceeded 110 mph and that Uncle Hugh's fast wheeling son had added nitrobenzene to the gas tank to enhance engine performance. Boy, what an absurdity. Nitrobenzene...you've got to be kidding...nobody in our parts had ever heard of such a fuel unless it was Toby Bell, an aspiring chemist and honor student. Furthermore, everyone I knew in Sunflower County was so ignorant they couldn't even pronounce alcohol...they called it alkeyhaul, so it's unlikely Sonny was out buying exotic nitrobenzene at $5.00 /gallon before the fateful race up to Ruleville.

Another "strange as it seems occurrence" happened in the aftermath of Sonny Boy's Le Mans lap to Moorhead. The passenger side front door of the old Chevy had been missing its inside door handle for at least a year which necessitated the opening of the door from the outside. But it seems on this night of miracles; John cleanly and expeditiously exited the front passenger side door without help, as evidenced by the door being wide open after the fire was put out. Could it be, Johnny's angel of succor had been up at Ruleville watching that same basketball game that night and hitched a ride home with the rapid moving passengers not realizing it? I think that likely explains the door being ajar, don't you John? I would venture to agree... your ghostly patroness did and continues to perform admirable work.

As a postscript to Sonny's infamous night ride in the 1950's, his notoriety at SAHS peaked in about a week, but for a couple of days, he was "the cock of the walk" about town. The tale of the Ruleville Cannon Ball run to Moorhead made the rounds of gossip for a while then died out and Sonny became just old Sonny Boy but I must say he was in heavy demand at the outset. His recounting of the story was actually more a denial of the fictitious aspects of the escapade than it was of him exalting the actual circumstances. The embellishment of nitrobenzene and all that stuff was debunked in short order but nonetheless the myth of 110 mph lived on. I still chuckle when I think about the episode...his passengers certainly didn't help matters because the lot of us being, the practical jokesters, that we were, continued to hype the most ridiculous elements of the incident, just like I'm doing now.

As everyone agrees, with age comes prescience and I at age 70 look back and think to myself, if I had had the foresight then that I have now, we could have made old Sonny a rock star. Jokingly, I'm saying this...We could have contacted General Motors Corp. in Detroit and informed them that we had this guy down in central Mississippi who had set a world speed record in one of their 1950 slopeback Chevys and we would encourage their Publicity Dept. to come down and interview the fellow and the associates who would verify the record. If things went according to plan, I could envision Sonny signing a big barnstorming contract that would take him around the country with the Matthews' Green Chevrolet showpiece situated on a big trailer. The rig would have a big Marquee Sign sitting on top with the following caption:

Sonny Boy Matthews & his Flying Fleetline
Owns World Speed Record for Six Cylinders
(Unmodified Engine)
110 MPH with Passenger Load of 6 Men
"Have to see it to believe it"

I truly believe Sonny could have made a million dollars off of his hot rod reputation. He could easily have been the first to have the name "Fireball" because "Fireball" Roberts had not entered the headlines in 1955. "Fireball Matthews" has a snazzy catchiness to it. Yes, that name combination would have been his ticket to everlasting fame and notoriety. I like it…yes I do…"*Fireball Matthews and his Flying Fleetline*, fastest 1950 slopeback Chevy in the world, circa 1955." And to think, ole Sonny wasn't even a rum runner like the early NASCAR drivers.

Part Eight

Subsequent to the aftermath of the block and piston comedy, in an attempt to water down the filial redundancy of my storyline, I'd like to digress a little and shine the light on some of the characters that Sonny Boy and yours truly hobnobbed with in those days of wholesomeness. Hopefully, looking in depth at some of my buddies, will add a little flavor to the overall perspective of the rural small town culture in the amazing fifties. The good Lord saw fit to place us and our buddies into this microcosmic community…how fortuitous for the Moorhead posse. We came of age in an enviable era and on a remarkable location on planet Earth. The following characterizations are meant to be more aligned with humor than seriousness:

Sonny: I think everyone has heard enough about Sonny Boy Matthews to have him figured out pretty well. He was a good person, very considerate and obedient to his parents and teachers. Owing to his parents influence, Sonny was somewhat pious but at times could be hypocritical. His abhorrence of alcohol and those who abused it was worn quite visibly on his sleeve. He was a year older than me but his maturity level was on a par with mine. We differed in the way our thought processes worked; I was more introspective while Sonny was more spontaneous in his indiscretions, in other words he could be impetuous like his tendency to gun that old Chevy roadster to unsafe speeds. I didn't drive so I didn't have the temptation to be reckless but I firmly believed if given the chance, I would have been more subdued in my pursuit of the finish line than Sonny.

Funny, engaging, attractive, and happy, Sonny could be the good natured butt of jokes and he could dish out prankish jokes with the same intensity. Although, he was for the most part cool and collected, he could on occasion exhibit testiness if provoked. He and Roy locked horns on a couple of occasions when some kidding got out of hand, but it was unusual to see him mad at anybody. We both liked girls but our shyness hindered our pursuit of the fairer sex. For whatever reason, we lacked self confidence. I believe my problem related to not driving and I'm not sure what Sonny's problem was…most of the girls liked him, thought he was cute and he could sing like Elvis, as a matter of fact he could do a heck of an impersonation of the big name artists in the 50's, for example Carl Perkins, Roy Orbison and Gene Vincent. The Greenwood gals gravitated to him but I don't ever remember him going steady. Let me remind you, these were our early days in high school…as we got older and our peach fuzz turned to wire brush, we became more brazen and daring and our dating schedules picked up.

Sonny was on the football team and was a good player despite his lack of weight. He could hit and was fast. Because my father needed me in the fields for after school work, Bud and I weren't allowed to play until my junior year and Bud's senior year. Coach Wade was expecting great things out of me in my senior year but Dad reversed course and wouldn't let me play football. This turn of events so incensed Coach Wade that he vowed to ban me from the basketball team that season. That decision was rescinded when he surreptitiously observed ole Billy Ray hitting 10 jump shots in a row from the corner in a pickup game. Although he was tall, Sonny didn't play basketball, but like I said, he was good at football and was instrumental in the SAHS Aggies winning about 80% of its games. The team was considered good but not of championship caliber.

Billy T: One of our regular pack, Billy was an exceptional all around good guy. He was honorable to parents and teachers, friendly to all, generous to a fault, easy going, a decent student and sports lover. Sports trivia was his forte...he knew batting averages, earned run averages of all the major league pitchers, records of college football teams especially Ole Miss and Mississippi State. Played guard on the SAHS football team and made All Central Delta Conference his senior year.

Billy's father owned a mini–grocery store and the son clerked in the store when he wasn't in school or playing football. He always had money which was the reverse of Sonny's and my situation ...we never had any; nonetheless, he was a very giving soul and was continually buying us hamburgers and drinks. He had a car and hauled us everywhere except during those times that Sonny was rawhiding Uncle

Hugh's green zephyr and we were with him in dazed astonishment as our young lives flashed before our eyes.

Billy was a little on the gullible side, so Sonny and I conspired to convince him that he was the best bopper in Moorhead. We did it by steadily reinforcing the superfluous idea… telling him repeatedly that all the girls were impressed with his sleight of foot and thought he was by far the best dancer at the SJC canteen. Ole Billy lapped it up and was soon thinking Sonny and I were a couple of club footers the way we danced. Yep, Billy gobbled up our deception, hook, line and sinker. Before long he was prancing out on the dance floor with his chest puffed out asking all the classy girls for a dance. All the pretty girls were hoping the college football players would ask them for a dance but ole Billy would appear out of nowhere and take their hand for a spin on the dance floor intercepting their attempts to flirt with the finely chiseled athletes. After a while most of the girls went home or made a dash for the girl's dormitory to get away from this wannabe Fred Astaire. Ha.

Billy's sister was in my 10th grade high school class and we had been classmates since first grade. A pretty girl and an excellent student, she no doubt helped her brother with his dance steps but I'm sorry to say her instructions settled out in left field. Billy tried awfully hard but he just didn't have that flare to become a bopping prodigy. The same went for Sonny and me…we were impossible but none of us knew how bad we were. I guess that's how some of us low achievers get through life…we deceive ourselves. But I don't want to downplay Sonny's dancing ability and agility; he was a quantum leap ahead of me. I'm sure his sister, Carolyn helped him with his steps and too, they had a new 45rpm record player to dance by. I had to do my practicing out in the soy bean field, away from my brothers who would have murdered me with abuse…especially my older brother Stan. Yep, he would have had a ball critiquing my Roger Bannister bopping style. By the way for those who don't remember Roger, he was the first two legged Homo sapien to break the four minute mile barrier. I was the first to break it, bopping.

I don't believe Sonny or I ever told Billy we were just joshing him regarding the superiority of his dance moves. Maybe it was just as well…sometimes believing is the same as doing and we certainly didn't want to burst our good friend's bubble.

Billy wasn't as girl crazy as we were but he did have a girlfriend over at Greenwood. He had average looks and his self-esteem was probably average compared to the group. He was quiet with a calm and humble demeanor. We all got along admirably…we were very compatible. We were whatcha call bosom buddies.

Inflicted with the disease asthma, Billy's parents sought to relieve his symptoms by air conditioning their house. I remember we would occasionally drop by the refrigerated home in Moorhead (he was a city boy) on some of those July days and nights in the 50s and soak up the unbelievable cool air. No one else had air conditioning so it was hard to fathom such comfort. Of course our good friend had to have it as it probably saved his life, because every now and then he would have asthmatic attacks that threatened his life. Even with our youthful callousness, we all empathized with the debilitation of his sickness.

This very good person, Billy, had the perseverance to stay in college, received a degree and became a high school football coach in the 1960s. It was his life's ambition.

Roy M: Another one of my good slumming buddies; Roy was Mr. Personality and was extremely fun to be around ...he was our residing court jester and he kept us laughing with his comedic jinks. I hate to be repetitive but Roy followed the mold of all our circle's members...we all were courteous to adults and teachers...it was a natural way to be...old folks were revered... back talk was anathema.

Roy lived in the corridor in an old house much like mine and Sonny's. Roy was a first cousin to Sonny but no relation to me. His father had been a cotton farmer but had given up on the futility of that profession, so Roy, though he lived out there in our environment; was not a member of the hoe handle fraternity. He had an older sister and younger brother. I assumed she taught her teenage brother to dance...yes, I'll admit Roy was a pretty good foot flopper. His girlfriend also contributed to his bopping prowess.

It was hard to comprehend that our humorous court jester would ever deign to get into a fist fight but it did happen one night. He and an unnamed person in our aggregate got into a verbal altercation that didn't amount to a hill of beans. Roy took exception to this person's point of view regarding "acts of a fool" as in acting a fool and proceeded to square off and assume a "John L. Sullivan" boxing posture. Roy did ok for himself, but everyone in our posse agreed that Roy needed to upgrade his boxing technique to perhaps Marciano's style, inasmuch as the Sullivan defensive stance allowed his opponent to bust our court jester's flawless proboscis and realign it slightly. In summing up the pugilistic rooster fight that just occurred, everyone agreed that Roy was the recipient of a closed eye roundhouse right. A bony fist somehow crashed through Roy's slightly impregnable defense, producing a modicum of damage to his smelling orifice. The fight ended as quickly as it started. Concluding the fisticuffs, and with all seriousness aside, Roy and his anonymous welterweight adversary were soon walking down the streets of Moorhead arm in arm, good buddies to the end. It was all part of the "Rite of passage" of a bunch of upright kids from the sticks.

Unlike his dumb runaround buddies, Roy was a polyglot, i.e. he was multilingual in three standard tongues… English, Southern drawl and pig Latin. His fluency in pig Latin was remarkable and he gave everyone a moniker… Sonny was onny-say, Billy was illy-bay, Bob was ob-bay, Billy Ray was illy-bay ay-ray, John was ohn-jay and Bud was ud-bay and last but not least Roy was oy-ray. You bet, ole Roy could spout pig Latin without missing a beat. The rest of us struggled with the smooth delivery that Roy had mastered…to the contrary, we had to think about what we were going to articulate beforehand and its halting impact lost its effect. But Roy was smooth. Mister Cool was he.

Roy was a tall handsome young man who had good bulk. In fact he was a damn good football player and played end on the SAHS team. Roy wasn't the swiftest guy in the world but he had good technique and could block with the best of them.

In my junior year, Coach Wade caught our starting ends, Roy and Sonny smoking cigarettes and drinking Coca Colas and suspended them for a game. That led to my elevation to the starting end position and I happened to score a touchdown against a weak opponent. Although it was nothing but luck on my part, Sonny and Roy shunned me for a week. They soon rejoined the team and I was back warming the pine planks and attracting splinters as a second stringer. In reality, my football career never really got off the ground and Roy and Sonny came back determined to be the best football players they could be. Coach Wade's psychology worked that time.

Like me, Roy didn't have a car. Well, let me correct that statement. Roy's Dad had a car but Roy rarely drove the car while we were in high school. He was usually bumming a ride with Billy or Sonny just like me. Roy's family finally moved to Moorhead and Roy became a city slicker but we didn't snub him…he was still one of us.

Roy ended up marrying one of my "Class of 58" classmates after finishing high school. He became a world class helicopter pilot and made flying his career. His main claim to fame was his Hollywood stunt flying in some of Sylvester Stallone's action movies on location in the Middle East. His name is listed in the movie credits and I'm happy to say proudly… "I used to run with that famous helicopter dare devil, Roy Matthews."

John A: Although John didn't run with our group on a regular basis, he nevertheless was in the group the night Sonny's green phantom launched its motor into suborbital flight. Since John was somewhat outside the group's fraternal definition, I thought his addition would add some luster to the group's overall star power. Collectively, we needed all the help we could get to boost the credibility of our clique.

John's mother was a teacher down at the junior college and she, John and a sister lived in an apartment on campus. Yes, I would have to categorize him as a city boy but he fit in pretty well with us as a whole, so I couldn't use it against him. Furthermore, he had no control over where he lived. What really set him apart was his book smarts…he was an excellent student and he hit the books, but you know, one would expect him to be education oriented due to his mother being in the teaching profession. Also, I think she was pretty strict and I'm sure she and John's prominent grandparents had a hand in planning for his college education. As far as the rest of us boys, our parent's involvement in laying out a critical path to a college education was a blank concern.

I could tell John was goal oriented even in high school. I believe he had a young uncle who was a fighter pilot in the military and his influence on his nephew encouraged a definite curriculum as a prerequisite to following in his uncle's footsteps.

Another factor that made him compatible, at least with me was the fact that we had been classmates since first grade at Moorhead Grammar School. We played on the peewee football team and suffered through bloody noses and the entire trauma that went along with growing into adolescence in the early 50s.

We held the same moral standards, but that wasn't unusual, as every individual that we tipped our hats to at that time had an identical moral compass. Each and every one toed the line and deferred to their parents almost without fail. Those that refused to walk the straight and narrow path were shunned as outcasts. That's the way the culture was then. It dealt harshly with immorality. If a person, was a known thief, had been in jail or even cheated on school tests, his stock in the eyes of his peers dropped sharply.

Pregnancy was the ultimate shame. In this day and age, getting knocked up is not even frowned on by the public and the girls with that condition accept it as a badge of achievement. Not so in the 50s, the stigma of pregnancy was irreparable and a badge of shame was instantly placed on the girl. I can safely say that none of the girls that drew my acquaintance in the 50s had any problem with the previously mentioned predicament. The culture wouldn't permit it and the bounds were extremely tight.

Dadgummit, how did I get off on knocked up teenagers? Sorry about that John...I'll try to step away from the sermonizing long enough to complete your profile.

Being a city boy and having an educator for a Mom, John was looked upon by us country boys as being a classy guy. He dressed nicer than us and the mother drove a nice car. In my old age, it's hard for me to understand how we teenagers were so narrow minded that we thought anyone who had a big car and lived in town were superior to us, but that's how warped we were in our prejudice of self. By the same token, we country boys thought we belonged at the bottom rung of society. How crazy...where did we come up with that unfounded idea? It was truly ridiculous. But that craziness pervaded our way of thinking.

I think at the time, John was dating some of the Indianola high society girls, you know, the ones that wouldn't give us sodbusters a second look. So that development by itself put John in a class slightly higher than our social station but in our view, going out with Indianola girls wasn't that much of a feather in your cap. He also went out with some of the SAHS girls, but he was like us in the dating game, we played the field but the incidence rate was on the low side of "not many". In defense of our low number on the popularity index, the quantity of dates or lack thereof was strictly a function of cash reserves. John was probably a little better heeled than were we (Sonny and me) therefore his popularity rating trumped us without any sweat.

But all in all, John outstripped us in, dress and élan. Being smart and well read made him a good conversationalist. I never double dated with John, therefore I was never witness to his gift of gab…I knew for sure, conversation was not my strong suit…once my date and I covered weather and sports my mind went vacant. I guess ole Sonny Boy was a better social talker cause once he finished with weather and sports, he went to racing, telling his date how to double clutch, shift and accelerate in a synchronous motion to maximize a cars thrust in a drag race. Since I didn't drive at that time, racing was completely out of my sphere of knowledge except in a passive role, i.e. riding shotgun. Too, if Sonny was at a loss for words he had the ability to sing.

In truth, John blossomed into a handsome bloke, grew tall and slim, was a good football player as an interior lineman and as I said before, he was an excellent student as evidenced by the college preparatory subjects he took in high school. While I was taking courses in shop, agriculture and music appreciation, John was matriculating in chemistry, trig, science and biology. It was an intelligent move on his part…a nonsensical move on my part. One would have thought I was prepping for a career in agriculture…Ha. How laughable? Farming as a vocation was the farthest thing from my mind at that time in history. To tell the truth, I had no idea what I wanted to do in my future.

These mentioned attributes made John different from the boys in our country boy fraternity but even so John was an easy going level headed youth and I considered him a friend, not a bosom buddy but a good friend nevertheless.

After finishing high school in 1958, John went to Mississippi State, graduated and received an Air Force commission. He married one of SAHS' beauty queens from "our class of 58". During the Vietnam War, John flew dangerous bombing missions over North Vietnam. After the war, back in the states, he became a commercial pilot with Delta Airlines. After a long career of flying, writing was added to his resume upon retirement and this man of letters has written several novels. I must say John did ok for himself, he was yet another Sunflower Agricultural High School alum who had done well in the annals of life.

Bob C: Being a couple of years younger than our regular crew, Bob preferred to run with a couple of boys in his grade class, but on occasion, he did pal around with the more advanced and mature crowd (that would be the group that I identified with). Another factor entering into the equation was the fact that he and Billy were good friends due mainly to the close proximity of Bob's father's Mechanic Shop to the latter's family mini-grocery. Bob hung out and did casual work for his father at the shop but at every chance, he was over visiting with his good friend at the little grocery store. Billy had a boxing ring set up in back of the store and a lot of guys in the neighborhood would meet there to advance their fighting skills.

Mr. Clark was the town's master mechanic. There were no jobs that he wouldn't take and his shop was always full of broken down cars, trucks, tractors and other miscellaneous farm equipment. He also was not averse to making house calls to farm sites where equipment most likely and variously broke down on the spot. It was not like a farmer could log a big piece of broken down farm equipment to the town's mechanic shop, therefore Bob's Dad, between shop jobs and call jobs, had a thriving business in the little town of Moorhead, Mississippi smack dab in the middle of the Yazoo Delta. Next door to Clark's Mechanic Shop was Hickman's Service Station, another landmark that no one probably remembers but I thought its annotation to Clark's place would bring back a few memories if not for the general public then maybe for the Clark boys and their offspring.

Not to get too redundant, these little indistinct human snippets are put in this story to add some zest to a weak story. For the interest of the reader, these humanscapes are intended to add substance to the narrow, bland and ordinariness of my familial retrospection. One important thing to remember is the whole lot of us had fathers who worked solidly for 10 hours a day which didn't give them much time to overprotect their boys much less help shape their future aspirations. Since we didn't look much farther than the ends of our nose, we were pretty much on our own but we had the best of role models and the straightest of rules to guide our behavior plus we never wanted to disappoint our parents. That strictness was the glue that reined us in fairly close to a center line and minimized our devilment.

Bob was a big kid and was tough as nails. He had a daring spirit and wasn't averse to busting a mouth or two in horseplay. He tried out for the high school football as an eighth grader but ended up playing on the Grammar School team as the result of a rule technicality. Those poor sixth, seventh and eighth graders that year caught hell as big Bob mowed them down in practice and in games. Surrounded by smallish juveniles on his high school team, Coach Wade salivated to get Bob into his lineup as quickly as possible which came in Bob's freshman year and the coach was rewarded with an all-star Tight End. In those days, football players played both defense and offense and the big freshman excelled at both specialties. In my opinion Bob was better at defensive play because of his explosive power and too, if he had a flaw as a football player it was an inability to catch a pass on offense. He had tremendously large hands but for some strange reason, finesse at pass catching escaped him.

Although Bob was physically equal to us older guys, he was not as well versed and didn't possess our savoir faire in social situations. Does that surprise the reader? I noticed that you were taken aback slightly when you read that assertion. No...

really what I'm trying to say is we brought Bob along for the ride but we weren't that crazy about his gun slinging tall tales.

But he was a good kid, always smiling and laughing, ready for the receipt or dishing out of a practical joke. No trouble maker he…but he could on occasion stir up some mischievous undercurrents, e.g. he and his good buddy, the grocery clerk, shielded by bushes and using a realistic rubber snake with string attached, they would startle poor pedestrians as they strolled by on their way to the grocery store. It was a harmless diversion but the poor victims as they danced to high heaven, certainly didn't think it was that cute.

Another example of his dare devilish approach to life was the time out near Mossy Lake, he and some of his cohorts (not the regular debonair set) were out making a fool of themselves in an old pickup, running in and off the road in what amounted to a game of "chicken", I guess. I only heard the story, I never took the time to corroborate it… the scars were prove enough. But as the story goes, Bob riding on the running board of the old truck received a barbed wire garroting of the legs, when the weaving vehicle ran into a ditch near a pasture that was protected by a barbed wire fence. Needless to say the sideswiping of the fence for a short distance left poor Bob's legs in a severely gouged and lacerated state. Can one imagine the agonizing pain caused by the deep ripping to the lower appendages which had no place to hide? Bob bore the scars of that traumatic event for years to come. It was just one more rite of passage for a bunch of rambunctious underage dolts.

One fortuitous happenstance about having Bob along the night Sonny blew the engine in Uncle Hugh's Fleetline was the fact that he had a standby referral to a mechanic shop that could quickly tow and change out the motor for a small fortune. Phone calls weren't necessary. Bob could handle the notification and would more than likely get a bonus for picking up some new business. How fortunate for Sonny Boy.

With a lot of luck, Bob made it through high school and junior college without succumbing to the wiles of the "grim reaper" (talk about somebody who needed a guardian angel, his was a classic case of justifiable intervention). With his inherent football talent and size and surrounded by some good players, his high school and junior college teams won conference and state championships in the early 1960s. Out of that hometown success, Bob received a football scholarship to Tulsa University and went on to marry his high school sweetheart, who was also a distinguished class beauty and a graduate of Southern Mississippi University.

You know…as I sit here writing, I just made the connection… it seems all the members of our pack married beautiful women. Does that not say… even at an early age, we all had an embryonic eye for esthetics? Who would ever think that this bunch of uncultured boys would show promise in the discernment of all things beautiful and classy. Yep, I can safely say that in good conscience and vouch for its validity. We all had an eye for pretty girls and as I think back to that time long ago, a question comes to mind: Were girls attracted to us as individual gems or were they drawn to us because of our bopping skills?

In summary, this group of adolescents coalesced around a genuine spirit of commonality and camaraderie. We enjoyed the collective company of all. I believe traits alien to our personalities like arrogance, greed, sullenness; selfishness and vanity defined us more than our true qualities of friendliness, humility, and affiliation. There was no phoniness in any of these comrades. Taken in sum, these guys and most of their equals at SAHS were bona fide gentlemen in all respects.

Part Nine

The efficacy of the Griffin's money making enterprises could be considered a success by most rules of thumb, but the truth of the matter was; there was still a shortfall to the tune of about $6.00. We weren't even sure Bud could take time off to go on a vacation because of his job at Tehnet's Service Station. In all likelihood, Mr. Tehnet would want no interruption of services from his favorite gas pumper and windshield cleaner. With that likely possibility staring us in our face, Bud's IOU for $10 stood to be in jeopardy. Nonetheless, it looked as if Stan's contribution was a done deal. His shoo-in was a big relief, but still, if Bud's amount were to be added back in, the shortfall looked to be insurmountable at this late date.

As a result, we were a little desperate but as a last resort we could opt to borrow money from Bud and pay it back after the vacation was over, perhaps in September or later in the fall. One way or the other, that vacation of a lifetime was going to happen.

Unbeknownst to all the vacation seekers, Mom had been selling eggs and milk to a couple of black ladies in Moorhead who were on welfare. It wasn't a lot but after two weeks she had accumulated $3.00 and expected to duplicate that amount in the next two weeks for a total of $6.00.

Meanwhile, the last of the field work was progressing nicely and we were about two thirds done with the hoeing and final plowing. The main taskmaster had retired his hoe for the year and was concentrated on making a last plow-through before the cotton crop was put on standby until the picking season commenced in September. It was still the first week in August and the cotton was maturing at a fast rate. It was Benny, Stan and Bill's race against the old clock to finish the hoeing before August 14, the designated day of departure to the glorious mountains.

Optimistically, our crops looked like they may be good ones. That meant we could expect to break even, i.e. our yield would equal the amount of money Dad owed C.M. Davis at the Bank of Moorhead. That was good, because contrary to that scenario, we would be losing ground to the debt ogre. Another prime factor to consider was the land payment... it had to be paid regardless... or share cropping would become an irrevocable eventuality and no one could stomach that thought. Normally though, if a one had a good crop it meant the "furnish and the land payment" would be met with a little cash left over for a few winter time amenities like Christmas purchases and obtainment of a few cold weather clothes for the boys.

Let's see, we still need $10.00 discounting Bud's portion. So what are we to do...I had just about run out of ideas.

I got out the road maps of Mississippi, Alabama, Tennessee and North Carolina and measured the mileage to Asheville via the route that Dad had traced with a red pencil. The total came to 545 miles one way or 1100 miles round trip. Our old 1952 six cylinder Chevy got 18 miles to the gallon, divided into 1100 miles came to a requirement of 62 gallons of gas at $.24 / gal = $15.00. Hey, that's about $10.00 less than our earlier estimation. From a critical standpoint, maybe our vacation stash was more substantial than first assumed.

I relaxed so much that I almost crumbled…indeed at last, out there in the mists of doubt; a sighting of "eureka" was a distinct probability. After telling my father and mother about the funding error, they felt as good about the situation as we did and in a generous reflex gave us the afternoon off.

Instinctively, I headed off to the Moorhead Swimming Pool to see if I could perform some belly flops off the high diving board, but my real motive was to rendezvous with Katie Jean in the shallow end where hands would not be necessary to stay afloat. Please remember I was fifteen and one knows what puberty does to growing boys. Furthermore, I knew Sonny and my other friends were working in the fields and won't be there to harass me…that was the second best part of my afternoon at the Moorhead Aquaworld. By the way, Katie Jean was a looker and she was well on her way to what the word "nubile" implies. But our intentions weren't really amorous in nature, we were just physically curious. So with that reportage, this depiction of two springers is about as risqué as this story will get.

I don't know what Stan or Benny did for the afternoon, but I suspect Benny had gone down to play with his cousin Thomas Edgar who was the same age. Stan being a guitar aficionada had been practicing nonstop for several months therefore in all probability, he spent the afternoon picking out tunes on his Gibson...and the night spent chasing girls over at Belzoni.

Like clockwork, we were back in the fields the next morning bright and early. The hoeing pace had picked up because the cotton field that we were working in was much cleaner…there was virtually no crab grass and cocoa grass under the cotton plants. At this speed, our target of finishing the field work on August 13 could be moved back to August 11, which would give us a couple of extra days to prepare for the trip.

Not to be outdone by the specter of destitution, Benny and I were determined to make one last stab at making a payday to help with expenses. One of my town buddies had been cutting a yard for an elderly lady whose house faced the Moorhead Bayou across the street from the Methodist Church, but for some reason he needed a substitute and word got around town. All the smart boys declined the offer and by the time I heard about it I was the only one interested in tackling the project for $3.00 on the barrelhead. The yard was a monster and covered about a half-acre of Bermuda entangled land. The lady knowing I had no mower of my own to cut the grass, offered to let me use her reel type push mower (as in manual push). Having no concept of the brutal work ahead for Benny and his labor broker brother, the job was readily accepted. Fortunately or unfortunately the mowing job coincided with August 11 and as we finished in the cotton patch, the big yard in Moorhead sat beckoning. Talk about underestimating a job, the two ole cotton patch hoers (oops) worked five hours to level that lawn. After that day of prostration, I made a vow that I would never use such an inadequate mowing contrivance for the rest of my life and I've kept my word. A reel mower is a cuss word, a really bad cuss word! Poor Benny, I apologize for getting him in that crack. The real value of cutting that lady's grass on an August day should have fetched $20.00 not the measly $3.00 we received. As we recovered that night after drinking 2 quarts of iced tea each, we spastically (our muscles were in knots) gave the three sweat stained greenbacks to Dad and went to bed early before the shooting stars started their performance in the eastern sky.

Incidentally, a question that had cropped up several weeks before regarding the setting of the Folklore tune "*She'll be coming round the mountain*" was finally put to rest when I visited Sonny Boy's house a few days prior to this date. While there with the acknowledgment of Carolyn's erudite knowledge of music, I asked the question and she not only provided the answer, she pulled out the sheet music for the old standard. It seems the Alleghany Mountains were the source and setting of the piece written in the late 1800's, not the Ozark Mountains as I had supposed. Well so much for the accuracy of my contention...Troy would be satisfied to know the correct location although he more than likely had forgotten it had been discussed in our cotton patch arena. I say that facetiously because my Dad had a claptrap mind and retained information like a sponge. No way would he have forgotten that particular discussion.

Part Ten

With just a few days before blast off, we were all concentrating on preparations. Dad had hit the high points but Mom was the real detail person. One thing that I've failed to mention up to this point was the addition of another son to the family in 1951. Baby brother Bishop was now four years old and his presence would require some special planning, like where to store his baby bottle and diapers…ha …just kidding. He was certainly weaned and ready for the outside world.

Stan had taken the 1952 Chevy, changed the oil and filter and washed it and dared Bud to get it dirty before the trip. By now, Bud had been turned down for a week off at the service station, so he was past the stage of hoping. In addition to missing out on a vacation, Bud would also have the unpalatable chores of milking the cow and feeding the pigs. Stan was also a good mechanic and gave the old car a tune-up by changing the spark plugs and points. We wanted as good a gas mileage as we could get owing to the scarcity of greenbacks. The tires including the spare were checked and appeared to be tread worthy for the 1100-mile round trip.

Finally on a hot muggy day in the middle of August, we all went to bed early, so we could arise at 2:00 AM to start our trip to Asheville, NC. Even with the heat, we slept soundly as the cool air from Dad's latest invention flowed over our bodies. The invention was a makeshift air conditioner constructed of a big cypress enclosure positioned around a big window fan. The cypress enclosure had walls stuffed with straw and a perforated piece of copper tubing attached to a water hose supplied a dripping source of water that kept the straw moist. As the window fan drew air from outside through the moist straw, evaporation took place, causing the temperature to drop. For water to evaporate, it has to absorb heat from the air, thus a cooling effect takes place. I tell you my Dad was relatively unschooled but he was a wizard when it came to figuring out mechanical contraptions and the like.

After eating breakfast, everyone hustled to load the car in preparation for takeoff. Mom's one piece of luggage contained her and dad's clothes plus the youngest boy's few short pants and underwear. Stan, Benny and I packed our stuff into a cardboard box in the corner of the car trunk. At Dad's behest, several blankets and pillows were thrown into the trunk on top of the other items. He knew that once we reached mountainous elevations, coldness could creep into the picture especially at night and blankets would be a welcome accessory. Mom had packed a picnic lunch of ham sandwiches and tomatoes for our lunch time meal which we would eat on the fly. The plan was to stop and get cold drinks and then find a place off the highway to eat our picnic meal. The sandwiches had been chilled overnight in the refrigerator and wrapped in cellophane to protect against spoilage until noon. The tomatoes taken individually would be sliced at the picnic site.

Bud saw us off and returned to his bed. Without having to listen to the first rooster crow of the day, we pulled out, loaded to bear, at 3:30 AM and headed east on Hwy 82. The Clampetts (no, I mean the Griffins) were on their way to their very first **Vacation.** We were stacked in the old Chevy like sardines with no air conditioning (unheard of in those days). Stan was driving with Dad on the passenger side and Bishop in the middle. In back, Mom sat with Benny and me. At last our dream vacation was coming to fruition and how wonderful it was to think that in a few hours on this very day, we would be witnessing the grandeur of majestic mountains.

In essence, the same route that the School Bus caravan took in 1952 was the same that Troy was navigating today. But to be safe, maps were marked and placed in the glove compartment for easy access. Hwy 82 was a major two-lane federal highway that traversed Mississippi from Greenville to Columbus and continued on through Alabama into Georgia. Stan methodically proceeded east toward Columbus but with daylight still a couple of hours away, Benny and I dropped off to sleep as there was nothing to interest us at this point in time. Once in a car, Mom never slept…I don't think she totally trusted any driver regardless of who they were. Bill Vukovich could have been driving and she still would have remained wide eyed.

Once in the "Hills", as daylight approached in the eastern sky, Stan quietly steered the car through Eupora, a little town on the other side of Winona, Mississippi and suddenly the car engine started sputtering and missing causing the car to come to an abrupt halt. After a couple of attempts to restart the motor with no luck, Dad, Benny and I got out and with Stan steering, pushed the car to a vacant parking lot in the middle of town.

Under the hood, our two master mechanics determined there was a problem with the ignition distributer. Immediately my brain was awash with thoughts of the Griffin family having to abort their magnificent vacation trip before it had even started. If one spoke in aerospace terms, our ignominious plight was analogous to a moon rocket burning up before it reached the treetops after launching. We were all devastated at the sorry turn of events and couldn't believe it was happening after all the work we had put into the trip. I kept muttering to myself…"I ain't believing this…ain't believing this…ain't believing this." One of the first questions that popped in my mind was: "what will my peers think about ole Billy Ray's big shot vacation getting cancelled…heck, they hardly got out of Moorhead's city limits…what a joke." Ha-ha. "Who ever heard of a bunch of poor rednecks going on a vacation anyway?" Ha-ha. I could see them making fun of my unfortunate circumstances. Depression was setting in quickly and my self-esteem was taking a beating.

I walked up and down the street several times while Dad analyzed the situation. With a broad smile, he informed us that he had good news for the novice vacationers huddled around the car…he thought he could repair the distributer if he could purchase a certain part (I don't remember what the part was). A policeman came by and asked if he could assist us in any way. After being assessed of our dilemma, he told dad we were in luck, there was an Auto Parts place in the downtown area which would open at 7:00 AM. It was now 6:00 AM, thus a delay of one hour could be expected but that was a better alternative than turning back --- to the central Delta flatlands where no one took vacations except maybe the rich.

Shortly after 7:30, the distributer was fixed and the old Chevy was once again pointed east and clocking a 60 mph gallop. "Hallelujah… Lord is with us… we might make it yet."

And that was the way it went down, we had a delay but the parade went on as planned. The Clampetts (I mean the Griffins) were on their way for the second time in four hours.

The farthest place I had ever been away from the Delta was Memphis, TN, but the roads to that major city were the same variety as we had around Moorhead, i.e. flat and straight. Actually in the trip to Memphis we never left the Delta, so the monotony of the landscape was just a continuation of starkness. At age fourteen, a good friend of mine who worked at Kincade's Drug Store treated me to a Greyhound Bus trip to the **Midsouth State Fair** and we went up there for the day. After spending the night with my good friend in town, (his father was the Moorhead Cotton Gin manager) we arrived at the Bus Station before daylight and boarded the big bus to Memphis, Tennessee. We rode all the big rides including the Zephyr roller coaster and Ferris wheel and ingested all kinds of junk candy, popcorn, peanuts, name it, we ate it. That was an experience I never forgot and I've never forgotten Twyman's generosity.

However, the point I'm trying to make here, is that once the Griffin party passed Winona we were in unknown hill country and I was fascinated. As we whizzed along at 60 mph my eyes followed and absorbed a kaleidoscope of hills, pine trees, houses and small towns, not interesting to most folks but to me, it was a treat for an ole country boy that had never been anywhere in his life. To use a country witticism "I was really takin it all in."

With Stan still driving and Benny peering through the windshield from the back seat like a Meer Kat, nervously rotating his uplifted head trying to see over the oncoming hills,

Columbus, Mississippi was reached and soon the Alabama state line was in the rear view mirror. I think some of Benny's apprehension was partially due to Stan's driving but as far as I could see he was very restrained in his foot pressure as a consequence of our parents being in the car. Benny knew full well that Stan was a lot like his cousin, Sonny Matthews, or in a more descriptive vein "Fireball Matthews." It was a known fact in Moorhead Alley that they both liked to maximize the boilerplate ratings on the old gas burners they were driving. But I must say, as we enter Jasper, AL, Stan is doing just fine because I knew if Dad took the wheel, we probably wouldn't make it past Murphy, NC before darkness caught us. It was a must that we make the first mountains by 14:00 hours.

I was still getting an eyeful of Alabama's rural vistas but was happy when we stopped in Jasper, Alabama for a pit stop. Some cold drinks were purchased and Mom brought out some sliced chocolate cake for a snack (chocolate not a good idea). Due to the summer heat, even at so early an hour the cake icing had melted. It was a little after 9:00 AM and with a Double Cola in hand and my mouth smacking of chocolate cake, I caught a glimpse of a couple of nice looking farm girls walking by the store, thought to myself "I bet they have some really cute girls in Alabama" because a Miss America came from the state a couple of years back.

The reason I knew that bit of trivia was due to my recent attendance of a 1954 Miss Louisiana beauty pageant during a visit to my cousin's house in Lake Providence, Louisiana. A program handed out at the door of the auditorium contained a picture and a profile of each young beauty from Louisiana and the previous four or five Miss Americas, including the girl from Mobile, Alabama. She struck me as being a uniquely beautiful girl and with her southern manners and charm she exuded a wholesomeness that was mighty appealing to a young sprout like me. Now why did I need to get so wordy, when I could have just said she was flat out gorgeous? Anyway, one could see what my mind was centered on or should I say where my thoughts were collecting. Yes I would say the gray matter between my ears was alternating its output between ac – dc, with the ac being fast moving scenery and dc producing thoughts of girls. The drone of the car and the virgin scenery elevated my awareness to a sharpness that was paranormal. Maybe that's the reason vacations are so highly acclaimed.

While my mind was in the dc mode, I sought to get a thing or two off my chest that had lingered in my thoughts for some time now. As I sat in my mental cocoon on the back seat, enjoying a reflective moment or two, I thought maybe I could purge my mind of a perplexing, yet exhilarating puzzlement, which had gripped me since the end of the spring semester. Talking to myself under my breath, I thought perhaps the troublesome aspect of this seemingly improbable fixation could somehow be disproved, thus sparing my mind of any future emotional distress. It dealt with a fantasy that had come true (in my mind) but in reality there had been no realization of such. It's the sort of thing that a juvenile boy would definitely dream about and I certainly had done my share of that since school turned out for summer.

As I learned later, her name was Sarah (fictitious), last name unknown and she was from a small town north of

Indianola, MS, maybe it was Shaw or maybe it was Shelby. She was a freshman student at Sunflower Junior College and she boarded in the women's dormitory on campus. My guess was…her age was probably 19 years.

I first met her eye and she mine, in the Moorhead Baptist Church on a Wednesday evening in late winter. Don't get me wrong , if you're thinking I was a habitual church patron, I'd like to quickly dispel that notion… however, on the other hand I did, as an ulterior motive, like to attend church for social reasons. One's life had to be pretty boring if an individual needed to opt for a church venue to gain social satisfaction over a teenage Bop session at the school canteen. But I did occasionally take that opportunity to act like a practicing Baptist. The older parishioners thought Sonny and I were such nice young men…yep; ole Sonny was a heathen just like me but he could sing the hymns like a songbird. Unfortunately, I added no such complement to the soothing hymnal music that emanated from the pews and choir.

On this particular evening, this very mature and handsome older girl was singing in the choir and it seemed every time I looked in the direction of the choir loft, her eyes were cast on my countenance. No, it can't be…her eye contact has to be a fabrication of my imagination. No way would a lady as classy as her be looking approvingly at a 6 foot tall 15 year old springer with "Snicker" induced patches of acne on his face. Get real and expunge that thought… "It's totally outrageous to assume such a preposterous idea."

I shrugged it off and went about my business for the next week but being intrigued by this 19 year old college girl, I made it a point to attend the next Wednesday night service. She was a no show so I temporarily forgot about my reason for being in church and focused my attention on the pool sharks down at the Moorhead Pool Hall, not to mention attending some drag races out on Hwy 3 going to Inverness*.

> **All the accolades that Sonny had accrued after the "Fireball" escapade were forfeited when he lost two drag races in one night during the competitions mentioned here. The Flying Fleetline lost to a Henry J and a Kaiser four door, in back to back races. Talk about humiliating... Sonny blamed it on the rebuilt six cylinder engine that the Mechanic Shop installed in his green Chevy plus he said his tires were pretty slick and couldn't catch any traction. At the end, Sonny finally nipped Johnny Gardner's 1949 Plymouth by a hood ornament, so he didn't go home completely empty handed. But that win was no consolation because he went home that night with his racing reputation shot to hell.*

The Baptist preacher at that time probably thought he had a promising youth deacon on his hands but little did he know, ole Billy Ray was not very good timbre for a mission of that importance. In fact I'm sorry to admit, *Illybay Aray*, that's what Roy called "*Billy Ray*" in pig Latin... was nothing less than an imposter on the prowl.

Since the SAHS and SJC campus was one and the same, both high school and college students were in close contact going to and from classrooms and to the cafeteria. I happened to see this older girl, Sarah in the cafeteria but she was too far away for me to even nod a "hello." The next week, Sonny and I decided to act like good Baptists and attend the Wednesday night service. This older girl who had attracted my attention for the last few weeks was there again, lighting up the choir loft. Once again, I was overcome with this sensation that she had me under her watchful eye, but my good sense kept denying the notion that her gaze was trained on me. I let it ride and tried to keep my eyes on the hymnal but every time I looked up, my boyish frame without a doubt was in her line of sight. Feeling subconscious, I kept feeling my face to make sure I didn't have some caramel smudges but there was none to be wiped away. Wow, I was stunned, but still had extreme doubts that she was flirting. No, it couldn't be.

When the service was over, the choir exited the aisle that Sonny and I would have to file out. As the college age girl sauntered by, I gulped as we made eye contact. She smiled slightly and nodded so imperceptibly, the motion was almost unnoticeable. I was so thunderstruck; I walked toward the pulpit which was in the wrong direction (the preacher had his eye on me...I think he thought I was coming to him for an unscheduled communion). Sonny grabbed me by the arm and directed me to the exit of the church where I noticed a group of college girls walking off the church steps in the direction of the SJC campus. Sonny was in a hurry to get home so without hesitation we jumped into the Chevy and went on home leaving me to ponder what to make of my continuing eye contact with this female stranger.

Although I was only 15 and she probably 19, the age difference made a flirtation totally out of the question. I saw her several times on campus after that and she always acknowledged me with a nod and a smile but I was too intimidated to stop and talk. Furthermore, what would I talk about...the weather or maybe crops, yes I'm sure those topics would have interested her passionately. It was a no win situation but it was exciting to think this attractive older college girl had shown some interest in me or maybe it was just a figment of my active imagination. Genuine cynicism continued to reinforce my doubts and finally I let the emotional mind game play itself out. It was a boyhood fantasy and that was all it was, pure and simple. Then at last I thought I had figured it out, perhaps it boiled down to this basic premise: my appearance reminded her of a brother or cousin or something as simple as that and the looks that she gave me were totally platonic. I accepted that rationale but had a hard time erasing her countenance from my brain's drawing board.

During the last days of the spring semester, I overheard a teacher say that Sarah's mother was seriously ill and she (Sarah) would not return for the fall semester. As I sit here, writing these passages half a century later, I can safely record that I never set eyes on her again. All I can say in retrospect is...Life is built on hard realities and little fantasies like the one just revealed. There are others that are sealed in the memory bank that will stay entombed forever. So this ends my melancholic soliloquy. Owing to his inclination to tease and rag his buddies about girlfriends, I never told Sonny about my perceived admirer. All in all, I think it was the prudent thing to do. He'll be surprised when he reads this excerpt, more than likely he has no idea who I'm talking about…and it's just as well.

The time line closeness to the coexistence of my infatuation with the college coed to "the vacation" is what brought the subject to the surface on a highway between Jasper, Alabama and Cullman. After all that deep contemplation, I was now ready to get back to some serious panoramic sightseeing, inasmuch as the Hills were starting to get higher and craggier and I had a 50 yard line stadium seat in the back seat of the 1952 Chevrolet that was serving as a fast transit system to the mountains of western North Carolina.

Part Eleven

One's memory is imprinted with visions that invoke a rush of adrenaline that firmly embosses an image into the brain's safekeeping gray matter. The folds of the brain record the images and they can be brought to life again and again by the thought process. That's the way it was as we approached Guntersville, Alabama…I remember it well and I'm sure Benny does too, with his Meer Kat attentiveness.

Indeed, as I recall, we came off this high hill and looking down on the city of Guntersville, lying at the head of a lake valley, the beauty of the view was awe inspiring. The city, with its clean main street, radiating side streets and nice stores on each side dissolved into a pristine lake in the backdrop. After passing through the town proper, a long causeway connected Guntersville with the northeast side of a big lake. Thoroughly impressed with the whole vista, I sopped up the attractive view as Stan made his way through the town. The combination of high hills (actually small mountains), the quaint town, and the large placid lake on an August day made an impression that I wouldn't soon forget. Once through the town, and over the long bridge, we stayed parallel to the beautiful lake for many miles until it narrowed into the Tennessee River which was the source of Lake Guntersville. Continuing on a northeast course, we made our way toward Chattanooga, TN. The car's odometer had registered roughly 300 miles so far and in another 35 miles the vacationers would be in the vicinity of Chattanooga, Tennessee home of Lookout Mountain.

I thought it was coincidental, in fact, downright uncanny that a big sign advertising "Lookout Mountain" was painted on the roof of a big barn at the end of Sheffield Road on Hwy 82. Every time we went to Moorhead and returned, the sign was right there in full view bigger than life as we turned into Sheffield Road, three quarters of a mile from our house.

Visit Lookout Mountain
Chattanooga, Tennessee

Here we are about a half an hour out of Chattanooga and the Griffin family will be looking at the real Lookout Mountain instead of a logo painted on a barn roof. Yep, we are now mainstream major league vacationers. But who cares about that status stuff, I'm starving and... I'm ready for some ham and tomato sandwiches on light bread, topped off with a big Barq's Orange Soda and another piece of that gooey chocolate cake. A roadside grocery store about 10 miles short of Chattanooga, served our need for beverages, a rest stop and gasoline. Two miles later we pulled into a shaded area on the Tennessee River and Mom pulled out the picnic box and we all enjoyed the food, drink and a short refrain from cramped legs and hot wind blowing in our faces (remember the windows had to let down to avert suffocation and heat exhaustion). Our picnic area was covered with soft grass and some hardwood trees afforded some cooling shade for the car and its human cargo. With the doors flung open we enjoyed our brief pause by the fairly large rock cleansing river…its water almost devoid of discoloration, which in comparison, old Quiver River was a turbid creek, whose banks were overgrown with cockleburs and ragweed. I must say from an esthetic point of view, the Tennessee River was vastly superior. Is anyone surprised?

Due to being behind schedule, we rushed through our meal and Dad, after consulting his maps, took over the driving. It was his driving experience through Chattanooga on two occasions that precipitated the change in drivers, not fatigue on Stan's part. I think Stan was enjoying his role as lead driver…so it was not the fact that Stan was tired, it all boiled down to city driving experience. Stan had none. Too, this was the time before Interstate Highways but there were truck routes around the large cities and that was a bypass strategy that Troy was counting on to get us around and through the city as quickly as possible. As I recollect, because of the River and the mountains, the choice of staying out of the middle of the largest city that we would have to go through was not an option, however we seemed to make good time and was soon on the northeastern side and headed to Cleveland, Tennessee. Not being able to see Lookout Mountain up close was a disappointment but the fact that we saw the massive mound of stone from a distance was a feather in the cap.

We vacationers could now make the claim that Lookout Mountain had been part of our itinerary. That would lend some credence to our legitimacy as big time journeymongers. But please don't get me wrong, my jesting about being uppity travelers is a total fraud on my part...actually it is dishonest to characterize my family in this light because they never put on "airs" in any context. Please accept my facetiousness as making fun of myself and that's all it was. I know for a fact that no one in our party was out to make a favorable impression on anyone...we were having the most fun in our life just being ourselves.

By now, it was 1:00 PM and we were making good time. There was virtually no conversation between the passengers because the wind noise produced by the open windows was close to deafening but it wasn't a requisite that we talk, none of the family members were big talkers to start with, besides we had run out of things to say. We were just enjoying the novelty of traveling for the first time and our eyes were roving big time. I believe Benny had the right idea...assume a Meer Kat's posture and take it all in...in rapid scans. No doubt, we were in mountains but I guess they were considered to be of the piedmont (foothills) variety. With the exception of Lookout Mountain, most of the stuff rolling before our sight receptors currently was in the 1000 foot elevation category, moderately impressive but nothing like we were to see later in the afternoon.

What about all that mountain coolness everyone spoke of...to me it was still hot as Greenwood, Miss'sippi in the dog days of summer. In reality the temperature had dropped a couple of degrees but it was hard to judge comfort level when we were compacted in the car sitting next to a heat producing family member. I stood to be corrected…Dad informed me over the stridency of rushing air that the humidity had dropped and the cooling effect blowing across our bodies was an improvement. Never one to disagree with my parents, I nodded my acceptance of the fact that I was getting cooler. Indeed, no one would get any complaints from me…I was used to heat but I wasn't used to the topography being projected outside my window.

Before a redneck grammar school graduate could drawl the word ***antidisestablishmentarism***, the North Carolina border sucked wind as it was parted by the green Chevy loaded to the hilt with Deltonians. In a few minutes we were soon pulling into Murphy, NC, a smallish town on the west side of the Smoky Mountains. Our quest to reach the foothills of the Smokies would soon be realized as surely as today was a Tuesday.

It was now 3:00 PM and if we expected to do any mountain sightseeing we would have to hustle. Stopping on the east side of Murphy, refreshments were purchased for a cool down before we made that last leg to reach the base of the tallest mountains. Mom had brought a camera and she made a couple of pictures that captured the tall 5000-foot Smoky Mountains in the background. The mountains appeared as dark undulating silhouettes behind the smaller mountains in the foreground.

Leaving Murphy, we made our way into Nantahala National Forest following Hwy 74. In the mid 1800's this road was known as the "Trail of Tears" named in honor of the Cherokee Nation whose tribe members were forced off their land by the US Government and forcibly led by US Army troops to an Oklahoma reservation. The saddest part of this forced relocation was the death of about half of the migrating Native Americans.

As we climbed in elevation, we soon found ourselves alongside a fast flowing clear water stream that was carrying people in rubber rafts and canoes. The air had cooled noticeably and the tree foliage overhanging the road cast a shade that made the air even more pleasant. As progress was made into the National Forest we could see empty buses parked along the Nantahala River. It appeared the buses were taking loads of canoeists and rafters to upstream locations, dropping them off and then going downstream for several miles to wait on the same group riding the rapids. I thought to myself...gosh doggit..." that rafting looks like fun and I'd like to try it" but I knew it was totally out of the question.

We stopped a couple of times and Stan, Benny and I scampered down the walls of the rock festooned waterway taking giant steps from polished boulder to polished boulder. We couldn't get over the clarity of the river water, it took discipline to resist an urge to scoop up a handful and drink the clear pristine water. My mother was busy clicking photographs of us and the fine scenery. The youngest of our group, Bishop, age four was taking his cue from his older siblings in his reactions to the roiling water and rocky underpinnings. He leaped from small rock to small rock taking care not to get too rambunctious, while the semi - perplexed grin on his face exhibited his less than complete enthusiasm for dipping his feet in the 45-degree water. However, after Benny rolled up his pants legs cuffs and dangled his feet into the cold crystal clear liquid, Bishop followed suit.

I could see Dad had a look of serenity on his face, because he was reveling in his family's enrapted enjoyment of this beautiful natural setting. Although he wasn't what you would call a religious man, he nevertheless believed that nature's engineered beauty and perfection was the handiwork of a superior being and proved beyond a doubt the embodiment of God and Christ. In times of stress he always sought nature to gain a peaceful state of mind. I'll have to admit his form of spiritualism rubbed off on me and at an early age I became a devotee of his method of neutralizing the demons of discord. Nature is a best friend and both Dad and I embraced God's created instruments...that which is called **Nature.** We both realized unequivocally that nature is the epitome of perfection and contrarily, mankind is the epitome of imperfection.

Although my father was taciturn and spared his words haltingly, I had a knack for interpreting his thoughts. After my mother died in 1991 and Dad became the sole occupant of his lonely little house outside of Moorhead, I would drive up from south Alabama and visit on weekends. We would always have a great time...I would take him to Indianola for dinner to some of the worst food I'd ever laid a spoon on but he thought it was delicious. That was fine and I didn't object because if he thought it was great food, I thought it was great too. In the winter months, we would sit around his wood burning stove and chew the cud. Like I said he had trouble putting his thoughts to words but because we were so much alike, I knew what he was trying to say because I understood him through his personality and actions, his likes and dislikes, his kind of friendships, his habits, how he treated people and all those definitive clues that come together to define a person. I had him typed to a tee.

Using my intuition to its fullest, here is some of what I determined to be Dad's slant on the spiritual. On the subject of religiosity, in simplistic terms, he would have believed that God created nature, i.e. animals and plant life with the following engineered omniscience in mind: Animals were given an involuntary survival instinct to guide and protect their being from harm but animals were not blessed with free will or a conscience, just instinct. Plants were not given free will, conscience or instinct. All God gave plant life was the kernel of life in a seed or a root and an engineered blueprint for growth, regeneration and propagation. If there are doubters in this world who infer there is no God or Christ, in his mind…for proof of a Lord, all one has to do is look at nature and its perfection. Nature comes from perfect engineering; fabricated by a superior being. There is no way, nature or man, came from randomness…from chaos. There is absolutely no rationale, not one iota of logic that will ever convince a perceptive thinker that somehow this heavenly conceived firmament, earth and life just happened to materialize.

As far as mankind, God empowered the human with all the gifts that he had to offer using himself as a pattern. He embodied man with a well sculpted machine of a body, instinct, intuition, conscience, ability to propagate and free will. But ominously… free will, left to the human recipient is the flaw that leads to imperfection. Infirmity adds to that imperfection. That's not to say infirm people cannot strive to be perfect but certain infirmities like mental illness are impossible to mend, briefly put, free will is and will always be compromised. God makes us, winds us up like a toy and lets us loose. He watches over us and encourages our supplication to him but our free will is the most damning element of our existence. I know that philosophers and theologians have written millions of books and articles on the subjects of free will and supplication but it is not my wish to trivialize the subject by saying what I said in so few words, so if you will, please skip over this section quickly and that's all I have to say on behalf of my father's wisdom of life. He was a simple man and this is the way he looked at the universe. He believed in Christian principles, adhered to those principles in his own way, treated his fellow man kindly but he was not a devout church practitioner.

Troy had always had this strong desire to bring his family back to the mountains to observe the sights he had relished and thought others would have to see the wonders to believe it. And thus, as he viewed his spouse and offspring soaking up the natural flora, he was overcome but he didn't shed a tear. He was not the emotional type. The only time I ever saw him cry was the event of his realization that he was dying in old age... His passing was not the reason for his sadness…it was the sobering fact that he was witnessing his loved ones, one by one, for the last time in this life.

In a final tribute to Troy Lee Griffin, I think he would have approved without reservation the family's selection of a natural Cherry wood casket in which he was laid to rest. Cherry and Black walnut were two of his favorite woods.

Part Twelve

Deep in the Nantahala Mountains, we made our way through and around overhanging forest, gorges, hair pin curves, cliffs, precipices, creeks, rivers, valleys and meadows. Even though everyone was a bit tired, inasmuch as we had been on the road for 15 hours, the pastoral splendor of the mountains kept our energetic vigil fixed on the ever changing views always sparking an anticipation of what comes next. Sure enough our impatience paid off and we were treated to the sighting of bears in an observation area where trash cans were on display. Initially there were three of them but the appearance of people scared off two but one black bear was either bold or semi tame He stood his ground and the car was able to get fairly close to the bear as he salvaged food from the trash cans. Of course there were warning signs cautioning tourist to stay away from the animals and we heeded the warning and moved on after taking a couple of pictures.

At another point on the roadside, two more bears were spotted...they were very docile...lounging and observing the vehicles as they passed. That's really all the wildlife that was observed with the exception of a couple of red squirrels and some chickadees.

At this juncture, our route took us to the rim of the Great Smoky Mountains National Park and into the Cherokee

Indian Reservation. Within the reservation, the town of Cherokee, NC was situated at the confluence of a creek and a river and a couple of highways, one of which lead into the GSMP. The other highway (19) worked its way to Waynesville and we took it when we exited the small settlement. But first, the Griffin envoy stopped in the middle of the business district (if that is what one could call it), and strolled the streets, peering into the store display windows, to see what the businesses offered. One store's merchandise consisted of polished rocks and quartz crystal. I ended up buying some token specimens for a modicum of outlay. In another store, leather goods were on display but their cost made their purchase prohibitive…I knew I had to conserve my meager vacation money for doing a few things after reaching Asheville, therefore I backed off the impulse to buy more of the gaudy trinkets and other items of interest, although a large selection of knives drew my attention but after seeing the prices, I backed off and looked for a grocery store to see if their cold box contained a Red Rock Cola. Not able to find one, I concluded the Cherokee natives didn't know what they were missing, plunged my hand into the cold water basin and pulled out a chilled RC Cola. That was the most soothing drink since Murphy. My thirst had been exacerbated by the inviting crystal clear water in the upland rivers. Like I said earlier, it took resolve not to drop to a knee and drink deeply from the seemingly harmless water bubbling up from the rocks.

Mom, Dad and Bishop wandered around and looked but did not buy anything other than cigarettes and George Washington pipe tobacco for their own consumption. Bishop and Benny got cones of ice cream and Stan, off by himself found some bone guitar picks and leather strapping for his Gibson guitar. That was the extent of the group's shopping, besides the day was long in the tooth and we needed to get on down the road since we still had a far piece to go. On top of that, we were all pretty much wasted after being awake for 14 and ½ hrs.

As I was standing there in the little village of Cherokee getting ready to board the car for the final leg to Asheville, I was overcome with a feeling somewhat like I experienced when I had a premonition of Sonny's inadvertent destruction of the engine in Uncle Hugh's green Chevy Fleetline. I was laid low with an eerie feeling of calm and a vague connection with the mountain terra firma on which we were standing. It wasn't a feeling of doom like with Sonny; it was more like a magnetism pulling or tugging at my body admonishing me to return to these mountains. "Come back son...come back soon." I knew there was Cherokee blood in the Griffin bloodline, so maybe my ancestors were beckoning me from the Happy Hunting Grounds. Like with all my premonitions, I never discussed this supernatural extrasensory stuff with any of my family but I always wondered if any of them had a similar glow. I might add...yes I returned to these mountains countless times over the years, in fact my employment for 6 and ½ years in the early 1990's required my crossing of this same mountain range on a six week frequency. The area became almost as familiar to me as my root based Yazoo Delta.

Well so much for vapors. Where the heck am I in this narrative anyway?

As we filed into the car to continue our mission to Asheville, it was obvious the shadows were getting long...extremely long. At best, we were still a couple of hours from Asheville and then it would take time to find Uncle Grady's house. It would be pitch black in 45 minutes, making it impossible to track down Grady's address in the dark. Perhaps the plan was to call him on the phone and he would meet us on the outskirts of Asheville and escort us in. Nope, stunningly, there was no such plan; as a matter of fact my parents did not have Grady's phone number nor did Stan. An address was all they had.

As our car's headlights found Waynesville's city limits at shortly after 7:00 pm, our destination was still an hour away and that was just to the Asheville city limits. After consulting the map, it was decided, the group had no choice but to try to find a place to sleep. As we groped our way in moonless blackness, the little town of Enka, a suburb of Asheville on Hwy 19 offered that respite and it was a Bed and Breakfast suitable for the six of us. The proprietor was a sweet old widow who was so accommodating it was unbelievable. I likened her to my Grandmother Moore...she really was saintly and we were in such adverse straits we badly needed an angel. It was too late for supper but she insisted we eat a sandwich before hitting the sack. The place had no air conditioning which was not unusual in 1955 but there was not a need for cooling, the mountain air was already naturally conditioned and refreshing. I was dead tired and passed into a deep slumber as soon as my head hit the pillow. Likewise, instant sleep overtook the four boys and probably the same went for the elders in another bedroom.

We all awoke the next morning, well rested and energized, ready for our rendezvous with our uncle and his young family over in Asheville. Dad and the boys went outside to appraise our location since the nighttime had obscured any real view of the old Victorian house where the bunch of us had settled for the night. It was off the road a lengthy distance but very close to the petite downtown. Big hardwoods in the front of the house muffled the sounds of the road, but considering the fatigued state the group was in upon arrival, road noise was of no importance.

The temperature was 62 degrees and it felt like a fall day in the Delta… it was nice, real nice. We all went back inside where the kind old lady had fixed a large breakfast of the usual fare that we were accustomed to with the exception of biscuits…toast replaced biscuits which was just fine. A deviation from biscuits was actually a welcome change for us boys, but Dad was a "dyed in the wool" biscuit eater and couldn't stomach the thought of a substitute, although on this day he accepted the toast without complaint. Mom was not as inflexible as Dad in her dining likes and dislikes, toast was fine with her. I would venture to say figuratively speaking, that Troy had eggs, bacon or ham and biscuits for breakfast on every day of his life. If he missed that sunrise combination it was a rarity.

Before we departed, wandering around in the big backyard, I thought about Bud at home by himself. Mr.Tehnet, his boss at the service station had agreed to come out to the house on Sheffield Road and pick him up in the morning and return him home in the evening. I could imagine Bud enjoying his freedom but not so much feeding pigs and milking the cow. Mom had made a big banana pudding and left it in the refrigerator for Bud to snack on. Knowing Bud, I visualized him knocking out that large dessert in one day, two at the most. There was no danger of the pudding lapsing into spoliation with Bud around.

After paying the $8 charge for unanticipated lodging, the green Chevy was filled with $.23 / gallon gas and we were on our way to the largest city in western North Carolina. Cruising down Hwy 19 into Asheville, the question of finding Grady's house came up and the truth came out. Surprise, surprise! Grady and his wife, Norma had no idea they were getting ready to have company. Troy had **not** notified Grady of our impendent five-day visitation.

In hindsight this atrocious imposition seems like a lack of propriety, but to be fair, Dad and Mom had always adhered to the country custom of visiting kinfolk unannounced. Since there were no telephones in our realm of living, country folks would typically visit and have dinner with relatives on Sunday without the lucky recipients knowing beforehand that company was coming. That was always the way it worked and it was a way of life. Normally a Sunday meal was built around fried chicken and with country families there was never a shortage of fat pullets running around the yard ready for plucking. Since, one didn't have to run to town to pick up the fixings for an unexpected meal, having company for Sunday dinner was always a treat for the host and the guests. In return, reciprocity was expected.

I guess it never occurred to the Griffins to write a letter to their unsuspecting vacation hosts announcing their trip intentions. Unfortunately, it didn't happen and here we were sitting on their doorsteps. I was pretty naïve but even I thought it a bit presumptuous that we came all this way without knowing whether they'd be home or not. What if they were on vacation? We'd be up the creek would we not? I guess Dad's logic was ... it took a long day to get here ...we could easily retreat to the Delta in the same length of time.

Although my Dad wasn't much of a long range planner, he nevertheless was a genius when it came to getting out of fixes. His mind could work buttonholes when he was backed into a corner like now. He was a wizard at extrication and it occurred to him the best way to find Grady was not at his house but at his place of employment which was the US Weather Service in downtown Asheville. The proper thing to do was to go downtown and ask directions to the federal building.

It's really priceless the way the meeting with Grady transpired. The memory superimposed in my brain of that scene is forever sealed in indelible sepia and slow motion. The scene, eternally solidified, can only be erased by apoplexy, Alzheimer's or death.

Directions to the US Weather Bureau building were proffered by an old stooped gentleman in a black sweater covered with dandruff, who must have been in his eighties. Yes, he was a native and he said he knew where everything in Asheville was located and he happily and precisely gave us directions. In 1955, Asheville was fairly compact and we had no difficulty finding the big multi-story building. Parking meters were out front and Stan pulled into one of the parallel spaces in line with the sidewalk fronting the marble and glass building. Dad, Stan and I exited the car and walked along a big plate glass window heading to the entrance marked with a US Government medallion. Stan happened to glance sideways into the large window and there was Grady hunched over a file cabinet in full view of pedestrian traffic. Simultaneously my eye caught sight of my uncle's visage and as Stan wheeled around catching Dad by his elbow and pointing to his brother inside. It was almost if Grady sensed someone watching him and looking up through the window he broke out in a big grin. So surprised was he, his composure was abandoned temporarily as he broke into a run through the front door and into our midst giving us bear hugs and vigorous handshakes. Can one imagine his total shock…he was flabbergasted…he had no idea that any of his kinfolks would ever come to see him in Asheville, especially any that would be so audacious as to sneak up on him like this. It was obvious Grady was overtaken with total gladness at seeing his older brother. A genuine look of pleasure enveloped his outward features and there was no denial that he welcomed us with all his heart. I could see his thought process working ninety to nothing formulating places of interest that he could show his inquisitive brother (he was well aware of Troy's love affair with mountains). There was a sigh of relief to see the open armed reception that we received because I was a little queasy that the arrival of six bodies to feed and lodge would be overwhelming to our unsuspecting host. Of course Grady's reception was heartwarming but what about his lovely wife, Norma. Would she be as taken with the arrival of Troy's bunch as my uncle seemed to be? We would soon find out.

Once it was determined our stay would be several days, Grady went back into the office and notified his boss that he would be taking the rest of the week off. I don't think it ever entered Grady's mind that for all he knew, we were just passing through on our way to take in some Broadway shows in New York City. Knowing our cosmopolitan ways, I always wondered why that thought never entered his mind. Ha.

He retrieved his personal car from the federal parking lot and led us through the downtown area and out into the suburbs. As we sped away, I took note of the city's landmarks which could be characterized as moderately low height ... most buildings were only a few stories tall and the streets snaked over... steep inclines and curving two lane streets. The hub of the city seemed to cater to the tourist industry as there were lots of cafes and curio / gift shops intermingled with routine places of business. At 10:00 in the morning, there was a hush in human activity as I spied very few people on the streets.

Benny had tired of his neck extension exercises to see over the inclines and sat relaxed in the middle of the back seat. It's amazing how quickly one becomes inured to the vacillations and nuances of big time travel. I guess one would now have to consider him a pro, this serious minded 10 year old tri-state traveler. Ha. Bishop was doing fine, as he didn't grasp what was really going on. He was just along for the ride in this wobbly mountain world.

Stan was calm and collected as he concentrated on his driving. He had his ears attuned to the sounds of the car motor, trying to discern if anything was awry with the workings of the previously dysfunctional distributer. The old car never missed a beat, was clicking like a well-oiled sewing machine, so Stan could relax and focus his attention on Grady's license plate. One thing I admired about Stan was his ability to concentrate intensely as the circumstance dictated, unlike his middle brother who had a wandering and active psychedelic mind (an exaggeration) that was hard to restrain even in times of stress. Stan could rise to the occasion and take charge...that was his forte. Speaking of the psychedelic reference, I thank my lucky stars that my coming of age in the mid-fifties predated the drug craze in the sixties. We were never subjected to street drugs, as a matter of fact, we never heard of them. As such, I can safely say, my psychedelic ruminations were all naturally induced.

Mom was doing great, after that good night snooze in Enka, she was enjoying the carnival ride to destiny and was looking forward to seeing her good friend Norma. I think Grady phoned Norma from his office, so she was prepared for the shock that would eventuate when the car pulled into her driveway.

Dad was mellow in his passenger side cockpit and the George Washington tobacco smoke was billowing forth like a paddlewheel on fire. He had brought the ship to port and the next few days would bring such a joyous round of sightseeing you wouldn't believe. We were in store for a once in a lifetime experience. And so it was. In retrospect, the enjoyment of that week spent in Asheville and surrounding countryside was never equaled in later life. It was the quintessential vacation. It was sublime and I didn't even know what sublime meant in those days of innocence.

And that leaves Bud...the only non-traveler who was at home in Moorhead. No telling what he was doing other than working and milking cows but I would venture to go out on a limb and contend the banana pudding alluded to yesterday was no longer part of the refrigerator inventory. In lieu of banana pudding, sno-balls and stage planks were probably filling the void.

Part Thirteen

The circumstances that brought Dad's younger brother to North Carolina is recapped as follows: after farming for two or three years in the Sheffield corridor, Grady sold his land and went to work for the US Weather Service as a meteorologist, a specialty that he attained in the Armed Services during World War II. I believe he spent some time training in New Orleans and was then transferred to Asheville in 1951. So at this point in time, the couple and their three children had been residents of Asheville for four years.

Grady's good wife Norma and her three children came expectantly out of their house as we pulled into the drive behind Grady. By all indications the whole family was glad to see some familiar family members coming up from Mississippi to see them. We had lived on Grady's place in 1948, 1949 and part of 1950, so with the exception of Cherry, the baby, the oldest children, Scot and Gail knew us if not well then well enough to recognize us. I believe Scot was probably 9 years old, Gail 7 and Cherry 3.

While we were still outside, and before the car was unloaded, we were given a tour of the property. If I remember, the house and lot were located at the end of a dead end street. The ranch style house was brick, 3 bedrooms and 1 bath, on a quarter acre lot with a few nice trees. The house was not joined to a carport or a garage. It was nothing fancy but it was a nice livable house, much better than the one we lived in on the farm.

As far as we were concerned the accommodations rated five stars, but we were far from choosy and to our delight, the novelty of a television set rounded out the fifth star. It was really a crowning culmination to an unexpected turn of events that our hospitable hosts could offer entertainment that was almost totally foreign to us. The only family in our neck of the woods who possessed a TV set was another uncle and aunt not previously mentioned, the Browns. On infrequent occasions, we would go to their house on Saturday nights and watch "Hit Parade" and "Have Gun will Travel" on the tiny screen that displayed enough snow to white out most of the picture, but we would attentively watch it for two hours without missing a beat. It was bad viewing but the concept of television was tantalizing.

To relieve the burden of Norma having to feed the big crew the minute of our arrival, Mom had brought a big box of red juicy home grown tomatoes and the big group enjoyed tomato sandwiches and iced tea for lunch. In the afternoon, the men folk sat at the back of the house on a small patio and talked about old times and current events in the Delta. One could tell Grady missed living in the low country but it was evident his standard of living here was superior to anything he would ever find in Mississippi. We expressed out loud that he had *it made* in this mountain haven and he agreed it was a nice place to live and raise kids and the climate was unbeatable. The Asheville area including the southward down slope consisting of foothills was called "an Isothermal region" owing to its lack of temperature extremes during a year. That meant comfortable summers and not too cold winters.

At Dad's request, Grady enlightened the group on what he knew about Asheville and summed it up with an overview of his home city.

In summary: this pristine city of Asheville in 1955 had a population of approximately 52,000 people, 90% white and 10% black. It was the largest city in western North Carolina and the people here are pretty progressive and liberal inasmuch as "The Arts" are a big thing here. The area was settled in 1792 and sits at the confluence of the French Broad and Swannanoa Rivers. The city lies in the Blue Ridge Mountains at an elevation of 2500 feet which depresses the temperature about 10 degrees compared to the Delta; for example, August in the Delta is 94 degrees and 84 degrees in Asheville. On average the area receives about 12 inches of snow annually.

From the start of the Great Depression through the present time, economic growth in Asheville was slow. During this time of financial stagnation, most of the buildings in the downtown district remained unaltered. This resulted in one of the most impressive, comprehensive collections of Art Deco architecture in the United States. Therefore, Art Deco sets the tone and flavor of Asheville Downtown.

This style of architecture is a design style which had its origins in Paris in the 1920's and continued to be employed until after World War II. Art Deco affected all areas of design throughout the 1920s and 1930, including architecture and industrial design, as well as the visual arts such as painting, graphic arts and film. At the time, this style was seen as elegant, glamorous and modern. In its earliest form Art Deco embraced soft pastel colors but moved away from those influences in the 1930s. Surviving examples of Art Deco may still be seen in Miami Beach, Los Angeles and New York City and of course on a smaller scale, Asheville. The Empire State Building and The Chrysler Building both in New York City are two of the largest and best known examples of the style in the United States.

I thought to myself…boy, my uncle is a good instructor…he was every bit as good as some of my teachers at SAHS who lectured us in History and Civics. Listening to my uncle's dissertation on Art Deco, the topic somehow went unabsorbed and didn't interest my brothers or me. Too, I think Troy was way in over his head with this Art Deco stuff. Jointly, the topic of architecture was really outside our narrow purview of international awareness. At first mention of Art Deco, I perked up a little as my mind turned over an idea that maybe the Sunflower Junior College buildings and campus being somewhat impressive in their own right were patterned after Art Deco. Later in my visit to Asheville, after viewing real Art Deco in downtown Asheville, I changed my mind about the Junior College's possible architectural style.

Grady went on to say that he would take us back downtown and show us the buildings that were considered to be Art Deco. On the subject of touring he indicated he would also take the group to the world renown Grove Park Inn and the Biltmore Mansion. We were all anxious to see as much as possible, if he was willing to take the time to show us.

Part Fourteen

That first night, we were spread out like boy scouts at a jamboree campout. The living room/den having carpet was utilized as the main sleeping quarters for the three "B" boys, who would have been Bill, Ben & Bish on pallets with Stan bedded down on the sofa. Likewise, the leaders of the pack had commandeered one of the children's rooms. It goes without saying, the night was comfortably cool with low humidity and we all slept better than we did at home where the night air in August was low eighties at bedtime. I must say this mountain living is A-ok.

That night before we all went to bed, after our uncle had time to settle down and think about attractions in the Asheville area he decided for tomorrow's itinerary, he would take the flatlanders up on the Blue Ridge Parkway for some real mountain sightseeing, i.e. mountains in the 5000 to 6000 foot range. Most roads in the highlands meander through valleys at elevations that are moderately low level, but that's not true of the Blue Ridge Parkway…its main attraction is its specific design to carry conveyances along the highest elevations that can be safely attained, in other words, along the peaks.

With Mom's agreement, it was decided the forthcoming day's excursion would be an all-male affair with Grady and Scot taking Jo's and Bishop's place in the sightseeing coach, which was Grady's fairly new Chevrolet sedan. As far as my mother was concerned she looked forward to sitting, drinking coffee and socializing with Norma for the day. It was suggested they might go into Asheville for a while and then buy groceries to meet the needs of the hungry travelers. Being the fair-minded person that she was, Jo insisted on paying her share of the groceries. Of course Norma was in full resistance mode as one would expect from any southern lady of good breeding. It was a long entrenched custom for any southern host to provide complete food and lodging for any and all guests regardless of the party's number. But everyone knew the circumstances were different in this case, after all, they lived in the city and didn't have the benefit of a garden, cows and pigs to supplement their food supply. Mom knew that and she insisted vehemently that she would buy some main course items and prepare some of the meals. As a Matter of fact on this very evening she bought a couple of chickens and prepared her specialty of southern style pan fried chicken, with creamed potatoes and gravy. In southern dialect "that's a meal that's hard to beat" even if one is "coming around the mountain driving six white horses."

In her own right, Norma was very prudent in ways to stretch out the food budget which was standard fare for any mother back in those penurious days of monetary restraint. One highlight of her innovative genius was the steadfast breakfast menu that was served the entire time we stayed there. Pancakes and maple syrup...yes-sir-ree I loved it. Her stroke of smarts derived from her way of making maple syrup…instead of expensive bottles of the stuff, she made her own with sugar, water and maple flavoring and it was great. Country boys are very easily pleased when it comes to eating…no epicureans were we.

The sightseeing brigade, sated and overstuffed with pancakes, filling Grady's Belair four door sedan to overflowing, pulled out of the driveway and headed to the Biltmore Estate section of town. The Blue Ridge Parkway built by the Franklin Roosevelt Administration in the late 1930's skirted the eastern Asheville city limits near the big Vanderbilt summer home and that was our destination for access to the Parkway. By the way, the Parkway's jumping off point was about a mile north of Cherokee, NC and it didn't end until the two lane 45 mph highway reached into the state of Maine.

What an engineering feat… but on second thought this accomplishment was nothing a person should glorify because this magnificent road, tunnels and bridges were built by "The Greatest Generation", a generation of over achievers who never believed that impediments could short circuit achievement. They just went out and did it as another days work and the word "excuse" was not in their vocabulary. Amen, my admiration for that group and the World II set is hard to contain.

Sitting in this very car among boys were two men who fit that mold of stick-to-itiveness that empowered that generation. Grady had served in World War II and Troy even with his house full of kids was on the verge of being called and shipped out when the war ended in 1945. In 1944 he had gone to Camp Shelby for a physical and pre-induction paperwork that resulted in his placement on standby. If Japan had not surrendered when they did, Troy would have been in the Pacific Theater in short order. The atomic bomb intervened and Troy who would have been relegated to the Army Infantry, escaped the horrors of war by the skin of his teeth. Even without military service, Troy still qualified for recognition in the Greatest Generation owing to his age and membership in the Civil Conservation Corps (CCC) one of the same group of workers along with the WPA that built the Blue Ridge Parkway. He wasn't in North Carolina or Virginia for the Parkway project but he was doing civil work in the Desoto National Forest in south Mississippi. So without hesitation, I say he definitely deserves a place in that honorable group if only for his willingness to serve.

My generation is minor league compared to those heroes; moreover, it's almost inconceivable to think America will ever set eyes on a greater group of citizens.

As the Belair sedan reached the Parkway entrance, Benny was positioned in the middle front seat (this was done purposely) so he wouldn't have to crane his neck to see over the hills and mountains, as a matter fact, for the most part he would be looking down at vistas that were unimaginable. A picnic lunch and drinks were loaded in the trunk, Stan and Grady had on their shades, Dad had a fedora cocked on his head, and the rest of us were attired in blue jeans and short sleeve shirts. Short pants were not in vogue in that era; in addition we thought Bermuda shorts looked queer on the few old men that were seen wearing them. Norma had suggested that we might want to wear long sleeves owing to the coolness on Mount Mitchell but the Griffin underlings had not brought long sleeve shirts or light jackets. We felt like we could endure the cold air, and too, we weren't convinced it would be uncomfortably cold in late August anywhere in the USA.

The National Park rangers didn't tolerate speeding on the Parkway, therefore the 45-mph speed was observed for the entire day as we scooted along at 4000 feet riding the high elevations of the Blue Ridge Mountains ...but this was nothing compared to what we would see in about an hour and a half. We would be staring up at 6,600 foot Mt. Mitchell, the highest peak east of the Mississippi River. The road was much curved and our stomachs got up in our throats several times as we looked at the bottomless precipices that appeared on the edge of the road at certain points. We stopped at several Overlooks and soaked up the scenery and enjoyed the crispness of the cool air in full sunshine. At this elevation coupled with bright sunlight one would have to be careful of sunburn but even in this modern age, sunscreen was not even an afterthought. Our cotton patch sunbathing had toughened our skin to an elephantine consistency, therefore we didn't give sunburn a second thought but Scot and Grady were vulnerable but who cared, certainly not Grady or Scot. Furthermore, we wouldn't be out in the sun that much, however we were mistaken as both father and son blistered that day but not seriously...just a little blush. On the contrary, the hoe brothers added to their already fashionable Caribbean tans.

I regretted we were seeing no wildflowers, but I learned later that Mountain Laurel blooms in June and July so it was too late in the season to take notice of any flowers. At these high elevations and accompanying low humidity, colors of the spectrum are strikingly enhanced. Living in the Delta at virtually sea level, all one sees is shimmering heat and haze at this time of the year. But this brilliance in the mountains is something to behold. It would have been a treat to see flowers, although the verdant greens of the hard wood and conifer foliage were something else by its self. Admittedly, this time of year didn't compare with spring or autumn in showcasing the mountains; still it nevertheless was quite a slide show. Even the quaintness of the highway with its unique landscaping, overpasses and bridges had an attractive aura.

Since Grady was the travelmeister, he had planned our arrival at Mount Mitchell to coincide with lunchtime. A frailty of the Griffin bloodline, just under the surface at all times was a ceaseless hunger for food, that's to say, we all had ravenous appetites that never appeared to be satisfied. At least that's the way I felt. We were always ready to eat. There weren't many food items I would turn down. The only thing that I refused to eat was liver and Brussels sprouts… everything else in the food chain was considered a smorgasbord of edible fare. My brothers were the same with one exception … they would eat liver. It's a wonder we all weren't overweight but all of us were pretty beanpolish in body.

As soon as we pulled into the parking lot at the tallest mountain in the Blue Ridge, a picnic table was spotted and the lunch was brought out from the car trunk along with soft drinks. It was a little bit cool but the brilliant sunlight made it tolerable. There were lunch meat and goose liver sandwiches, take your pick. It made my choice of lunch meat a no brainer and we were all soon munching away and craning our necks to see what views we could pick up from the picnic area. Afterwards, everyone had a good time milling around and looking at the broad expanses the huge mountain's mile and a quarter high elevations afforded its viewers. A tower was available for an even more stratospheric vantage point for anyone wanting a higher look at the panorama. I thought my physical position was sufficiently elevated enough to see all I wanted to see but Stan opted to hit the tower as did Grady and Scot. Benny and Dad stayed grounded while Dad inhaled several milligrams of nicotine from the George Washington tobacco smoke plume that arose from his large briar pipe. On second thought, maybe that point of information needs to be clarified …what should have been said: he got his nicotine fix from the smoke that entered his lungs through the pipe stem, not the smoke that billowed from his beloved pipe bowl. Over the years, he had developed a tic whereby he used his forefinger on his right hand to constantly tamp the burning tobacco in his pipe bowl ever so slightly without burning his calloused finger. Go figure that… and while you are at it, guess where the callous came from.

I detected a glow of satisfaction on Grady's face that reflected in kind, the pleasure and fun everyone was enjoying on this journey up the Blue Ridge Parkway. I got the impression he was feeling much like our Dad had when he observed us on the Nantahala River but I'm sure Grady's emotion probably was not the deep spiritual pangs that Troy had evoked from observing his sons among the boulders. Introspectively, it was apparent Grady was enjoying himself because everyone was having such a bully good time. It was a collective expression of esprit de corps for the entire Griffin clan.

After the group had lapped up all the best of Mother Nature's paint strokes, looking north, south, east and west, Grady figured it was time to be moseying on back to the home base, i.e. back to the beautiful little city on the French Broad River. We jammed our smiling bodies in the Chevy Belair and sashayed (maybe that's not the right word, but the car was fishtailing a little due to overweight) our way back to Asheville making sure the 45 mph speed limit was not exceeded.

Arriving at home around 3:00 PM, the home standing ladies informed us they had journeyed downtown and Norma had shown my mother the Art Deco style buildings that comprised a lot of the downtown architecture and adjacent side streets. Mom didn't really know what Art Deco was owing to her insulated world devoid of newspapers, TV, and magazines. The sole medium besides radio, which the Griffins did receive, was the "Progressive Farmer" magazine but it was only good for informing farm folks what the latest **Farmall** tractor and **creeping rose trellis** looked like. Without media it was no wonder we weren't up to date on the latest fashions in clothing, furniture and architecture. Our kitchen cabinets were made out of apple crates and we thought they were pretty stylish but I guess perhaps we had over rated them given the fact that they didn't have doors. But they did have shelves and were passably functional! Ha. Just like the pie safe and our air conditioner. Not much to look at but these appurtenances of convenience got the job done.

Yes the women folk and little ones had had a good day just like we had. Over Norma's objections, Mom had purchased two fryers from the grocery store along with some hamburger meat and Irish potatoes. She was in the process of cutting the chickens into pieces in preparation for our meal of the evening, pan fried chicken, southern style. The hamburger meat would be converted to a meatloaf on Sunday evening which was two days hence. Norma had decided that Friday evening's menu would be spaghetti so with everything duly planned, the food arrangement was taken care of through Friday and on Saturday a picnic was in the offing at Pisgah National Forest on the south side of Asheville. The group would drive about 30 miles to a recreational area on a river that could provide swimming and picnic grounds, green forest and views of a mile high mountain, namely Mount Pisgah. The whole clan was looking forward to that outing.

Most of the older boys took a nap waiting for supper which was on the table at 6:00 PM. We dug into the chicken and mashed potatoes and soon had our fill. I believe Norma welcomed the respite of not having to cook since our mother took over the kitchen and shooed her out. After supper everyone but the youngest children settled down to watch TV which was a treat for us lowlanders because we didn't own a TV. The reception was excellent since there was a TV station transmitter on the highest mountain surrounding Asheville. In the Delta, the TV signal was beamed from Jackson, MS a distance of over 100 miles; therefore the reception was very poor in Moorhead. That was my impression during the times I watched a few programs on Uncle A.P. Brown's little Philco receiver.

Living in a closed world in the Delta, current events typically went unnoticed unless I picked up an old newspaper at my uncle's house down the road from our house. I did on occasion like to pour over a newspaper and absorb state and world events, especially sports. I did that at the SJC school library and was a fan of the "Sports Illustrated" and "Life" magazines, but in the summer months away from school, my literary assimilation suffered, big-time. So here I am, sitting in the Alps of the Carolinas, among intelligentsia, cocked back in an easy chair soaking up the best programming that world media could offer.

As far as current events, a fellow named John Cameron Swayze came on at 6:00 PM and read the news. In 1955 Dwight Eisenhower was the Republican president having succeeded Harry Truman in 1952. At this time in history, the nation was highly concerned about the shooting down of an Israeli Commercial flight by a communist country in the Eastern Bloc. All the newscasts were astir with that news but since that action was a world away it didn't interest me, but on the other hand, some of the entertainment programs grabbed my attention. In prime time, the whole lot of us was able to watch programs like: *Kraft TV Theatre, Ed Sullivan Show, Candid Camera, What's my Line, General Electric Theatre and Dragnet.* Since I was watching these programs for the first time, it was not surprising that I was totally captivated. *Candid Camera* was so uproariously funny; I almost got the hiccups from over laughing. And some of the Theatre presentations were as good as or better than a lot of movies I had seen in the movie houses.

Grady interrupted our TV viewing to announce that the tour schedule for Friday would be a downtown walkthrough and a trip to the Grove Park Inn, a landmark in Asheville. None in the family, me included, knew anything about this place called Grove Park Inn but from the picture Grady and Norma painted, it was a magnificent hotel and golf course set on a picturesque upslope highlighted by mountains in the background. We were assured that once we got there and toured the historical place, we would remember it forever. Not having seen a resort of this magnificence, or never having ever seen a resort period, I was really looking forward to seeing the place up close and getting the ole sticks out and playing a little golf pool. Ha, how ridiculous…what is this game called golf? If one could use a hoe handle for a club, I'd probably be a scratch golfer, but no, at that time golf was as abstract to me as a glass of Pinot Noir wine.

As far as going to downtown Asheville, its appeal was not that enticing owing to the fact that in passing through I had already seen parts of it and Art Deco flew over my head as not being anything that would amuse me or the group. I thought the façade of **Gray's Dry Goods Store** in Moorhead had as much class as the Art Deco style supposedly rendered to those who loved it. Yet, instead if we were to go to one of those touristy restaurants with tables and chairs out front, that would be nice. Mom could take some snapshots of me in that savoir vivre background embracing the good things in life. Yes, that would impress ole Sonny and Roy---a redneck in a flour sack shirt tipping a goblet of cabernet wine while eating lamb chops in a sidewalk bistro on Main Street in Asheville. Come on *illybay*, be realistic… you know good and well, the family can't afford to go to a restaurant...six hungry Griffin boys would break the bank. I know, but it was just a fleeting thought that popped in my head.

Thursday in Asheville dawned clear, as the first splinters of daybreak peeped over the mountaintops, but there were no rooster crows alarming the late sleepers. Norma and Mom were already up preparing pancakes and maple syrup. I knew Dad was aching for a big plate of eggs, biscuits and bacon but it was not to be. I marveled at his composure and diplomacy. He bit his tongue and ate his pancakes passively but one could clearly see a big Virginia ham dancing in that cartoon like light bulb suspended above his head. I would guess the caption pulsating from the bulb would have translated to "hey Troy would you like some Red – Eye gravy on your hominy grits?" With the humorous digs set aside, the hoe brothers and their patron all chowed down on the mealy delicacy and the aromatic syrup poured heavily atop the mounds, reminded us of a Vermont landscape. We were really reaping the manifold benefits of this vacation, to wit: Glorious Mountains within our eyesight and the aroma of Vermont maple forests floating into our nostrils. Wow, what more pleasurable pursuits could one ask?

With perfect candor, I loved those breakfast delights but oppositely, I could see that burnt out look in Dad's brown eyes and the sallow appearance of his protein deprived countenance. One could really see emaciation setting in…if Troy didn't get an infusion of eggs and bacon pretty soon, he would be in danger of a precipitous weight loss to below 230 pounds. He was used to heavy duty feedings and he had about had it with this chicken feed pancake stuff. But Troy was a gentleman and he wouldn't dare raise an objection to any part of the gracious hospitality that we were receiving. As a matter of fact, he never mentioned disliking pancakes; I'm making this up as I go along with this story.

As it turned out, with time to waste until the tours kicked off, I decided to scout out the neighborhood around Grady's house and started hiking the streets that crisscrossed the grid of a neighborhood. With no thought of getting lost, I strode down the streets observing the houses which could be defined as cookie cutter in design and convenience, i.e. they all pretty much looked the same. About the only feature that differed was the look of the lawns and landscaping. It occurred to me that although there was not a lot of originality built into the housing, they looked good to me compared to the homes in the rural area from which our family originated. Now that I look back on it, I'm sure most of the houses were government financed ... it was only ten years after the great war and I'm certain Grady easily qualified for a VA loan because his good job with the Feds provided him a reasonable income. I assumed all the homeowners had good jobs, certainly they didn't farm and I was jealous...given the fact that since entering my teenage years I had fantasized a great deal about living in an urban environment where I could go to school unencumbered and free of farm work, to which, I could play all the sports and have memberships in school activities that I wanted to participate in. Of course the glamour of living in a nice home in a town atmosphere was something I had always desired.

A poignant memory popped into my mind as I looked at the pretty little ranch houses in Asheville, N.C. stacked neatly on nice landscaped lots devoid of dilapidated barns and stinking hog pins. This little vignette forming in my memory on this splendidly cool morning related to my pipe dream of living in town and the time it almost happened. Here is essentially the way the true story played out:

A possibility of employment for my father had come unexpectedly a year predating this August day in Asheville. What made it such an encouraging possibility was the job was not related to farming, a profession always accompanied by its unpalatable and unpleasant baggage.

In the early to mid-1950s, a company called Ludlow built a plant in Indianola, a town about seven miles from our farm on Sheffield road out from Moorhead where we lived in a harmonious yet poor household. The textile plant manufactured jute twine, a natural product that had use in the rope, cordage and mat business. The attraction of this Massachusetts Corporation to the Delta region was cheap nonunion labor and the farm culture of the south filled that need to the tee. Any and all people who fit the minimum wage worker classification would work for $.30 an hour in the cotton fields but the company also needed some halfway educated and skilled people to run their plant equipment. A lot of the jobs were what is called grunt work where virtually no intelligence is required…just a strong back. The mechanical aspect of keeping the equipment maintained required management to seek employees with above average mechanical smarts. Unfortunately most of the men who fit that job requirement were car/tractor mechanics in repair shops and/or farmers who maintained their own equipment but most farmers were not apt to leave their love of farming and being their own boss to work in a tedious mass production factory for Yankee supervisors.

With Ludlow not having any luck finding employees to fill their mechanical jobs, the company had to assume a proactive reconsideration in the wage area. They were willing to pay $40 a week for 40 hours of work. So the word got around and several people who knew my father and his tool talents put a bug in his ear. Due to his love for farming, his ambivalence in seeking a job at Ludlow was understandable, but when Mom chanced on the rumor of opportunity, she went into high gear goading him to apply post haste. At her nudging, he rode over to Indianola and filled out an application, had an interview and was put on a waiting list.

In the meantime, the wife and son's imaginations soared at the thoughts of a $160 per month income and the luxuries that went along with such a prodigious bundle of money.

I envisioned us renting our house and acreage to a big farmer in the area and taking the rent money and moving to town, either Moorhead or Indianola. The rent money would offset the cost of the town dwelling. That would leave $160 a month to live high on the hog…shucks, the cloud nine of that thought was overwhelming. No more milking cows before catching the school bus, no more slopping those stinking hogs, no more chopping, hoeing and picking cotton, etc. and the countless possibilities of drumming up fun in urban America was limitless. We all got carried away in our world of make believe affluence.

Then, the letter came and informed Troy that a maintenance job was his. Please come to the plant, sign some papers, take a physical and be prepared to start work the following Monday with pay commensurate to the wage afore mentioned.

Upon receipt of such comforting but profound news, we all went into a state of elation. Never had I felt such relief that at last I was free of the onerous shackle of poverty and unremitting work. I didn't mind work but when it barred me from participating in school activities and pastimes, I thought it was unfair. I knew chores were a fact of life and doing my share was a non-problem.

In a confab with Mom, we carved out a scenario that some of my dreams had touched on like renting the place, but she discounted the possibility of renting out our house. If the place was rented, she felt the prudent thing to do was to stay in the house and fix it up. This was a little disconcerting to me because that meant we'd be keeping all the farm animals and vegetable garden for food supplement but I liked the idea of modernizing our house. It could use it. The planning of our new life was heady stuff and we were savoring all of its beneficial permutations.

We thought the new job was a done deal but the day that Dad returned from the Ludlow Factory and told us he had failed his physical because of a hernia, our approaching feel good world evaporated like a snowflake in south Alabama. I was miserable for a couple of days but I got over it. My outlook to the future reverted to the same as before the "Great Chance" caught our fancy in that summer of 1954. So my ticket out of the pits never got punched but I became a better person as a result of the hardships…that which does not kill me makes me stronger.

With another episodic disappointment down the drain, my dream weaving was being thwarted from every angle… maybe it was time to quit that stuff, but it was a hard habit to give up, arising from the fact that in a farm boy's realm, a rosy visualization of the future is the string and carrot that keeps him moving forward.

As I stood in real time near the tract houses in that Asheville, N.C. neighborhood, I refreshed my thinking process to align it to the current place and time and pondered: What if Dad got a job up here in Asheville…we could buy one of these nice little houses and I could go to Asheville High School…become a basketball star and court some of these mountain girls. Boy wouldn't that be something…a redneck with a southern drawl trying to understand a western Carolina or an eastern Tennessee twang. What would be the product of those two dialects? I hate to even think about it.

Dad's chances of getting a job up here were minuscule. He had never had that hernia repaired because of no health insurance and no money. Maybe he could get a job with the Weather Service, seeing as; he was good at predicting weather conditions with his careful way of gazing at rings around the nighttime moon. Without instruments and data, he could easily contribute weather forecasts to the TV and radio stations for a reasonable fee. Of course that line of thinking was totally irrational…I was just making fun of my (dead on arrival) idle hopes. I thought if I laughed it would keep me from crying.

No, please don't take me seriously I'm just kidding…might as well accept it, the Griffin boy's destinies were to be foremost and forever firmly grounded to the black gumbo land that fills the central Yazoo Delta. The only way to get out was to become of age, then hit the road.

But in no way did these feelings of self-pity detract from this once in a lifetime vacation that my family was in the middle of. We were having the time of our lives. My reinstated euphoria skunked the short-termed depression that had overtaken me as I recalled Dad's lost opportunity. With my mind clear of pessimism, I took a deep breath and proceeded to walk back to Grady's pretty place...yes, I had come full circle in my thinking out loud but with that behind me as I revisited the appearance of the neighborhood l came to the conclusion that his home was the prettiest of all the houses that I had witnessed that crystal clear morning in the suburbs of Asheville, NC.

Later on that Friday morning, Grady decided to forgo the walking tour of downtown Asheville and in its place, tour the city in his car. Norma stayed at home with the kids and Mom joined us for the tour which included downtown, Biltmore Village and the Beaucatcher Tunnel.

In the afternoon after lunch we rode over to the Grove Park Inn to get a look to see if it was all it was cracked up to be. I must admit it was pretty impressive situated astride a beautiful manicured golf course with mountains in the background. It's my understanding the golf course predated the construction of the Inn by about a dozen years. In fact the street accessing the golf course and Inn was a residential area, probably the first high class subdivision in Asheville at the turn of the century.

We entered a parking lot at the side of the vast multi-level hotel and Resort and entered the building at the lobby area. Since this was a working hotel and not a tourist attraction per se, Grady had to be our tourist guide. We walked around the lobby and observed the huge walk-in fireplaces on each side of the massive room. Everything was appointed with hugeness, none of the furnishings could be considered to be moderate or quaint. Everything was colossal in theme; the furniture, the fireplaces, the wings, the porches, the stonework, the size of the granite stones, the windows, the roofing, the landscaping, etc. and there was no lack of quality and as expected there was no lack of coddling the quests. Of course we were painfully out of place...I don't know what the cost of a room was but in the context of our meager income it had to be astronomical, but there was no crime in looking. As we pressed close to the viewing panes, wide eyed with mouths open we probably left some inadvertent smudges on the large picture windows. Grady herded us out to the porches and told us to sit while he told the adults a little bit about the history of the Inn.

The big Inn was built by a wealthy gentleman from Paris, Tennessee named Edwin Grove in 1912. As the story goes, Mr. Grove made his fortune from the manufacture and sale of a Chill Tonic that contained quinine. Apparently the medicine helped tame the debilitating chills brought on by Malaria. One time the number of bottles of Grove's tonic outsold the number of bottles of a famous brand of cola that everyone is familiar with. It seems rich Mr. Grove suffered from bouts of hiccups and his doctors sent him to Asheville to determine if the favorable climate would help reduce or cure his hiccups which lasted for weeks at a time. In essence, taking into account all the elements leading up to the construction of this famous hotel, one would have to say the monumental undertaking of building such a grand structure came from a snake oil salesman.

He began accumulating land for the Inn and for residential development in 1910. Construction began in 1912 and was completed in an amazing 11 months and 27 days. This feat was accomplished by paying high wages to the dedicated workers who lived in circus tents erected on the job site. The Inn opened July 12, 1913. The hotel was outfitted with furnishings from Roycrofters of East Aurora, New York, one of the most important designers, manufacturers of Arts and Crafts furniture, metal work and other accessories.

In the hallways of the Inn, especially those that branched off to the "wings" on each side of the lobby, large photographs of Famous Guests were hung in full view of people walking to their rooms or to the large convention rooms. Some of the prominent luminaries who roomed in this fabulous place included Thomas Edison, Henry Ford, William Jennings Bryan, Woodrow Wilson, John D. Rockefeller, Franklin Roosevelt, Herbert Hoover, Dwight Eisenhower, Enrico Caruso, Al Jolson, Will Rogers and many more.

Boy howdy, we were striding through the corridors of the famous and wealthy. Talk about being touched by culture… we were absorbing every ounce of the interesting surroundings. We were walking in tall cotton, but before our heads got too big, it was decided us ordinary folk had overstayed our welcome.

As we drove away, looking back at the grand view, I made a vow that I'd come back some day and stay at this place. And I did on a couple of occasions when my home was Charlotte. It didn't feel or look nearly as grandiose as it did in my wide-eyed youth in that impressionable summer of 1955.

Part Fifteen

The TV shows that were listed came on during the work week but Friday night was aimed at the male audience.

Gillette's Cavalcade of Sports presented boxing and that was of great interest to Grady and me. As stated earlier in the story, Troy had no interest in sports, therefore he took the liberty to retire to the back porch, lounge, smoke his pipe and enjoy the cool evening. After studying a city map for a good thirty minutes, Stan opted to drive downtown and walk around the commercial area in hopes of seeing a Carolina girl or two. I think he struck out because he never spoke of what he encountered that evening in Asheville but he did relate to my confidence, an encounter with a girl at an Asheville amusement park on the ensuing Sunday. I will issue more information on that conversation later.

The novelty of viewing a television picture attracted Benny's notice, so the boxing match had a three man audience in the less than crowded living room. I remember the fight distinctly, now that my recall has brightened...the marquee fighter on exhibit that night was Gene Fulmer from Utah, however I don't remember his opponent. If I'm not mistaken, Fulmer became Welterweight Champion of the World in the heyday of Sugar Ray Robinson and Carmen Basilio. Remember those guys? Anyway, it was an interesting fight and the circumstances that night locked it into my memory bank and I can still conjure up visions of Fulmer and his sharp boned face but nothing more...I don't remember if it was a championship fight or not.

"Early to bed, early to rise makes a man healthy, wealthy and wise" but Grady, Benny and I violated that Ben Franklin epigram because we were late getting to bed after the boxing match ran to about 11:00 P.M. Customarily by 10:00 pm our bed covers were parted because of our farm work habits.

It was déjà vu with pancakes jumping off our forks on this bright cool Saturday morning. I refuse to make any more snide remarks about our wonderful flat cakes and New England flavored syrup. Like I said, I loved my aunt's wonderful pancakes. By now Troy's palate was craving eggs and grits so intensely his habit of slurping his coffee, followed by a big appreciative sigh, was ignored in favor of gulping. However, all the other food delights that were put forth at lunch and dinner easily made up for his lack of enthusiasm for the sunrise menu. It was a little bit of an enigma that he never took a pass on breakfast…he sat there and ate as many of those saucer sized cakes as any of us. Deep down, I truly believe he loved those big humdingers. Maybe it was a macho thing…you know like: "real men don't eat quiche", perhaps he thought real men didn't eat pancakes.

After everyone had dressed and the cars were loaded for the day's outing in Pisgah National Forest, Stan headed our 1952 Chevy out following Grady's car. Pisgah* was located about 20 miles west of Asheville and the spot that Grady picked was on a big stream of slow moving ice water…if it was not a river then it was a large creek…just the right size for swimming and swinging on a rope suspended from a big hardwood tree.

** Not far from this picnic location in Pisgah National Forest sits 5700 foot Mount Pisgah. It's hard to believe but in 1992 when I lived in North Carolina, during a four day snowstorm in the* *month of May, Mount Pisgah received 60 inches of snow. It really was an astounding event for the month of May?*

A picnic table was selected near a cooking grill and the numerous trees made for a lot of shade...too, the table was close to the water way. Our accommodations were primetime...one couldn't ask for a better picnic site. With extra chairs unfolded, the adults lounged while the kids hit the breathtaking water headfirst. Grady stayed close to his children to make sure they kept their heads above water and Stan and I did the same on our little brother's behalf.

The ladies grilled hamburger patties and we all chowed down for a lunch break. Teasingly, I asked Dad if he wanted a couple of pancakes instead of buns to wrap around his hamburger...he gave me a big "harrumph" as he cleared his throat and glanced sideways at Norma who hadn't caught my dig.

To suggest that we were on the backward side of unworldly would be an understatement but I'll have to admit that was the first time, I at 15 years of age had ever tasted a homemade grilled hamburger patty. I had had hamburgers at some of the cafes and car hop places but at home the only hamburger patty that any of the Griffin Boys had ever tasted was a hamburger steak in gravy. So it was a new experience...just one of many that were infusing our senses in grand succession.

More swimming, hiking and lounging followed lunch until finally around 3:00 pm a halt was called to the activities and given that we were all bone tired, loaded up the cars and returned to Asheville for another leisurely spent evening watching TV and eating a hotdog supper.

Before we could snap our fingers, it was Sunday morning and we were looking forward to our last full day in Asheville. With our fabulous vacation winding down, a return plan called for the Troy Griffin troop to get up early on Monday morning, around 3:30 AM and hit the road at 4:15 to return to the motherland over yonder in cotton country.

Later in the day on this Sunday, the final activity of our stay was planned to take place at an amusement park in Asheville. We would all converge on the park, buy tickets to some of rides and enjoy a nice and cool Sunday afternoon before turning our thoughts of backtracking to the sweltering Delta.

I'm sure Norma was relieved to know that we were leaving in less than 24 hours. There was no doubt She and Grady had enjoyed our visit but let's be realistic, their routine had been upset to a high degree and I think all of us old enough to think about good manners acknowledged that our time was up…it was time for our gracious hosts to see our tail lights disappear in the early morning dawn never to be seen in these parts ever again. The same excitement that accompanied our arrival was now equally felt upon our soon to be departure. I could gamely see, our hosts were more than ready to abort the familial comradeship for a little prolonged peace and quiet. Happiness was certainly not their intent but unquestionably, glee was lurking just beneath the skin surface covering the smile muscles. Furthermore, the big box of pancake mix was just about depleted and Norma was starting to panic a little, concerned about Troy not getting his normal diet of delectable hot cakes. Post August 21, 1955, I can safely say that I never saw my father eat another pancake as long as he lived.

As a precursor to the amusement park outing, Mom made and cooked a large meatloaf for our lunch and supper. With our lunches tucked away in our alimentary canals, the vacation revelers, made a beeline to the neat amusement park located in the city limits of this touristy little city. The park was nothing like the Midsouth Fair in Memphis but it offered an assortment of rides, games and concessions. Since most of my activities had been in concert with the family, I was anxious to break away from the group for some solitude that would allow me a chance to compare the Carolina girls to the Delta belles. In so many words, I was aiming to do some girl watching. The same went for Stan because as soon as we entered the park he headed in a direction opposite to that of the adults. Although I wasn't as abrupt in taking leave of the group as Stan, I soon was on my own in the concession area where several girls were loitering. I sat down on a bench away from their view and sized them up with an occasional glance over my shoulder. In my discriminating opinion, a couple of the four teenagers were deemed to be on the cute side but the other two were pretty ordinary looking. For one thing they weren't as nattily dressed as the girls in the Delta...indeed that's one thing about the Mississippi girls that I knew, for certain they never went out into public without being smartly dressed and coiffured, even at casual events. But you know even if the mountain girls weren't that classy looking, they still were cute and giggly and they cornered my attention for a few minutes; then I was up and on my way to get some parched peanuts for which I had a hankering for.

With some of that loose change that I had saved for the trip now rolling off my fingertips like water cascading over rocks in the spring running through the Grove Park Inn golf course, I quickly became concerned about becoming penniless before sampling a great deal more of the attractions that the park had to offer. In quick succession I had spent a total of $2.00 on peanuts, an orange soda, The Ferris wheel, bumper cars, rifle alley and a basketball shooting contest. I lost my cool slightly when I realized the basketball rim was a smaller diameter than a normal goal but what could I say. They already had my $.15 and I wasn't about to make a scene, so I just walked away and took my lumps.

There's no doubt the carnival thrived on deceptive games that attracted country hicks, mountaineers and hillbillies. I didn't want to admit it then and there, but there might have been some validity in counting me in that group…no, on second thought, I'm not a hick but it's hard to type one's self in a situation like this. Maybe I should have gone back to those four girls and asked them if they thought I fit the definition of a country hick. My flour sack shirt was made from "Mothers Best" flour sack material and I'd heard that the cloth came from the best textile mills in South Carolina. You don't guess they discerned that my shirt was homemade, do you? The cloth was combed cotton. Naw, I was just pulling your leg on that one…actually my shirt was purchased from Diamond's Dry Goods store in Moorhead. The fib just voiced did in fact have some validation several years before this occurrence…to wit: my mother did make her boys flour sack shirts and swimming suits from cloth that came from flour sacks. In the late 1940s and early 50s it was a common practice for all the flour manufacturers to market their products in nicely patterned cotton cloth bags, its purpose being to provide families with cloth that could be used for sewn garments. A talented seamstress could make nice looking outfits out of the cloth for her children, whether it was dresses, blouses, shirts or underwear.

Relative to this somewhat politically incorrect topic considering Women's Rights and all that stuff, there had been a well-worn yet still long standing joke told by my Uncle Bunk Moore about a time that he went to a dance and witnessed a young lady, who in an exuberant dancing exhibition allowed her dress to rise above a critical level, to such an extent that her drawers were completely exposed to the bug eyed males in attendance. The young men were all eyes, but the sight they beheld was not what most people are thinking…what really awed them was the drawers…one side was made from "Mother's Best" and the other side from "Pillsbury" flour sack stock. Forever broadcast after that fateful night was a rumor that this particular young woman, owing to her partitioned drawers, suffered a long lasting humiliation that was hard to live down. Eventually the poor girl had to be institutionalized after being diagnosed with a split personality.

I had a big time that afternoon as I wandered around the grounds. At intervals the family group and I crossed paths as did Stan and I pass one another on a couple of occasions. We stopped only momentarily to compare notes to see what the other had seen or missed. One time, I caught a view of Stan talking to a nice looking young brunette in a blue skirt. Later on that evening, he told me about her and their meeting.

We finally called it a day as the shadows got long and everyone tired of the walking and standing. I was glad and sad at the same time because my money was all but spent except for $.50 that I kept in reserve to buy refreshments on the way home. After arriving back at Grady's house, Mom and Dad got busy loading up the old Chevy before darkness overtook the driveway area. As was his normal routine, Dad checked the oil level in the car and noted it was a half quart low. He made a hasty calculation in his mind and announced under his breath that the car could probably make it to Chattanooga before a quart would have to be added. Early on that Sunday morning, at Dad's urging Stan had taken the car to a nearby service station for a gas fill-up; hence all the pre-trip preparations were completed.

From all outward appearances, the two tone green cowcatcher was pointed southwest and ready to roll. All that was needed now was for the driver to get a decent night's sleep pursuant to an arduous 13-hour trip back to the Mississippi Delta.

Concluding a supper of leftover meatloaf and mashed potatoes, the TV addicts settled in the living room/den area to watch Ed Sullivan, Dad went out to smoke his pipe and Stan and I moseyed to the lounge chairs on the patio.

I sensed that Stan wanted to talk, to get something off his chest. Normally he was not the type to confide any of his feelings to his family, inasmuch as my parents were not wired properly for career planning dialogues that could be an inspiration to a young son stepping out into the future. I think Stan was just looking for a sounding board to expose a plan that had materialized in his mind over the summer months and had conceivably reached a climax on this day. I knew beforehand that he was struggling with a decision to further his education at SJC or to light out on his own to find a job and start making some money, so he could live by himself and buy a car. That thinking was short sighted but unfortunately that train of thought was common among country boys of that era.

That was the prelude that I was expecting but Stan opened up telling me about his encounter with a girl that he had met that afternoon. A picture of her pretty face immediately jumped from my brain's memory cells. Yes I remember seeing you and a young lady talking near the carousel early in the afternoon. Was that her…if I remember she had dark hair? Nodding, he started his recounting of their meeting and I settled back in the chaise lounge and perked up my ears.

Her name I don't remember, but she was seventeen years old and visiting relatives in Asheville. Her home town was Rutherfordton, North Carolina, located in the upstate country of the Carolinas, i.e. in the foothills of the Blue Ridge Mountains. She was at the amusement park with her cousins and aunt. Although she told Stan that she had a steady boyfriend back in Rutherfordton, the news of that development in no way deterred Stan from starting an exploratory conversation.

One thing about Stan, unlike me, was his assertiveness in the pursuit of the fairer sex. Stan was an attractive young man with reddish brown hair, athletic body, fairly tall; probably 5 foot 11inches in height, winsome smile and devilish personality…in other words, he possessed all the components that attract girls of that sort or for that matter any sort. Most females I've ever known have been attracted by some degree of recklessness and Stan had various amounts of that stamped in his DNA.

Using the ruse that he couldn't find a certain place in Asheville, he accosted the nice looking girl in the blue dress, asking her if she was a native of the city and at the same time informing her he was a visitor. From that introduction, they started a discussion that went on for a good 45 minutes…it was obvious she was interested to hear what the old boy from Mississippi had to say. She told him about her hometown, her high school, friends and Asheville cousins…in return, Stan being a bit unscrupulous found it unnecessary to tell her the complete truth about his less than modest circumstances in Moorhead. In so doing, he good naturedly regaled her with a few white lies (unsure if one could call them white lies or something more hardcore) but anyway, the young lady absorbed a story of Stan being the son of a large cotton plantation owner in the Mississippi Delta called the Quiver River View Plantation consisting of one thousand acres and a big ante bellum style house. I was really surprised that my older brother had so blatantly misled that girl and I expressed my annoyance with his deceit. Deep down, I reconciled my inner self that Stan was exaggerating the story for my benefit as he was relating it to me.

But you know what; I now believe the story that danced in my head and put me to sleep that evening in August, 1955 had played out exactly as Stan told it. In hindsight, later in early September, I recall a letter arriving at our mail box addressed to Stan's attention – Quiver River View Plantation. Our mail carrier, Mr. Hobbs got a big kick out of that farcical address and laughed about it for years to come. Needless to say the return address on the letter was Rutherfordton, NC.

To further the conversation that transpired that evening, Stan went at great lengths to tell me he was seriously thinking about passing on a college education, instead he had an idea that he was mulling over and that was to go to his Uncle Gene Moore's place in St. Louis, Missouri and see if he could find a job. He was only a few days away from becoming 18 years of age and he wanted to get out on his own. He certainly didn't aspire to be a farmer or any related profession thereof. With my dearth of experience, I willingly seconded his announced choice of making his way to St Louis. I had always viewed my St. Louis relatives as being classy people with their big flashy up-to- date cars being symbolic of their prosperity. Stan would do well to become a part of their good life and separate himself from the rural way of life which almost always guaranteed a lack of opportunity.

By now it was close to 9:30 PM, so everyone knowing the ritual of getting an early start the next morning hit the makeshift sleeping pallets, sofa and bed. This was our last night in the beautiful city of Asheville and if the rest of my family felt the same wistful pangs as me, it would not surprise me. I had trouble sleeping, but thankfully, Stan and Dad, our delegated chauffeurs for tomorrow's journey were cutting "Zzzzs" like nobody's business.

Before we knew it, the wee hours of Monday morning rolled around and everyone got up and at 'em. Since all the pancake mix had been consumed the previous day, Norma and her guests had to settle for a breakfast of coffee, toast and jelly. That was fine with us and we soon were saying our parting goodbyes to the Grady Griffin family. Our return trip to the hallowed grounds of the Yazoo Delta would be starting as soon as Stan pushed the key into the keyway on the dashboard of the car. In five minutes, we were stopped at the first red light heading out of Asheville while Stan listened intently to the sounds of the six cylinder engine. The steady clicking of the lifters and a glance at the oil pressure gauge reassured the pilot in charge the old car was primed and good to go. There was virtually no traffic as we eased our way to the city limits and beyond. Benny and Bishop were already nodding off but Mom was wide awake and so was I. We had a long day ahead of us.

As the sun came up, we were passing through Sylva, NC working our way to Franklin with our far sights on Murphy. When viewed through the rear window the really tall mountains started to recede ever so slowly. Almost imperceptibly the air got warmer and warmer and the humidity got heavier and heavier as the highlands became foothills.

No one was talking because the overall mood was decidedly subdued. It stood to reason that the high all of us had been on for six days was slowly but surely waning...there was no getting around it. My elevated thought machine that was so energized on the way to the mountains was now frayed and fuzzy. No supercharged reminisces or thoughts of the future were firing off today. It was almost like being bipolar, i.e. the manic phase had run its course...now it was the pits...no not really, I'm exaggerating but the downside was definitely palpable.

With the old Chevy ginning like a brand new Singer Sewing Machine and with Stan's foot accelerating slightly on the heavy side, the cruising speed leveled out at 65 mph on the straight away. Granted, we had started at a 2500 foot elevation and were working down to sea level or below, but it seemed like the continual downgrade was aiding our progress much like a tail wind. Before we knew it were back in the beautiful little town of Guntersville at which point we stopped at a grocery store before treating ourselves to a typical cotton patch lunch, i.e. cheese and crackers, Vienna sausage, Hostess cupcakes and cold drinks under a shade tree on Lake Guntersville.

All that delightful coolness that we had enjoyed in the mountains was nowhere to be found in these climes and the travelers had to decompress to counteract the high humidity. All our shirts were soaked with sweat in the oppressive heat of late August and the shade provided by the big oak only minimally alleviated the discomfort on this breezeless day. At least the wind generated by the speeding car created evaporation in the occupant's clothing which in turn tempered the heat. It became immediately clear that eating our lunches quickly and returning to a moving car was the right option at the time. No doubt, the misery index of the subtropical south had kicked into high numbers with a vengeance and if the truth be known, the Griffins hadn't even breached the outer limits of the true Deep South.

I dreaded to think what it was going to be like in our old uninsulated house tonight upon our arrival, but then I reminded myself that Dad's window fan air conditioner would be our life saver. Yep, I had forgotten about that contrived piece of genius.

Stan was determined to drive the whole way and Dad wasn't objecting. The smallish mountains turned to monotonous little hills and low river bottoms in equivalence to the sun in the west as it dipped lower and lower…so low in fact that glare was hindering our determined chauffeur but he made adjustments to the visor and hunkered down for the final stretch. Suddenly those who were fully conscious exhaled an extended sigh of relief when the Mississippi state line was crossed.

Sightseeing was now an exercise in boredom inasmuch as the countryside was in reversion with nothing fresh to see. It was like watching a picture show for the third time in a 105 degrees Fahrenheit theatre.

My psyche was ill equipped for my return home. My head was still in the clouds (of North Carolina) even as my physical presence was quickly descending to sea level.

With absolute irony, we were all at the point of wanting this vacation to end. Of course it was only natural that this return phase of the vacation would engender a let-down but none of us were about to voice any displeasure. It just wouldn't be right after all the enjoyment we had had for six full days. No way would there be any complaints. We had reaped memories that would be with us for the rest of our lives.

And then in the distance, there was a sign just off Highway 82 signifying our approach to Valley Hill, a demarcation point between red hills and black Delta. As we descended the big hill leading into the flat farm strewn Delta, my heart beat picked up its pace. It wasn't joy but yes maybe it was a slight twinge of contentment to be back on home soil as much as I hated to admit it. As ugly as the Delta seemed to be to most of its inhabitants it was nevertheless the land of my birth and even with its warts and flaws I still had an admiration for the old grubby flatland. I certainly did and I didn't know why? It had brought my family a lot of heartaches over the decades.

The sun was slipping below the horizon when Stan took a right turn off Highway 82 onto Sheffield road and in a couple of minutes the tour car pulled into the driveway of the Troy Griffin Estate. After seven rousing days on the road and 1200 miles of extended travel, our first and only family vacation was jogged into history.

This vacation of a lifetime was now a memory but its ending was forever engraved in my mind in a "Treasured Archive" never to be tarnished, fazed or forgotten. I made a personal vow to one day retrace my footprints to that inspirational and profound garden of beauty that forever lingers under the gaze of those blue tinged mountains.

CHAPTER TWO

Part One

This is the second part of a serialized narrative containing a number of nostalgic anecdotes; actually the ramblings seen here are drawn from the fading memories of a simple and humble country boy whose body and soul was staked and tethered to the turning rows of the Yazoo Delta six decades past.

Before ratcheting forward to 1958... kindly accept this attempt to establish a connection to the past, moving forward in time from 1955. The plot begs the reader to respectfully examine this brief foreword as its provision is meant to fill in a few gaps of the larger picture. In the resulting disclosure, are a couple of relevant events that followed the North Carolina vacation of 1955 which serve as a springboard to the 1958 story contained in this article?

To set the record in motion, after a day or two of decompressing from cloud nine succeeding "the grandest of vacations", the humdrum world found the Griffins settling back into a well-established routine of work for the adults and school for the boys except for the oldest son Stan who almost immediately migrated to St. Louis where he gained employment at a plant that made industrial and commercial size refrigerators. Second son Bud and third male, Bill entered their junior and sophomore years at SAHS and Benny moved up to fifth grade at Moorhead Grammar School. The youngest of the brood, Bishop, was still a preschooler.

The demography of the Sheffield enclave and corridor had changed measurably from a neighborhood richly populated with pre-pubescent kids in 1949 to one that was moderately spiked with a mixture of variably aged youngsters. The Melvin's with their seven children (six boys and finally a girl child) had moved to a new farm south of Moorhead near Highway 3, the Roy Matthews family relocated to the town of Moorhead, all the Sheffield boys except the youngest son were gone either to the military, college or into careers , the Henley's who sharecropped on the Sheffield's farm had moved away from Moorhead with their five offspring and their vacant house was soon occupied by a hard working black family whose head of family was Willie Junior...his last name I never knew. There were probably at least eight in that crowded household.

The Houston Cooks, with their two daughters and a son, now lived in the old house where the Griffin's "Christmas Story" setting took place. The son, Leroy was a year older than my brother Benny and they became good friends as they roamed the same pastoral nooks and crannies that we older boys did in our pre-adolescent ages. My Dad gave Benny's running mate a nickname that I've always remembered to this day. He called him "Leroy Snavely Gray" and the name was a glove fit for this playful yet humble Huck Finn urchin child of a sharecropper. He fit the bill with his ragtag short breeches and his tough as elephant hide bare feet. No...Snavely was not an urchin, he was actually a humble and sweet boy. Urchin suggests poverty and he and his family certainly owned a piece of that common chattel. In retrospect although I'm a little hazy with my recollection, his two sisters were no doubt very nice looking girls but who would have known it in those days as it seems feminine attractiveness in the country was almost always masked by plain clothes, poor hairdo's and lack of makeup. Had these two girls been attended by modern cosmetics and fashionable clothes there is no doubt they would have been knockouts. But I do remember they had alluring figures and they didn't suffer from male inattention. They were older and I was younger, so in effect, my view of their beauty was lost in other diversions.

So let's see, doing the math, the population of youngsters had declined in number from 29 to 13 not counting the black children of which there was a houseful. They were extraordinarily good people but in the 1950s, segregation was the social law of the state of Mississippi, therefore mixing of the races was frowned on. Furthermore, we were older and playing with younger kids whether white or black didn't jibe with our interests. Obviously my standpoint toward issues of race was superficial due to my lack of analytical dissection. The civil right laws changed social habits in the 1960s but by then, I was long gone from that place smack dab in the middle of the Yazoo Delta where "the Southern crosses the Dog".

In the ensuing three years moving forward from 1955, the Griffin family continued farming the 56 acres of land that Troy Griffin owned in the corridor. The year 1956 turned out to be an excellent cotton crop year and the good yield allowed enough lagniappe for the household to buy a 21" Westinghouse Television set for the family. It was a dream come true...the Griffin boys felt almost as privileged as we did when the 1952 Custom Deluxe Chevy showed up in their driveway. The television reception wasn't that good but we, with squinted eyes endured and enjoyed any and all programs that were televised over the north Mississippi airwaves. We could pick up a channel out of Jackson, MS and on occasion receive one out of Memphis, TN. Some nights the snow on the phosphor screen was such a blizzard, we primarily just listened to the audio coming over like listening to a radio and conjuring up images of the action taking place on the sizzling screen. It was much like the old sports announcers in the 1920s that read ticker tape results at the end of each inning and made up the belated action for the enjoyment of an unwary radio audience.

The reason for the inclusion of the television acquisition as a significant event was not intended as a boastful remark. I put it in this passage because in my way of thinking, television in its infancy was a remarkable tool for educating the masses and as an added medium, its ability to distribute news, including political and current event analyses, was priceless. Since at that point in my young life, I was a keen observer of news and sports, the new television served my need for news acquirement that was heretofore sorely missing from our household. As I said before, we never subscribed to a newspaper, so it was left to me to gather the reports of current events in school libraries and from old newspapers stashed at my uncle's houses. They never threw anything away especially magazines and newspapers. I even had my choice of day old newspapers if I had the will to go get them, to wit: **The Memphis Commercial Appeal** at the Sheffield house and **The Jackson Daily News** at the Hugh Matthews house. I sopped up all facets of current events, including politics and world events but had no one to discuss the issues with. My parents and brothers were disinterested...the same for my running buddies...could one imagine seeing and hearing Sonny Boy discuss politics drawing on a one cent Pall Mall cigarette just purchased at Wu's Grocery Store? No I didn't think so. But reiterating my point, television in those days was innocent and politically nonpartisan and it showed the small town and country kids how the rest of the nation lived. It didn't remove the country kids from their provincial environment but it brought the world to the kids. Sorry I can't say the same for television today, its value to society is worthless; in fact its detrimental impact on society today is the reverse of what it was in the 1950s. Enough said.

The preceding trifling potpourri was inserted in this story to provide a link to the year 1958 which is the timeframe of the following narrative:

Part Two

In a deep drink of backward reflection, the year 1958 is brought back to a state of animation…it's almost like watching an old grainy 8 mm Kodak Brownie film. I can see myself sitting on a touring bus in a semi-comatose state (half asleep) when I hear Ellen call my name…" Billy Ray"…followed by a pause… here it came again…"Billy Ray" from the front of the bus where she was standing next to the bus driver. Immediately my heart started to race due to my urgent concern that something was seriously wrong. I was being called to the front of the bus to face potentially bad news from home. For some strange reason that was the first thought that popped in my head. But I couldn't have been more wrong. Stumbling up the aisle from about half way back in the giant bus, my heart quieted when Ellen wished me a happy birthday, handed me a birthday card and asked all the seated passengers to join in to sing the old standard birthday song. Boy did they catch me by surprise…I had hardly given my birthday a second thought that morning as I arose from my bed out in the country near Moorhead, Mississippi. As a matter of fact, my birth anniversary had never crossed my mind as other impending events superseded my God given personal day. Yes, it was May 5th 1958. My face reddened from embarrassment…after all I didn't like attention unless it was on the basketball court. I was eighteen years old.

Such a strange coincidence, here I am, trucking along in space, not far removed from the very place the Griffins had spent their one and only glorious vacation in the summer of 1955. It is three years later, my body and about thirty of my classmates are humming along on a highway nearing the Blue Ridge Mountains destined for Cherokee, North Carolina at which point we would spend our first night on the road.

I think it goes without saying; the graduating seniors of Sunflower Agricultural High School "Class of 58" were well into their first day of their **Senior Trip to Washington DC** in the spring of that seminal yet unforgettable year 1958.

I returned to my seat on this big Trailways touring bus and sat down with my seating partner Thomas. After opening the envelope and pulling out my birthday card, I found that all the kids on the bus, our sponsor, Coach Wade and chaperon Mrs. Harmon had all signed the card. As a keepsake, I hoarded that card for safekeeping but sorry to say it disappeared from my memento trove after I left home a couple of years later.

Taking senior trips was a long standing tradition at SAHS and I was the third son in my family to participate in this much anticipated event. Starting in our freshman year and extending through the senior year, money making activities were pursued relentlessly for the entirety of four years in an effort to raise funds for that trip. If I recall, some of the fund raising activities included "spaghetti suppers, raffles, cake sales, etc." but the most lucrative money making proposition was having a year's license dedicated to our class for the high school football and basketball game concession rights for our senior year. The final reward was a paid week trip to our nation's capital and other historical places along the way. Upon our return, we would all get the chance to walk to the podium in the SAHS auditorium in cap and gown to receive our high school diplomas.

Harkening back to the day's perfect morning, the "Class of 58" had congregated on the SAHS/SJC campus in front of the girl's dormitory for boarding on that Monday morning (if memory serves me). There was luggage galore, but I think it was mostly female stuff because all the farm boys had one little suitcase each stuffed with a few changes of clothes and some white socks. I'll have to admit though that I had crammed a white sport coat (one that brother Stan had used for his senior prom) into the small case that my mother had loaned me. The coat's wearing would probably not be in good taste this time of year but what the heck, who in Washington DC cared?

To tell the truth, as I stood ready to board the bus, I breathed a sigh of relief owing to my good fortune at not being a sick leave casualty. Only two weeks prior to our scheduled takeoff to Washington, a "mumps" epidemic had raged through our part of the country and one of my younger brothers had caught the disease. Having never been infected with mumps in my eighteen years of life, I naturally succumbed to a dire thought of coming down with that awful disease which at this time in my life was totally devastating. How unpropitious...the timing of a spreading disease as serious as mumps couldn't have been worse. In the previous two weeks, my first impulse as soon as I awakened from sleep each morning was to place my hands below the ear lobes and make a cursory examination to satisfy my fear that there was no swelling. How agonizing those two weeks were. Even today as I stepped on the bus, the fear of coming down with mumps was resonating in my brain.

It was imperative for me to make it through the week. It never crossed my mind as to what would happen in the middle of the trip if I came down with the mumps. Certainly there was no way I could have stayed on the bus in a sickly and contagious condition. What would have happened to me? No health insurance and no way to get home. Wow that was a major league dilemma that I didn't comprehend at the time but luck was on my side…I stayed healthy for the entire trip and never in my life contracted mumps.

Let me see…counting on all my fingers, toes and other protrusions, the senior class members making the trip were: Doris, Claire, Ellen, Johnny Anderson, Thomas, Nan, A.M., Sissy, David Hervey, Betty, Boyd, Toby, Barbara, Jean, Billy Ray, Catherine, Dave Pearce, Charles Dixon, Doug Pannell, Bob Denman, Charles Boyer, Camille, Johnny Lancaster, Keats, Haley, Lance, Oscar, Sam, Lynn and Ruth. Hope I didn't miss anyone.

For information's sake, the SAHS student body was made up of boys and girls from the Mississippi communities of Blaine, Doddsville, Sunflower, and Baird and of course Moorhead. The "Class of 58" consisted of twelve students from the previously mentioned smaller communities as opposed to eighteen from Moorhead. It was almost a given if you were from the villages up north of Hwy 82, you were a farmer's kid and the basic premise for that contention was assigned to the reasoning that with Blaine and Sunflower being so small… the odds of someone actually living in those small towns instead of in the country was remote. We all got along admirably and certainly there was never any internecine rivalry between the

North Sunflower school sectors versus the Moorhead faction. In grammar school days we had been rivals in basketball but now we were all one big happy family congregated together on perhaps the biggest trip most of us had ever hoped to take.

This group of seventeen and eighteen year olds represented a good cross section of the type people one could expect to find in the Yazoo Delta. About half of the names listed were country kids living on a farm. The rest were students who primarily lived in town, i.e. their parent's livelihoods were independent of outright farming although some had jobs that related indirectly to farming, for example, farm supply merchants and other associated farm services, lumber yards, grocery stores, an oil processing mill and the like. At least four of the senior passengers had parents who depended on educational services for their primary income and one outlying Phi Beta Kappaian (probably not a word but he was… smart as hell) whose father was a prison warden.

As I sit here writing, It has been fifty + years since this trip took place in 1958 and to be truthful I have to admit I struggled an ounce or two trying to recapture some of the details through a veil of fogginess that tends to overtake old brains saturated with Amyloidal plaques. So with that qualifier inserted for lucidity and if you still think this story's accuracy is suspect in some of my professed remembrances, I humbly beg your forbearance and request that you please don't take offense but instead offer your condolences to my pitiful shortcomings in my old age.

Once loaded on the bus, a seating pattern developed where for the most part, friends paired off, based on gender although

I believe there may have been a couple of mixed couples who were going steady. As mentioned previously, Thomas and I sat in the same seat. We had become friends after he moved to Moorhead from Ruleville in his freshman year. His domestic circumstances were similar to mine in the correlation that his father farmed cotton and had a house full of hungry kids. Coupled with the presence of a hand to mouth existence and poor crops we lived a life of monetary shortfall and the resultant anxiety that goes with it. The sad state of those trying times proved to be difficult but not insurmountable. Our temporary lack of a car and a shortage of rags in our chifforobes were only short term inconveniences. In 1954 & 1955 Thomas, like yours truly didn't drive anything but a tractor but by the time of our senior years, we were driving our family cars and trucks, albeit intermittently.

Of course those two insignificant items of concern were not the worst thing that could happen to a couple of eighteen year old lively, athletic and intelligent (may be a stretch) young men. A lot of the kids on this very exalted bus ride to the Capitalist Mecca of the world were in the same boat and none including Thomas and me were bemoaning our standing in life. At our age, we were on the cusp of shedding our birth circumstances, so our attitudes had assumed a high order of zeal and enthusiasm as we reached out to the future. Yes, Thomas and I were two peas in a pod. As will be seen later in this volume, we both hit the road simultaneously later that summer… on a Greyhound bus to Memphis, Tennessee in a futile effort to probe the outside world to see if we wanted a bite of it. As a contingency, had that superficial probe into destiny proven to be over rated, our default strategy was Sunflower Jr. College. I wasn't really sweating options at that point in my life? As I looked at life, I felt I could easily adapt to the fickle winds of fate. Details of that venture will be discussed later in this non fictional account.

Looking around the bus interior I could see other pairings of friends...Boyd and Toby, Hervey and Sam, Oscar and Dave, Betty and Barbara, Camille and Ellen, Boyer and Lancaster, Lance and Doug to name a few, but that was not to say that the group as a whole didn't mingle because they did. Afterwards, on any given day the seating arrangements changed depending on the individual's preference.

Repeating what was said earlier, Coach Wade and Mrs. Harmon were the only adults on board and they sat at the front of the bus. "As revealed previously, Mrs. Harmon, whose daughter Camille was an eminent member of the "Class of 58", rode "shotgun" as a chaperon whose presence possibly influenced her daughter to be on her best behavior but I don't think so? Actually, Mrs. Harmon had an easy job; no influence was needed because all the girls on the bus, including Camille were well behaved and comported. However, Camille was very outgoing and fun loving and would mix it up with anyone willing to play a practical joke on another student and I think a couple of pranks were played as the bus rolled along. It was nothing malicious, just good natured fun among the sprawling travelers. But on second thought, I could be wrong about the prankster, maybe the joke was played on Camille and not the other way around, but anyway, she was a good sport and cut up as much as the jokesters. I might add, Camille and I had known each other for twelve years...in fact, we both started first grade at Moorhead Grammar School and had gone every step of the way in our pursuit of an education up to this point in time. Her mother, like Nan's mother had always been involved in our lives as a room mother. She was a swell lady and she made an ideal chaperon for the "Class of 58" heading to the nation's capital".

In the same vein, I wouldn't go out on a limb and say the same about the males of the group. Sometimes when given full rein, they could exceed the bounds of good judgment without working up a good sweat. But for the most part all the girls and boys were ultra conservative in their attitudes and actions compared to some of the behaviors that are seen in today's adolescents in these modern times. I'm not aware of any disciplinary incidents requiring authoritative intercession as far as the trip went. But on second thought, maybe there was one itsy bitty one or two. However, being unmanageable was certainly not on any body's mind as the loaded bus headed east on Hwy 82. The whole lot of us had waited four long years for this much anticipated departure and we didn't want any interference in its success.

By and large, coming of age in the 50s proved to be a once in a lifetime experience for a group of individuals who were lucky enough to be born at the right time and in the right place in the march of history. In the context of perfect timing, the 1954 to 1958 time slot, turned out to be the ideal chronological niche for a certain group of exceptional youngsters who were riding the bus that day.

Not that anybody ever noticed, but ostensibly from every small town having a core of businesses as compared to those towns that just had a post office, there are always a couple of prominent families who have risen above the mainstream and are looked upon as being "upper crust". On our bus ride to the far reaches of exotica (no! not erotica, you naughty person, I know what you're thinking), sat a young man who was the consummate rich man's son and I hope it adds a little spice to this story if he is highlighted ever so gingerly in a brief descriptive sketch. By all means, I'm not trying to paint this fellow as a good or bad representative of our class; the sketch more or less is entered to add an outlying aspect to the overall personality of the group as a whole.

Part Three

As stated earlier in this narrative, about half of the busload was comprised of rural kids and the other half, city kids who could probably be categorized as middle class in those days of the late 50s. But this one young man named David stood out because of his family's purported wealth as compared to the rest of us. In addition to being a substantial land owner, his father owned a lumber yard/supply business that had been around for years and had the Jr. College plant as a steady and high volume customer. As an only son living with his parents in a large stucco house on beautiful grounds in a secluded and privately wooded location, David enjoyed the things in life that were noticeably superior to those of his classmates. I think anyone living in Moorhead would affirm the assumption that

David's household status was right up there with the C.M. Davis family, Moorhead's most prestigious banker.

Whoa, wait a minute. Why am I being so cautious tip toeing around in this story about this interesting character. Please excuse my lack of propriety but I'm gonna come right out and say it...Herseby was his name and he was a friend of long association with whom I had been a classmate for twelve years...yes, we were first graders under Mrs. Boone and we walked side by side in every grade at Moorhead Grammar School and then on into SAHS. I'm proud to say Herseby, even though he had the trappings of the rich, never was an elitist when it came to social interaction... decidedly... he was just one of the boys with a little more chump change in his pocket. In grammar school, one would see him at all the places one would see the redneck kids, e.g. the swimming pool, picture show, the pigeon palace (remember that place), the gin, downtown, the pool hall, the alleys behind the juke joints, Boy Scout hut, Pee Wee football practice field, SJC football stadium, ad infinitum. From a social order standpoint, I don't believe Herseby's parents put any halters on him at all. All the farm boys befriended David in a similar fashion true to the way the city boys embraced him. I'm sure his folks had big plans for him in the future but in the early years he was allowed to run with the hyenas.

As I look back on those times, I get a chuckle out of the remembrance of Herseby's first year in high school. Of course being only 14 and not having a driver's license, in lieu of walking or riding a bike, his father arranged for his son's transportation around town and school by providing at his disposal, a big long maroon Chrysler manned by a black chauffeur. While my posse and I were out wearing out shoe leather, old Herseby was tooling around town in a chauffeur driven limousine. But that didn't lower our opinion of Herseby, nor did he look down on us.

Upon reaching the age of having a driver's license, David showed up at school one day in a sweet looking two tone Ford Victoria. I'm not sure if my recollection is right but I believe David wrecked that car not too long after he got it. Instead of getting the Ford reworked he changed his mind and found a beautiful three tone Dodge coupe that suited his fancy. Boy was that a fine car…it had classy looking fins that were synonymous with the 1955 -1956 Chrysler product cars. The most important enhancement for the lumber yard baron's son was the cars attraction to the females of the human species. They flocked to ole Herseby like flies on honey.

I recall a cool day in early October of 1957, David asked me to ride down to Jackson, MS with him to pick up some new winter clothes at an upscale haberdashery. The reason I can pinpoint that date in my memory is the juxtaposition of that trip to the world headlining news of Russia's launch of the "Sputnik" satellite. Every informed American was riddled with fear of the breaking news, especially owing to the fact that the satellite could be seen trekking across America's skies. That was not good, huh? That meant the Russians; a fanatical Marxist enemy of the USA could easily spy on us and could even perhaps drop an "A" bomb from that contraption. And the poor USA didn't come close to having a comeback. But so much for history, the point I was trying to make was my ability to zero in on the date of that fleeting trip to Jackson highlighted by Herseby's fine car and his cultivation of fine clothes. Oh yes this young purveyor of style had a flair for fashion and fine clothes…just ask the girls.

I guess the real significance of recalling that little trip owes to the point that it was the first time I had ridden in the swanky looking Dodge that Herseby squired all those good looking women around in. It was a fine looking vehicle…although it was two or three tone, its prominent color was coral or burnt orange and with the classic fins of that year, the combination of features made for a nice, really nice car.

Then in 1958, things got even better for him when his dad bought him a Corvette. I assumed it was a high school graduation present, but I could have been wrong on that account because it may have been a perk for making a "B" in his Algebra course. For all I knew, as a graduation gift, he may have received a deed to a 640 acre tract of land but I could be wrong. Don't take me seriously, I'm just funning. In my situation, if I had made straight "A's" on every course that I took in high school, my reward from my parents may have been a new Case pocket knife. Not to belittle his good fortune, I'm presently taking a moment to make light of my personal situation which was… not only did I not have a fine car, I hardly ever drove a car.

To wrap up this modest dissertation on David, I must say he was a nice warm friendly person with a pretty heavy dose of humility in his makeup. He was fun loving and I expected all of us would be having the best time of our young lives in the next 6 or 7 days. And I also knew intuitively that once we all grabbed that high school diploma on graduation day, in all probability, Master David would not be seen hanging his hat in these parts much longer. I knew SJC was not in his grand plan, but I had heard that Ole Miss was his next educational train stop which was totally expected. I had known for years that David was an Ole Miss diehard; as a matter of fact he had turned me into an Ole Miss Football fan in the early fifties. Emulating David's uncompromising habit of listening to all the Ole Miss Rebel games on radio I started following the team when Eagle Day was their quarterback and hardly missed listening to any games myself in the 1950s. I was a very devout John Vaught fan until the mid-1960s at which time my allegiance changed to LSU where my brother Benny played in 1965, 1966 and 1967.

Speaking of personalities, if one takes a look at the older guy sitting up front, there sat our Senior Class sponsor, Coach Darry Wade. The way the system worked, when a freshman class entered the high school, that class was assigned a sponsor and to tell the truth I am not sure who made that determination but I would guess the decision came from the high school principal. As a result of this system of selection, Coach Wade was appointed the "Class of 58" senior trip sponsor. He would be instrumental in money raising schemes and in planning the logistics related to the trip. Of course there was already a blueprint established by previous classes therefore mapping, transportation, accommodations and sightseeing itineraries were presupposed and consequently the trip didn't require a lot of original preplanning. But anyway, Coach was the focal point of authority and Mrs. Harmon was along to help in that department.

Coach Wade, SAHS' head football and basketball coach was probably in his mid-thirties and had been at our school for four or five years. I was well acquainted with him since I played football for him one year and basketball two years. Needless to say in his coaching approach he was a fiery bantam rooster who got the most out of his players by exhorting them to be better players than most thought they were capable. Since arriving in Moorhead, he had gradually built the football and basketball teams into winners. Without an abundance of material, the football team was on the verge of winning a conference championship in 1958 and the basketball team had already reached that goal two years running in 1957 and 1958. Coach was an honorable man but he didn't put up with any crap inasmuch as he wouldn't physically lay a hand on you but he wasn't averse to blistering a recipient's ears with dainty epithets.

Granted he was only a one man coaching team, so it makes sense that he would have to be stern to shape up a gaggle of wet behind the ears juveniles. As I look back, it was an amazing feat for Wade to be able to teach and coach 30 players in practice situations every day and have any success. One thing for sure and it was true for all coaches of that era, the players could not drink water during the practice sessions…usually at the end of practice all the players stripped hurriedly and entered the shower stalls, making sure the nozzles were aimed at their mouths for at least five minutes to hydrate the body. As I view football players today drinking water and Gatorade constantly on the sidelines, I think back to our time and wonder how the team made it through a year without someone dying of heatstroke. We were lucky but we were also tough and sinewy. Concluding several weeks of two hour drills in 95 degree heat, any baby fat remaining on any one individual was hard to find…that's what I meant when I say sinewy. For the most part most of the athletes were finely tuned because of their pastime of cavorting in the cotton fields and a bias for diets of turnip greens, Crowder peas, okra and corn bread.

Coach Wade was a paradox to me, given his inclination to be a nice guy as a teacher and a bogeyman as a coach. My young age had something to do with that bafflement I guess, inasmuch as youth only sees the surface of one's demeanor but with age comes a growing ability to see what lies below the surface. Later on in this trip and years afterwards I saw through Coach Wade's ornery side. The mean streak that beset him as a coach was just a façade that he adopted to get some effort out of his troops. Although he did have an explosive temper and could revert to it with little provocation, he pretty much kept his fulminations under wraps in the classroom.

And on this trip, our sponsor was in full control of his wits and was putting forth an affable and considerate bearing. Yes, he was our class overseer and he was in charge of keeping a flock of eighteen year olds in some reasonable control. He would be what's called our "roving conscience" in case some of us forgot our "rearing".

Actually I had a lot of respect for Coach and I could easily see that he was enjoying the company of his young male and female underlings. God knows he had ample experience with girls because he had a houseful of daughters. I was convinced he was up to the challenge ...it goes without second guessing...whoever made the decision to make him the "Class of 58" sponsor knew what they were doing. As it turned out the trip under the auspices of Wade and Mrs. Harmon went without a hitch.

Part Four

The big coach (bus) was headed east toward Columbus, Mississippi on Highway 82. It was early and the morning air being cool and humid impaired visibility to some degree but it didn't seem to concern the bus driver. However as the day heated up a couple of degrees the fog quickly burned off.

The current driver of the bus was a sub and he was advised to give way to another driver in Columbus who was to be the dedicated driver for the entire trip. As it turned out the trip driver was a second cousin to Sonny Matthews but he admitted he hardly knew his Moorhead relatives. I don't remember his name but word was out that had been the driver for several previous SAHS senior trips, so that fact served to relax any of the students who might have been nervous about the professional credentials of our Washington bound chauffeur. I must say he proved his mettle later in the day as darkness caught us in the Smoky Mountains with its road's extreme curves and hairpins. I never suffered such strain unless it was on a roller coaster at the Midsouth Fair in Memphis. He pulled off a commendable tightrope performance in the face of adverse driving conditions and deposited us at an over-night lodge in Cherokee, NC. We were late in the night getting there but we were safe without mishap.

Before arriving in Cherokee on that first day of that long awaited expedition, the bus made a stop in Cullman, Alabama for lunch at a downtown S & W Cafeteria. Our bus driver informed our long serpentine line queuing up for service at that S & W cafeteria stood for Stand and Wait. Later in the afternoon, Chattanooga's Lookout Mountain was the scene of another tour stop for the Moorhead sightseers. It was part of the itinerary to tour the lookout and Rock City Gardens of this well-known tourist attraction besides everyone was keen to see the actual attraction since everyone knew the big advertising logo on a barn right outside Moorhead heading west on Hwy 82. We'd all been looking at that big marquee sign for years, now we were walking and looking at the real site in real life.

After spending an hour at Lookout Mountain, the group and bus were back on the road speeding to Chattanooga and from there toward the Blue Ridge Mountains. As I said earlier, the bus hit the high mountains concurrently with long shadows and eventual total darkness. It was a harrowing drive in the topsy-turvy mountain terrain before we reached Cherokee around 9:00 PM. The bus had been gyrating like a ship in distressed seas but thank God we had a veteran professional at the wheel. The relieved passengers grabbed luggage and made their way in total darkness into their assigned motel rooms that night. Our place of lodging was called the Boundary Tree Motor Court. I don't remember any extracurricular frolicking that night by Coach Wade's young charges, besides it was too late to do anything besides grabbing a soda to sip. Cherokee was a remote village right in the middle of the Cherokee Indian Reservation bordering the Great Smoky Mountain National Park making it not in any way conducive to any night time forays by the inquisitive male troopers.

The next morning in the cool surroundings of the 5000 foot tall mountains, all the traveling students had donned jackets most of which for the boys were athletic letter jackets. Likewise some of the girl athletes had followed suit with their same but smaller size "S" jackets. By the way that jacket was my one and only cold weather garb for this trip and that also went for most of the other guys too. But realize it was May in the mountains and for the record some of the heaviest snowfalls had fallen in that month at the higher elevations. So it shouldn't have been a big surprise to step out into the 40 degree weather that morning. That was especially true of an ole veteran traveler like yours truly…remember I had trekked these same mountains a couple of years prior.

Getting a late start the next morning deep in the Blue Ridge Mountain chain, the bus snaked its way to Asheville. On this day, unlike last evening, there was bright sunlight, which facilitated our party's viewing of the mountainous scenery and landscapes that the area was so noted for. I had seen it before but I wanted another extended gander at the high mountains. I believe on this second day out, I was sitting with Charles Boyer, who unbeknown to both of us at that time, we would become roommates in the SJC athletic dorm in October when roundball practice started for the 1958 – 1959 Trojan basketball season.

Coach Bellipani had given us a half scholarship to play basketball for SJC after we had concluded our high school careers at SAHS in the spring. A half scholarship was appropriate for local boys who could reside at home until basketball season kicked off ... at that point, the college would board and feed the Sunflower county athletes free of charge until the season ended. The scholarship also paid for tuition but not for books

Boyer, like me, was taken with the sights outside the bus window but I noticed a lot of the other seniors were chatting away and paying no attention to the outside Technicolor slide show. But what the heck, everyone marches to a different drummer and to some people looking out a window was a boring exercise particularly if one had this exciting well versed person sitting next to them. I could see that Boyd and Toby were in a deep conversation...my guess...they were discussing **The Periodic Table of Elements** and then there was Jean and Barbara...probably talking about their handsome boyfriends who they were leaving behind, unsupervised, for a week. I'm sure they were nervous about that exposure. Apparently everything worked out fine for Barbara and her boyfriend because she got married that summer. Ditto for Jean too...she and the same boyfriend tied the knot a couple of years later.

As we were boarding the bus to depart Moorhead the previous day, one of the girls had warned us all not to pull the stunt that her fiancé had committed on the 1957 senior trip. Apparently he had chewed on a bar of soap for some unknown reason (I'm sure it was for a perfectly legit reason). The result of that bit of craziness was an outbreak of fever blisters, hence this unnamed girl being the smart person that she was, was urging us sometimes rowdy boys to be a little more wizened than her future husband had been on his trip to the nation's capital. The worst part of her affianced's affliction was the fact that no kisses were exchanged for a couple of weeks after his ship came in. I always wondered what the fun loving rascal was thinking about when he nibbled on that lye stick. Was it an act of self-immolation to atone for cussing? Or maybe it was for drinking aftershave lotion or something like that (years later a little birdy told me the item was ink). I guess I'll never know...one of these days I'll have to ask the perpetrator what his end game was on that ill-fated spring day in 1957 up there in Dwight D. Eisenhower's rent free white washed house (as in White House) and golfing vacationland.

The big bus was rolling now...the terrain had flattened out on the other side of Asheville as we worked our way down to Hickory and then Greensboro, NC. The lunch stop today was a cafeteria in Hickory but it was around 13:00 hours and we were all starved. We didn't don jackets as we departed the bus ...the weather in upstate North Carolina was warm and comfortable.

For the sake of me, I don't remember stopping for any tourist attractions on that second day out. We pulled into Danville, Virginia later in the afternoon and checked into the multi-storied Hotel Danville in the downtown area. After room assignments were finalized and luggage tucked away, several of us including a couple of the girls walked down the street to a drive-in café...it appeared to be possibly a Frosty Top drive –in, I don't know, it is conceivable that franchise didn't exist in those days, but we enjoyed a soda and returned to the hotel. The evening must have been uneventful because I don't even remember eating dinner...was it a group affair or were we allowed to get food on our own? I seriously doubt it was an individual affair inasmuch as the hotel had the capability to accommodate dinner for the whole crew with no problem.

The next morning after boarding the bus for the final leg to Washington DC, we settled in our seats and almost immediately the grapevine heated up. Scuttlebutt jumped from seat to seat like a baton handoff in a track meet. A rumor was floating around to the effect that one of our illustrious students had gotten into a wee bit of trouble for accidently breaking a mirror in his room. It seems a mirror (which he had to pay for) was dislodged from its hanger during an energetic burst of bop related hi-stepping on a dresser top. Because it was an unavoidable accident, the person involved in that little innocent episode will not be revealed, likewise, another event that was even more innocuous involving a security guard who had to admonish one of our strait laced girls to remove her head from outside a window she was using to communicate with another person in an upper floor window. Because it was only a warning, it really was no big deal. So what do you expect from a bunch of blustery kids on a junket away from parental control. The rumor mill soon cooled off and everyone forgot about the previous night and started thinking about our arrival in Washington DC that would happen in the afternoon of the same day.

Even in the flatlands of Virginia farm country around Richmond the weather was cool and damp necessitating a need to keep our "S" and "M" letter jackets on standby. In current time, 2011, looking at a picture of our group on the capitol steps made in 1958, I notice that John Anderson was wearing an "M" monogrammed jacket. I'm not absolutely sure but I believe our esteemed Sunflower Agricultural High School name was changed to Moorhead High School in our senior year and that was the reason for the "M" jacket. Since John had lettered in his early days at the school and earned a free "S" felt jacket, I assume he had the option to purchase the "M" leather jacket at his own expense. I could have done the same but didn't have the wherewithal to make a purchase of the new attractive jacket. By the way I still have my red and gray felt "S" jacket, though it's a little moth scuffed after 54 years of existence.

As my memory waxes and wanes, I remember distinctly as we rolled along in the big touring bus each day, the sound of popular music emanating from a mysterious source. I can still hear the Everly Brothers singing "Kathy's Clown" and "Wake up little Susie". Was the sound coming from the bus sound system (not sure such existed) or was it coming from a hand held transistor radio that one of my fellow classmates held in their hand. I don't know but I believe those small radios were around at that time if one could afford the high cost. I'm sure there were other memorable songs but the Everly Brother Records are the only hit parade relics that surface in my recollection as I sit here writing.

The fads in wearing attire in 1958 were in full modeling mode by my distinguished classmates as exemplified by the variety of rags worn by the busload of Tab Hunters and Sandra Dee look-alikes. I don't remember a lot of resemblances to Tab Hunter but a lot of our girls would qualify as Sandra Dees or even better.

Pink and gray were the "in" colors. I say that with reservation because I don't remember anyone wearing those colors, so it's possible 1957 was the year of pink and gray. Most of the boys wore dark colored khaki and Rayon trousers while the girls mostly wore full skirts with petticoats and/or straight fitted dresses that showed off the figure ever so tastefully. In that era, boys had to have an acute imagination to discern what was under those Burka like wardrobes the girls draped over their bodies. In all modesty, there were never any provocative displays of skin showing from any fashions that were popular in the late fifties unless that skin was on the ankle. But I would like to put my two cents worth in the pot and go on record to say that the imagination is so powerful in young men that a few rags draped on a female body is a zero deterrent at subduing their visualizations of flawless bodies. In other words, older boys, especially those that shave, see a lot more in a woman's cloaked figure than meets the eye. Add more clothing and the young man's vivid imagination can adjust instantaneously, actually its part of the same physiological system that allows one to breathe without thinking. And that's the way it was in the 1950s, and I only speak for myself, i.e. young men were left to their own imaginative devices in sizing up young ladies. I've always wondered if girls have the same capacity to use that xray dimension to gawk at boys. Hmmm, maybe it's time to depart from this train of thought before I paint myself into a corner.

Now back to the ordinary attributes of dress and grooming as it relates to the SAHS group. For the boys, hair styles were mixed, e.g. flat tops for some and reasonably shortened long hair for the remainder, including yours truly. The girl hairdos were also mixed i.e. short hair styles and moderately longer do's were the menu of the day. Taking into consideration our rural ties, we were all well dressed in the latest fashions if the letter jackets were exempted.

As morning light hit the bus driver and his crew of trip seekers square in their sleepy eyed faces, the big Trailways Silverliner rolled out of the Hotel Danville (what a unique name?) parking lot, and aimed its truncated nose in the direction of Richmond, Virginia commonly known as the Old Confederate Capital. After intersecting Richmond, our itinerary called for a tour of Williamsburg, Jamestown and Yorktown, Virginia.

Since Danville is not a vast distance from Washington, I thought surely our arrival at the Plaza Hotel in the downtown DC area would be somewhere around midafternoon. To the contrary, I miscalculated severely...I had thought the side trip to the James River area would not take very long, we'd eat lunch and then scoot on up to DC in a couple of hours. Not true, because in reality the bus didn't get to the hotel until an hour or two after darkness fell. .

Once the bus passed through Richmond, the schedule called for a detour off the main thoroughfare to Washington

(Highway 301) and a jog over to the historical towns of Williamsburg and Jamestown. Notably, today, Williamsburg is a well know tourist attraction but in 1958 the restoration of Virginia's first capital city was incomplete but the group of students still toured the old Virginia Capitol, the Governor's Palace and the George Wythe House to name a couple of the attractions. Dave Pearce and Doug Pannell were especially enthralled with the antique furniture displays and the bus had to wait on them while they lingered for a critical second look. Not true, it's a joke. Never in my life could I ever imagine those two guys even taking a first look at antiques.

The stop at Jamestown was not earth shattering…all I remember is a walk down to a river landing and seeing some stones in the sand. I think I saw that scene but my memory may be playing tricks on my recall…I won't swear that's what I saw, my recollection was that Jamestown was on the Atlantic coast but I stood to be corrected because it sat on the James River. I believe Jamestown was the place where John Smith wed Pocahontas but I wouldn't swear on it?

Then it was on to Yorktown where George Washington whupped ole Cornwallis' British army in the Revolutionary War's last battle. Then the bus had to reverse course and retrace its tracks back to Highway 301. It was late in the evening when we left there, making our arrival at the Plaza Hotel* in DC around 09:00 PM.

* *The memory of the hotel's name was initially lost in the cobwebs of drifting time, but one of my classmates resurrected the name of the Washington*

DC hotel from his records, as well as the other lodging places where we stayed during those six nights on the road. Thanks, Hervey.

As luck of the draw would have it, I ended up with Coach Wade as my roommate. What a dastardly* turn of events.

* *A particular rhyming word would have been more appropriate if not for its illicit inference.*

Here I was trying to divorce my presence for a half fortnight from parental oversight and I'll be doggone if I didn't get stuck with the only adult male on board. How was I gonna raise any hell with the captain looking down my throat. Shoot, I doubted seriously if I would be able to even drink a coke in his presence much less a beer with the boys in our rare unsupervised forays into the surrounds of the nation's capital. The odds of him smelling my breath when I returned to the hotel room to get some sleep was obviously elevated, bearing in mind, Wade's fine-tuned technique of catching his athletes smoking. He had a keen eye for reckless behavior and he utilized a shifty approach to surprise them in the midst of their youthful indiscretions. Just ask Old Sonny Boy and Roy about their experiences with the Coach. I knew I didn't have a chance to be a bad boy. Where's Student Deacon Boyd Horton when I needed him...he would have been the ideal candidate to room with our sponsor. It was not so much that I didn't respect our hoary athletic enforcer...it was just the uncomfortable feeling that I was under authoritative surveillance at close quarters.

But that was the way it was...it was a done deal, so as not to cry in my soup, I made up my mind to make the best of an uneasy situation. But as things turned out, the situation wasn't nearly as unsavory as I thought it would be. Coach Wade was very cordial and we had some good adult educational conversation. He tried to steer me in a noninvasive way to get more focused on going after a college education and instructed me how to do it. He was also very interested in my younger brother Benny as a football player of note who was making heads turn owing to his football exploits at Moorhead Grammar School. In the fall, Benny would enter the eighth grade and the year after that be eligible for Moorhead High School football (unfortunately the Griffin family moved to Baton Rouge in the fall of 1958 and the young football phenom ended up playing his high school there and college football at LSU).

Well so much for temporary living arrangements. At this point in my recollection process, my memories behave a little dimmed but I'll pretend to say that the "Class of 58" left the hotel the next morning on the same bus proceeding to engage in some serious sightseeing. First off, the bus took us through downtown Washington, passing the many foreign embassies, legations, Massachusetts Ave. through Potomac Park with stops at the Lincoln and Jefferson Memorials. I do remember that tour and have some pictures to back it up but I can't guarantee 100% the exact time frame but it makes sense that we had enough time left in the morning to see several more historical hotspots as we departed the bus for a look at the presidential memorials.

Note the fashionable belt and the cuffed shirt sleeves

With looks of wonder, this youthful array of girls and boys departing the bus steps, stared goggle eyed at the granite and marble structures of the Lincoln and Jefferson Memorials. Wandering around, we touched, observed, read the inscriptions in stone, took pictures and generally enjoyed stretching our legs for a half hour or so before heading back to the bus. We had all seen pictures of these national monuments in our history classes, encyclopedias, magazines and books but seeing the real object was something to be remembered.

I believe that very evening, all the class members boarded the *S.S. Mt. Vernon*, a big paddlewheel on the Potomac River for an excursion upriver to an amusement park. After the leisurely stroll up the river the boat parked and we had a few moments to visit the park and ride the rides. I don't really recall any details of the amusement park but the paddlewheel ride, I do remember because an orchestra was aboard.

Four days out from our Moorhead launch, the gang was now comfortably settled at a downtown hotel, and the group was raring to jump headfirst into the Washington DC sightseeing scene. Our predetermined itinerary called for a panoply of sights to be seen on the fifth day as available daylight would allow.

At Arlington Cemetery when the changing of the guard took place, we were all there in person in full deference to the ceremonial solemnity and reverence of the ritual, likewise the World War II monument depicting American soldiers raising the flag on Iwo Jima proved to be an inspiring sight. I couldn't speak for the other students but my viewing of these historical monuments and pageantry was riveting ...my enjoyment was obvious if anyone cared to take notice. Being at these places was like stepping out of a motion picture into a real world that didn't seem real at all because in my mind they only existed in phantasmagoria. To stand next to the real site was hard for the old brain to filter. It took me a moment to recover my senses once the context of being close enough to touch these famous edifices sunk in.

In the rain, the unfinished National Cathedral* was another place that the group toured and of course the Smithsonian Institute and Museum. It was all very fascinating to see the old flying machines, military memorabilia, dinosaurs, etc. etc.

**The National Cathedral, by means of an Episcopal Church sponsorship was constructed starting in 1907, but was not completed and dedicated until 1990.*

In the late afternoon, the Washington Monument crept into our crosshairs and some of us charged it like a herd of antelopes...I say some of us did...the crazy ones. The more intelligent of the group held back and rode the elevators but like I said the ones with dim wits including yours truly attacked the 897 step stairway to the top with mindless verve. We hit the stairs running and pretty much kept that pace all the way to the 555 foot pinnacle. As I think back, at 18 years of age we were in great shape and the run up the Washington Monument was nothing to us. The only thing about the trip up was not the energy it was taking but the extended time it took. We thought we'd never reach the top. The suffocating heat and humidity inside the tomb-like obelisk was oppressive but youthful invincibility has no limits. At the end of the chase, all competing stair steppers were soaked with sweat and the onerous feat of the downhill glide was still staring us in the face...but going down was a breeze compared to the 555 foot climb. I'm not sure if any of the girls took the stair route...if any of you are reading this account of the golden trip, please raise your hand if you care to admit to bounding the stairs that May day many years ago.

I can probably go out on a limb and safely say that if any of the young ladies climbed the stairs aimed at the "Father of our Country's" final resting place in the clouds, it would have been Catherine Noble, the Class of 58's most distinguished girl athlete. She was All Central Delta for at least three years in a row in basketball and was an all-star sprinter and broad jumper in track for her entire high school career. Shucks, she was almost a one girl track team now that I think about it; I believe she performed additional specialties like the baseball throw and high jump. Yep, she was a superbly turned gazelle of an athlete. And certainly it didn't detract from her athletic bearing to admit that her looks were also striking. It always amazes me when I look back to those times and see that I was surrounded by so much beauty, yet didn't realize it. That admission was quite an oversight on my part.

To further the subject of being in top condition, I guess the reason a good number of the boys made it to the top was due to the fact, most were in pretty good physical shape as a result of having just ended their track and field season a couple of weeks prior to this ascent to the highest of federal overlooks.

I stand to be corrected on this remembrance, but I believe the group as a whole was given the liberty to roam around the hotel's general vicinity without adult attendance, however, individuals were advised to grab at least one partner when venturing out. In other words, don't go it alone. I remember there was a small café up the street and around a corner and a good number of us boys went there for meals. While out touring, the group always assembled and ate in cafeterias and the like. We all had our own money for meals and in 1958, one could easily survive on a hamburger, French fries and a coke or malt at a cost of $.75 but overall I don't remember much about our taking of meals.

On one occasion in the mid hours of darkness, Thomas and I donned our stylish evening wear and proceeded surreptitiously to assemble with Hervey, A.M. and Sam at a bar and lounge that featured live music…I believe it was jazz…not our style but ok. We soaked up a couple of beers over a two hour period and made our way back to hotel in time to make curfew. Coach Wade was fast asleep but I made sure I kept my facial blowhole in a reverse position and far back of his supine body draped in his smallish single bed. He never awakened that night as I slipped in quietly with the subtlety of a chicken snake crawling into a hen's nest. He may have played possum but I assumed he never knew his carousing roommate had been out bar hopping that night in Washington's tenderloin district (that may be an exaggeration…the club we were in was pretty nice)

My cache of money had been set aside starting in the summer and fall of 1957. I was fortunate enough to gain part time employment at Lamb's Grocery Store and my parents insisted that I put a part of my wages in a kitty to fund my food and incidental expenses for my senior trip. Thank s to them, I had money in reserve for the trip, otherwise I would have been inconsolably broke if it had been left to my inherent financial irresponsibility. What is it about old folks that make them so sensible…but then again my parents were not that old…they were just 39 years old but they had been through hard times in the depression and they knew how to be practical in money matters.

Cutting up and packaging chickens, pork loins, beef and clerking behind the meat counter was my primary job at

Lamb's Grocery. The work was steady and not that hard but Lamb, a China native, and an old man in his seventies was a go-getter and seemed never to tire...was a regular buzz saw, not real fast but the guy worked from daylight to 11:00 every day except Sunday and I believe he and his wife stocked on that day. On Wednesday afternoons, the store was closed but I would report for work at 1:00 PM to help the old man cut and package meat. Like I said, I would cut up chickens and pack the parts in heat sealed plastic packages. On a band saw, pork chops were sliced off by the hundreds and packaged similarly to the chicken pieces...in the meantime; Lamb was cutting up the beef...round steak, sirloins, t-bones, rib eyes, etc. He never let me cleave the beef...I guess he didn't trust me but it was amazing how adept he was in the way he manipulated the big butcher knives as he worked relentlessly. It was almost musical; like he was a maestro leading an orchestra as the knife swished in broad strokes and parted the beautiful pieces of chilled meat. In between cuts he would flash the knife's edge across a sharpening stone held in his left hand, the sound of honed steel reverberating across the chopping block and beyond. It didn't matter if the sound was rasping because he and I were the only ears in the store. This meat cutting symphony...it was all done in an effortless but syncopated virtuosity by this ancient man who still had the attitude that he was a butterfly.

If I could somehow enlist a little of Lamb's high level of esprit vigor in my intellectual pursuits at Sunflower Junior College, I would no doubt have become a star pupil. But no, I didn't have it in me to stick my nose in a book and let it osmose for a while; however, I had no trouble flouncing like a carp in a farm pond as opposed to Lamb's butterfly metaphor. Admittedly, the word, "focus" was not part of my vocabulary in my butcher block days. I was content to flit.

It was left to me to take the individual cuts of beef and package them in the same clear plastic covered containers. Then the packages had to be weighed and a price label attached to the top of same. In recompense for my time and labor my pay was $.50 an hour. Not bad for an ole boy who could bebop in the soy bean fields to the tune of his own disjointed rendition of "Bebop a Lula". Yep, this mode of making a fifty cent piece was a step up from my honorary PhD degree in agronomy, you know, (cotton maintenance, i.e. hoeing and picking) that my good father bestowed on me when I reached the age of five.

Actually the reason I had the job was due to the necessity that I was a stand-in for Lamb's protégé and heir apparent, Jones Wong who was a young Chinese emigrant from the China mainland. Attending Delta State University required a lot of his daylight hours, thus Lamb had to have a person to fill Wong's duties during the weekday hours. For the record, Jones had been in our class for several years but being older, and after obtaining a good grasp of the English language he leapfrogged on to college ahead of the "Class of 58".

Lamb was a legendary worker and I had an unstinting respect for this pleasant industrious septuagenarian, a harder working human I have never known. Poor Lamb's legs were shot, causing him difficulty in walking but through sheer will power he just kept going and going for 16 hours a day. It was amazing… and on top of his persistent work regimen, he was a fine gentleman. I liked Lamb a lot.

SAHS Class of 1958 on Capitol steps

On our last full day in Washington, the White House was checked out as was the Capitol Building. At the conclusion of the Capitol tour, we had our picture taken with Mississippi Congressman Frank White on the steps of the most photographed backdrop in America. Claire Carr's father was a state politician and he had arranged our tours of government buildings and their chambers. I still have a copy of that picture with all of us posing in our letter jackets and well-scrubbed smiles. Later in the day the bus took us to Mount Vernon, Virginia for a whirlwind tour of George Washington's historic mansion and estate. It goes without saying, the novelty of viewing some of those historic places and furnishings had worn thin and most of the male culture seekers were getting a little jaded with the likes of repetitive views of revolutionary era boudoirs.

To enliven the interest level an octave or two, one of our lesser subdued fellows had a crafty way of producing a sound that mimicked flatulence and he was not averse to engage in the practice thereof. He was especially not shy in letting loose that distinctive reverberation in a room full of old spinsters viewing exquisite antique masterpieces, as was the case at Mount Vernon. Usually when our prankster friend cut one of his salvos, the startled ladies would immediately turn around and make eye contact with the perpetrator whose finger invariably would be pointing at one of his unsuspecting classmates. A lot of us innocent bystanders received countless looks of contempt from many of those well bred ladies. As a consequence, the offending culprit was left blameless and could be seen snickering in his cupped hand as he slithered unnoticed into a rearward room. At my young age, I thought my gauche classmate was a riot and always got a kick out of his "candid camera" antics. The victims of his fun poking (if that is what you could call it) were always nonplussed by the awkwardness of the situation and their expressions of disdain made me roll with laughter.

The next day was ""heading home" day and we departed DC, in the direction of Charlottesville, Virginia, where,

Monticello, the home of Thomas Jefferson's is located. This was Jefferson's home from 1772 until his death in 1826. He began the mansion in 1769 and moved into the completed portion when his father's home "Shadwell" burned in that year. Here Jefferson died, July 4, 1826, exactly fifty years after the Declaration of Independence. Ironically, John Adams died on the same day.

Part Five

Before time allotted for the telling of this most luminous of journeys plays out, I thought it would be an impartial gesture on my part to say something in depth about one of my female classmates, notwithstanding that most of my ink has been wasted on the dumber partners of the human coupling set. Ability to understand girls has never been one of my strong suits…remember my family was all boys, but I will try my best to do an attribution to this young lady who I've always admired platonically but I must admit perhaps in my earlier days, to the contrary, "a crush" may have been the better label. And that target of attention would be Quincy June, a native of Moorhead, in fact a city girl.

Repeating, it would only be fair to take an unbiased look at one of my "Class of 1958" classmates of the opposite sex, because I have spent a great amount of expressive wherewithal on my male friends and classmates.

I can start Quincy June's "reveal" according to BRG, by summing up this attractive star as an extraordinarily gifted individual who was and is blessed with an innate dignity and beauty inside and out. Saying "both inside and out" is a cliché but in Q.J.'s case it was totally applicable. Of course, in sum, these adjectives only touch on the topical first impressions of this gifted lady. Her qualities are manifold and I say this based on observations through her first nineteen years of age. Sorry to say, but I've only seen her one time since 1959 and that was at a Class reunion in 1978, so my "sizing up" is limited to her formative years from preschool through high school and maybe one year of junior college.

Before I get too deep into superlatives …one may think I'm belaboring the point but I've always viewed Quincy June through rose colored glasses. That's the way it had always been from Vacation Bible School in 1945 or 1946 to that last day on the Senior Trip in 1958. In my book, she deserved being placed on a pedestal and that's where she remained in those formative years. Likewise, I placed myself at a lower level out of reach. We were always friendly and respectful towards one another and that's pretty much the way our social contact remained. I viewed her as untouchable. That's crazy but I believe deeply that all boys in all environments have similar fixations from which they stay aloof. Unless a young male is supremely confident which is rare as dewdrops in the Sahara, he stays forever in the background and assertively goes after the girls that he feels equal to in looks and status. I might add, not to demean Quincy June but I developed the same "Snow white" syndrome toward Joy, another pretty little girl with golden hair and genius I.Q. Does that imply I was a two timer?

Well so much for the psychoanalysis of timorous boys.

Quincy June will be happy to know that I first caught a glimpse of her at the Moorhead Baptist Church (seems like I've been down this road before with that adoring co-ed in 1955). It was either 1945 or 1946...my family lived on the Ferguson place located on Highway 3, south of town. The hot summer had droned into July and Vacation Bible School was in its annual session, which meant a bus circulated out in the rural reaches of the parish to gather little children whose parents were aligned with the tenets of Christianity. My mother put her three oldest boys on the roving bus and away we went for some religious instruction.

My primary motivation for maintaining interest in the Biblical Stories that flowed from the mother teachers was our daily helping of cookies and various flavors of Penny-Aid drink. Yep, I looked forward to that trip to town every day for a week of absorbing parables and cups of grape Penny-Aid. One cent of Penny-Aid and a cup of sugar would make a quart of delicious beverage for the little students of Jesus' Ministry.

On top of my interest in grape dujour, I also picked up on the presence of this cute, very cute little girl in our preschool class. Now who would think a five or six year old child would be able to sense an aura of charisma in another child at that age and still remember it 70 years later. The human brain is an amazing devise. Thank you Lord.

But anyway, after our introduction in preschool, several months later I walked into my First Grade classroom and lo and behold there was that same little girl that I remembered from my Bible study days. She was even prettier...more than I remembered...and that was the way it was all through Grammar School and maybe to a lesser degree in High School.

It seemed she consistently had a boyfriend especially after seventh grade and into high school. But never me.

Another thing that made me have high regard for this girl was her mother. She was always extremely nice to me all those years and I sensed she had an undiluted respect for me that I otherwise didn't think was deserved because of my country boy status. She was a sweet lady and she was eternally a room mother to all us kids in the Moorhead group that started school in 1946.

Quincy June was forever the "A" student and was very active in a multitude of clubs, cheerleading, sports, etc. She was a force. Invariably, in high school she received many of the yearbook awards like "Most Friendly, Best all Around, Most Beautiful, Most Likely to succeed etc. etc."

And now as I look around the interior of the big Trailways Touring bus, I notice her and her boyfriend seated cozily together and their eyes transfixed on the other to the exclusion of everyone else on the *Hell bent for Moorhead* express. What an appealing couple…as it turned out they would eventually become man and wife. That little bright enchanting girl was now a mature beautiful enchanting woman and yes I believe all the young men on that same bus agreed that her boyfriend was indeed a lucky man.

For the life of me, I don't remember where we stayed on the way home from Washington. I do recall we visited Natural Bridge Virginia located west of Lynchburg. It's possible there was no overnight stopover that last day…yes, the more I think about it, we made a beeline to the home port… the express actually returned home non-stop, motel accommodations notwithstanding. The alternative sleeping arrangement included a big fatback retractable coach chair that induced sleep with no difficulty. I'm still a little stumped as to how our masterful bus driver could make that prolonged drive from our nation's Capital to Moorhead, a killer of a trip, in a full day and probably most of the night? But then, it was remembered that his home base was Columbus, Mississippi which meant his length of time in the driver's seat had been shortened a couple of hours but nevertheless that run took a lot of stamina*.

> **After writing the above paragraph, it came to past just recently, that one of the students on board that day retained a copy of the 1958 "Senior Trip Program" and let me use it for reference. Gleaned from that itinerary, I was able to determine that in fact we spent that 6th night on the road in Abington, VA at the famous* ***Martha Washington Inn.*** *Unfortunately, I don't remember that overnight stay at all. It could have been the result of my mind entering a catatonic state at that point in the trip. I regret that memory got wiped out. Maybe my mental computer needs to be defragged.*

The trip finale was fast approaching its last stop at the Sunflower JC campus. Our spirits, not totally unexpected were at low ebb caused by the end of this incomparable experience. Upon arrival, it was a tired bunch of homesick kids that departed the bus into the arms of waiting parents. As we went silently back to our home nests, our memories of that fast moving Senior Trip of 1958 were stamped into the brain cells for safekeeping. Although a lot of the details have faded over time, I would guarantee all the surviving classmates of that poignant year still get a little tingly when they direct their thoughts to that long ago event.

Part Six

Returning home from my Washington DC trip, my mother drove me home along Sheffield Road, where upon I sat taking note of the cotton and soy bean fields, I was aghast at the disturbing scene that was falling on my eyes. On both sides of the gravel road, high water was virtually lapping up against the roadbed… almost to the point of crevassing the road. The fields as far as one could see in any direction looked like Chinese rice terraces. "Wow, Mom… what has been going on with the weather since I've been gone." Her reply was dripping with pessimism and dread… "you wouldn't believe the rain that has fallen in the last week…the whole farm is flooded and water is up to the house steps." The old green Chevy made waves as we pulled into the driveway of our house. I noticed a bateau type boat anchored in the shop area of our home site. Mom wasn't kidding; I'd never seen anything to compare with this turn of events. Casting an eye in the direction of the "back forty" I could see nothing but lake like conditions. Sticking above the water one could make out the bushes and small trees covering the dredge ditch banks. The foliage and vines were protruding above the surface of the ripple free water. The shop and barn was knee deep in water and the cow was staked close to the pump house. At least when I resumed my milking chores, I wouldn't have to trudge through manure saturated stalls to access the old half breed Jersey milk machine.

With concern suddenly clouding my good humor imparted by the incumbent exhilarating joys of my senior trip, I grabbed my one piece of luggage from the back seat and stepped on tip toes to the back door of the nearly swamped house. What a rude reality check awaiting the Griffin boy clad in Levis, a new short sleeved shirt (a graduation gift), a letter jacket and a Washington DC banner waving from a buttonhole in his letter jacket. The man-child 12th grader was home but what was he coming back to. Times were tough enough even with ideal weather but this flood situation was demoralizing.

It all came crashing down…the reckoning of reality…this late in the spring the cotton crop was ruined. We had planted the cotton seed in early April and the small green plants had germinated from the seeds and numerously dotted the rows when I left for my trip in early May. I saw Dad and he had a look of gloom on his face but seeing how disturbed I was, he tried to keep his chin up and told me if the rain stopped, the water would recede eventually and a planting in May had been known to yield a good cotton crop. But I was a good ag student and a certified STATE FUTURE FARMER of AMERICA and I knew my stuff…the odds of making a decent cotton crop in 1958 was about as good as ole Sonny Boy Matthews beating David Hervey's Corvette in a drag race out on Highway 3 south of town.

A soy bean crop could be salvaged because the planting of that legume always took place in May a few weeks later than the cotton planting...good news there... but contrarily, a family of six could in no way survive on a bean crop.

The only hope we had as did all the farmers in the Delta was to pray for the rain to let up and miraculously it did. I only had a fleeting moment to savor my Senior Trip before jumping into the replanting process. I could go at it full time. My school work for my high school diploma was complete...all I had to do was attend Graduation ceremonies at the SJC auditorium to pick up my prized diploma. My ties with Moorhead High School were now behind me.

In a week, the waters had receded to the dredge ditches and in a couple of weeks the fields were dry enough for planting. All the farmers in the corridor worked feverishly from daybreak into the night for several days. Tractor headlights could be seen moving through the fields until the drivers and workers collapsed from fatigue. Their hard work did not go for naught...the first week in June came and the first cotton seedlings started to break through the alluvial crust. Like Dickens's preamble in one of his stories, "it was the best of times and it was the worst of times". The cotton crop was up but would it survive its late start...that was the big question? In all likelihood the cotton crop was doomed and with it any hope of repaying the bank furnish. How disappointing......the Griffin family was mired in an economic hole from the get go.

Armed with all the scientific knowledge absorbed into a blank skull from three years sitting in Pete Woods' Agriculture class, I tried to think of ways to give the little puny cotton plants a boost that would somehow catch them up with the April planting that died a watery death. But all the scientific pot stirring was in vain...I finally concluded if I wanted to know how best to make this cotton crop a success was to surrender to Troy Griffin's good judgment. If anyone could reverse nature's workings, my Dad could do it.

With everything said and done, now that I had come of mature age and was eligible to fight wars for my country but not drink whiskey publicly, I knew I would help my father through this year's crop but that would be it for me. I didn't really have a plan put together but like older brother Stan, I was working on it...in my mind I was working on a grand plan and my future was at stake. I had had enough of this game called farmer's roulette.

Part Seven

Self-consciously I strode across the stage and took ownership of a leather encased diploma handed to me by Mr. Hall, the school's Principal. Hopefully this gilded sheepskin was going to be a stepping stone to better things and fresh venues. However with my narrow understanding of what made a successful career get off the ground, I knew I needed more grooming in the fields of skill and language assimilation which meant more residence time in an educational setting.

But how? As Will Percy so aptly stated in ***Lanterns on the levee*** "What does one do with a life, or at any rate intend to do?" It was time to inventory my ambitions and, having selected one as paramount, to pursue it wholeheartedly." Yes that's what I wanted to do, but as I've said before, heck...I didn't have a clue as what my vocational desires were. No, wait a second; I do have this germ of a stirring to become a teacher and a coach. Maybe Coach Wade was more of an inspiration on that senior trip than he thought possible.

Not only was my experience and knowledge growing incrementally to my moderate energy input, my body was enlarging, not out but up. Since reaching 18 years of age there was this supposition that my growing days were complete, except maybe in the bulk area. I was six foot one and weighed 150 pounds, quite rangy for a boy who couldn't get enough to eat. My lissome athletic build was what some of the fooling boys called "hatchet ass". However I would like the readers of this piece to know that my growing up diet was crowded with too many garden varieties of green and yellow vegetables and not enough of carbohydrates and red meat. Out yonder in time: when I settled in at the SJC athletic dorm and started eating at the basketball team training table, my weight shot up to 175lbs and my hatchet derriere became a jug, one that a Coca Cola bottle could rest on. I've always remorsed a notion that had I been on a well-rounded diet in my early growing years perchance, my size could have easily matched my father's six foot two and 200 pound frame in his prime. If I had had those physical metrics, I think and know an inch or two of added height could have made me a better athlete. As it were, my basketball accolades only carried All Central Delta, All County and All Sub Regional, which was nothing to crow about but something to be proud of in a muted sort of way. My children to this day do not even know I was a basketball player in my jockey strap days.

The previous disclosure was not intended to evoke ego stroking …its inclusion is strictly for the record, hopefully for the benefit of nieces and nephews who never knew their Uncle Bill sprinted up and down a basketball court in those Wilt Chamberlin days when the jump shot was just coming into its own and the two hand set shot was in the throes of its last rites.

Getting back to the importance of career seeking, I had confidence that I had the bodily stature and brain power to make a run at college or a job but I had this flickering doubt that the high level of energy and patience required for a four year degree was not in my constitution at that stage of my life. I looked at Boyd, Toby, Charles, Nan, Keats, and John from a model standpoint and acknowledged, yes, they have the focus and staying power to make it happen. Me...hmmm...not sure.

Really, the medicine that I needed most in my life at the time was a bull mentor standing over me popping the whip. But as it came to be, no one stepped forward to be my drill sergeant and I was not a self-starter. Serendipitously, the way events were unfolding with the scholarship being handed to me, even though I had doubts, I was willing to go after a Physical Education Degree which required a lesser regimen of tough subjects. That was my long sighted plan as projected from a short linear nose, you know the old saying "We only looked into the future only as far as our nose". That suited the farmer's outlook and was actually part of his creed. It would be good if I could step up and shuck that label.

Part Eight

And here we go. High School was over, summer had arrived and it was hot as hell and still the cotton crop was still fledgingly stunted. With not much to do on the farm, I worked erratically at Lambs Grocery and Bill Colliers Service Station, picking up some change to defray some of my night life outlays.

Billy T, Billy Ray and Sonny Boy

You guessed it…my cruising partners were my old mainstays, Sonny Boy Matthews and Billy Tyner. By this time young Roy was madly in love and could not bear the thought of being away from his affianced leading lady long enough to go out with the "Sonny Billy Boys"; you know that rough bunch of beer drinking hard legs.

After graduating from high school the previous year, Sonny had elected to forgo college for the time being and was locked in a job at the Ludlow Textiles plant in Indianola. So did Roy, another good friend. Because of shift work, Sonny's availability for carousing was limited, which was ok with me because my tolerance threshold for a constant dose of beer drinking was indeed restricted to say the least. I could stand a few drinks on a Saturday night, but every night…no way.

Those alcoholic spirits always gave me a severe hangover, so as a favor to myself, I controlled my frequency and volumetrics of the happy juice. In my opinion, the fun of a drunken bender never came close to equating to the misery of a hangover. So in pure deductive reasoning the thought of a hangover almost always trumped the thought and onstart of a drinking binge.

In 1958, the town of Moorhead was still vibrant, but there were subtle indications that the business climate was not as flush as it appeared on the surface. The great Negro migration to the northern industrial cities had begun and would quickly pick up steam resulting in a resettlement of the southern black labor force to the factories of Detroit and Chicago. To compensate, the farmer was slowly mechanizing their operations and big cotton picking machines arose from the need. Since need is the mother of invention, the large manufacturers of farm equipment went into high gear designing and building all sorts of machines that would eventually replace every facet of traditional cotton cultivation and harvest. To the soothsayer, the hand writing was on the wall…the migration would grow exponentially, thus the inevitable labor shortage portended for the Delta could in no way be averted.

Those machines that took care of cotton hoeing process were being replaced with drop planting, new plowing techniques and grass eradicating herbicides that could be applied from a tractor and one driver. These early crop maintenance improvements were just a forerunner of what was to eventuate in the 1960's.

Troy Griffin's farming requirements had relied hardly at all on black labor, as long as he had four healthy and robust sons to handle the hoeing and picking of his cotton crops. But obviously the stock of his farm labor pool was in remission and the low number of hands still around behooved him to move more into the mechanical front. He was down to Benny age 13 and Bishop, still a not very dependable whippersnapper in 2nd grade. I was still slipping my shoes under the home bed on Sheffield road but to a hardy pragmatist like Dad, I was a dubious entry in the Griffin Bible who could hardly be relied on in the future and he knew it. Stan had been gone for almost a year, and Bud, a freshman in junior college had part time work as a county school bus driver but still lived at home although he was more or less on his own.

Still, Moorhead was doing all right and many of the stores that were in business in the Christmas Story in late 1949 were raking in customers at a provident clip. All the merchants and ancillary "hangers on" were making a living but the poor old farmers were pretty much at the mercy of Mother Nature in the early summer of 1958. And true to her fickleness, Mother Nature was being a bitch so far in the year of my high school graduation.

With his factory earnings, Sonny Boy went out and bought a very appealing light colored 1954 Ford Fairlane. I believe it was a soft green color or maybe it was tan…boy, now that I think about it; ole Sonny really had a fetish for green cars. This vehicle was now our tooling around buggy along with Billy's 1952 Chevy. With my brother Stan now out of the picture, I was driving the family's reincarnated Chevy more and more but Billy and Sonny preferred their cars whenever it was decided we would make a female seeking sortie to Indianola or Greenwood. For arguments sake, our sorties were almost as unsuccessful as the Libyan kamikaze pilot who just returned from his fourth successful mission.

I say that in jest...now that the Moorhead Lotharios were older and more self-assured, they were having better than middling luck with the Greenwood lasses. I remember one evening Billy and I dined with a couple of young ladies whose mothers had prepared a huge pot of boiled shrimp for our dining pleasure. I couldn't vouch for my compatriot's dining history but I'll have to admit that was the first time I had ever tasted that particular crustacean...maybe crawdads... but not high falutin jumbo shrimp. The shrimp entrée was out of this world and I still to this day love shrimp dishes of all varieties.

Admittedly, ole Billy and I were moving up in the world of sophistication...we had now elevated our gourmand pinings to select seafood delicacies as opposed to fried chicken and pork chops. Ole Sonny would have been envious if he only knew his suave colleagues were reared back in easy chairs with pretty damsels sitting close and savory shrimp morsels parting their lips while the "Platters" *Smoke gets in your eyes* drifted in from a sound system stuffed in the living room wall. YesSiree, if you could see us now, you'd be impressed with our acquired couthness. At the stroke of midnight, the two of us waltzed out of that handsome house and went home to sleep with a full awareness that we were "moving on up" in this world of refinement. If I remember correctly, the next day at suppertime, I volunteered to set the table for Mom and very confidently placed the forks to the left of the plates, true to good table manners and accepted etiquette. I think she habitually placed the tableware in its proper alignment but I don't think she gave place settings as an element of proper etiquette a second thought.

In parallel to our up and coming societal elevation, my associates and I were still bopping fools and in the process of cutting a rug, we had refined our dance steps to simulate the prevailing styles of national trendsetters like what we saw on **American Bandstand**. Billy had transformed his loopy style into a hybridized heel to toe move that was shocking to the eye but ole Sonny had us all beat with his reverse hip pivot and double clutch shuffle motion…it was innovative but it was really impossible to explain…groping for a definition, I would say it was almost like an Appaloosa show horse taking a bow after a performance of cut and rope. Since I'm the writer and have the prerogative to digress, I'll leave the reader in the dark as to my bopping transformation. I can say unequivocally…, my bopping had evolved into a step that was not as circuitous as my earlier efforts. I pretty much stayed put and let my dancing partner gyrate around me… using my leveraging hands more than my shuffling feet.

Part Nine

As events unfolded that summer of 1958, circumstances brought my senior trip buddy, Blansett and I to a closer comradeship due to our employment connection at Lambs Grocery. We were co-workers in Moorhead's nicest grocery store, the work being, if you will, amounted to meat counter jobs that were only part time but our menial labor was a channel to amassing some much needed legal tender and collateral. As a result of this path crossing, my butcher friend and I started putting our heads together on the job and off the job to the extent that over time a grand scheme was hatched that had fairly impractical implications if one cares to view it in hindsight. But youngness of spirit refutes logic so we thought we would sample the good life until such time that an alternate scheme dropped out of the sky on our heads and penetrated our brains. We weren't exactly what one would call thoughtful young men plotting our futures as potential college men or maybe in pursuit of some other daunting profession. The crux of the plan revolved around an idea that would take us to Memphis to find jobs that would facilitate living a dream of a big city life style...we both had relatives in that big city of sin and enticement. He had an uncle in West Memphis, Arkansas across the Mississippi River from Memphis and I had a couple of aunts living in the suburbs of the cotton capital of the south. Every chance we got after work or on our days off, we would get together and work on "the breaking out plan".

True to my breed, I was a clock watcher of the highest order. It seemed time crept ever so slowly when I entered Lambs glass fronted super market, grabbed an apron, washed my hands, positioned my body behind the counter and immediately started my routine of dispensing hog maul and pork neck bones, favorite items of the black patrons. Although I never did any shelve stocking, I believe Thomas did...he was multi-talented in all aspects of the primal skills required for grocery store administration. He was Lambs' right hand man.

I was his left hand, also known as the wrong hand. But Lamb and I were tight. He liked me and he liked Thomas.

The days rolled over and evaporated like quick steps through a field of dewy broadcast vetch. Before we could collectively count the money stash that was accumulating in a dresser drawer from butchering and doling out $.20 worth of lunch meat or hook cheese (it was actually "hoop") and the afore mentioned working man delicacies, the calendar indicated this commodity called time had oozed out another steaming month called July, 1958.

It was getting close to a "make or break" roll of the dice for the two butcher boys and part time hoers. With unanimity we nodded our crewcut heads, let's do it. Let's hit the road of possibilities, pronto. I knew Lamb would hate to see his vagabonds depart for the Land of Oz. He would be devastated…he had invested a lot of time in training these two sodbusters and Jones Wong had just finished his second year of college and would be trekking over to Delta State University five days a week very soon. Net result: no one to assist Lamb in the store besides his old wife. But we assured Lamb, that our sally up north was provisional and if things didn't work out, we'd be back in the bosoms of our families for the fall school season.

The cotton crop didn't look good, so my father and mother felt no qualms about letting me hit the road. I had helped my Dad intermittently with his cotton crop, you know, hoeing and the like, but the outlook for the measly looking cotton plants was about as promising as waiting on a cancer cure. The crop had fizzled due to its late start and at best the yield would not exceed 5 to 7 bales of cotton. The soy beans appeared to be promising but like I said earlier, a family couldn't live on a $1500 annual income. That's about all one could forecast for the rosiest of scenarios. To help out, Dad had taken a job at the Oil Mill working as weigh – in clerk on the dog shift. The job allowed him to pick up some scratch and at the same time continue to work his farm in daylight hours after picking up four hours of sleep in the morning hours.

Thomas and I were biding our time, waiting for the right opening to make our dash to Beale Street. Periodically, my friend and I, the grocery jack, would join Sonny and Billy for a night of cruising the Greenwood back streets but generally Thomas stuck close to home and hung around Moorhead, but who could blame him, considering the myriad attractions that this Sin City of the Delta offered.

Finally we sucked it up and committed to make our departure on the last Monday in July. We had both been helping our families with the farm work…our domestic situations were very similar, i.e. dependence on cotton farming and all the connotations that go along with that austere livelihood. As was the case throughout the Delta, all the cotton crops were failing because of the early May rains and subsequent flooding. We had done all we could to help out but the time had come to put up or shut up.

Our parents were informed of our intentions (my folks knew) and we made our final preparations which was not much. Once again I borrowed my mother's one piece of cardboard luggage and she packed it with the same care and forethought that she had sent Dad off to Oklahoma City. My Levis, my pairs of dark khaki and Rayon pants, a variety of short sleeve shirts (at least two were graduation presents) and white socks. My shoes, brown loafers, the only ones I owned were on my feet and fully engaged. I counted my money…about fifty dollars and change…I doubled checked my Greyhound bus ticket and before we knew it, thus arrived the appointed day, the glorious day the young man from Quiver River View plantation was ready for his much anticipated and unprecedented journey into another indeterminate realm. By unprecedented, I say that because on my behalf, the trip was pretty much a solo affair inasmuch as Thomas and I would part company after reaching Memphis. Heretofore all my trips had been within the safe confines of a group or a family. I did have the forethought to write my Aunt Nelle in Memphis to tell her about my plan and the approximate date of arrival and I also made sure her telephone number was safely tucked in my wallet…ditto for my older brother Stan's contact number and address in St. Louis, Mo.

Part Ten

Much like the day my good friend Twyman and I spent four years before, Thomas and I climbed aboard a big Greyhound bus at Kincade's Drugstore on this late in the month July day and ducked into two reclining seats which all but swallowed our gaunt bodies. Incidentally, Twyman dropped out of high school and joined the Navy when he reached eighteen years of age. I was always regretful about him not graduating with the Class of 1958 because we had gone through much of grade school together and of course high school until he decided to see the world.

The two temporarily unemployed grocery clerks were poised for the three hour ride into the reaches of destiny, namely Memphis, Tennessee. No, not really... *destiny* was too literary...I didn't know what Thomas' mindset was but inwardly I had already concluded, junior college was my end game and this trip was more or less a warm up lap for me. The Greyhound headed straight north on Highway 49, through a succession of small towns like Ruleville, Drew, Clarksdale, Tunica, etc. etc.

After a hundred stops or so it seemed (I began to wonder if everyone was leaving the Delta), our arrival at the downtown Memphis bus station coincided with the striking of 11:00 AM on a big bank clock that sat near the terminal. As we disembarked, Thomas found a phone and called his uncle in West Memphis. I knew my Aunt and Uncle were working so it was pointless at this time of day to try and reach them. I found out later that Nelle was not working that summer.

It was hotter than the Bonneville Salt Flats...the big city pavement trapped the heat and the temperature was hovering in the mid 90's but the two lost souls sitting on a bench out front of the terminal didn't notice. Heat was not an issue but queasiness had set in just a little bit because our surroundings were strange and foreign. Around noonish, Thomas' uncle wheeled into the station and we were soon on our way to West Memphis.

I must say, the community of the above mentioned hamlet was not the most pristine of places. To me it looked like a typical southern small town multiplied by 50 with a major highway splitting the town in half. Traffic noise was unrelenting, unnerving and rattled the brain. I was not impressed…but what can you say…an old boy from Moorhead, Mississippi passing judgment on another town. Ha. Up to this point, my dream weaving in the cotton fields had never presented images of northern towns looking like this. Ugh. Reality was starting to set in. The western bank of the big river, this place called West Memphis, was a busy jumping off point for traffic heading to Little Rock, Arkansas.

Thomas' uncle was a body shop mechanic and his main job was to smooth out dents in vehicles that had been kissed in collisions. I believe he was called a body man. After we had dined on hamburgers, we went back to his shop and watched him perform magic on a couple of car fenders and doors. In those days, lead was used to fill in dents that resisted hammering out. He was good…real good. But it wasn't long before we were bored stiff. This type ambiance wasn't exactly what I had in mind when my thoughts were previously reaching out for bright lights projected from classy store fronts and skyscrapers.

The uncle worked in West Memphis but lived in Memphis somewhere around Lamar Street…of which, I was not familiar … for that matter I was not familiar with any location in Memphis, including my Aunts' residential home fronts.

Finally after an eternity of killing time, we hopped in the uncle's car and headed back across the Mississippi River to the bus station where I was deposited to scramble of my own accord. In separation, my pal Thomas was now on his own and the same went for me but I knew my Aunts would take good care of me once I made contact and was enveloped in the ambiance of their homes. I wasn't so sure about Thomas' chance of getting a job but his uncle had indicated he would have something lined up for him. I learned later that my friend ended up in a boarding house after obtaining a job at a Kroger's Super Market in the downtown area of Memphis. Considering the hard times, I think Thomas did well finding that job as quickly as he did because I ended up not getting work at all. He stayed employed at Kroger's until he returned to Moorhead in September to start his college studies at Sunflower Junior College.

Never one to be underestimated, Thomas was a tall, slim and clean-cut young man, always starchly dressed in the clothing fads of the day which were an extension of styles worn on our senior trip. As evidenced by his 1959 SJC class picture, Thomas was quite the handsome boy. Always reserved and soft spoken, his speech, much like mine and everyone else that lived in the Delta was a Shelby Foote – like honey dripping drawl, a very thick honey at that, and he was resilient and headstrong in constitution owing to his rigid upbringing on the farm. Regarding his somewhat dubious circumstances, he resorted to his true unassuming nature which included the ability to easily roll with the punches. He proved his adaptability when he opted to work at Kroger's and live in a boarding house without transportation. He had to fend for himself in a big scary city, ridden with felonious crime shooting in (literally) from every direction. To repeat myself, I marveled at his buoyancy because I ended up having it comparatively easy, temporarily residing in my Aunt's comfortable and agreeable middle class home. Thomas showed maturity in getting a job and I showed immaturity in letting my aunt talk me out of seeking employment. I've reflected back on that happenstance many times over the years and I must admit I still have mucho respect for my good friend's ability to latch on to that job that quickly. His resume surely must have impressed the Kroger folks after they saw he was an experienced meat handler, clerk and stocker in a nice sized small town Super Market. They jumped at the opportunity to hire him.

Part Eleven

My father's younger sisters (my aunts, Kathleen and Nelle) migrated to Memphis in the mid 1940's to pursue careers in nursing for Kathleen and beautician school for Nelle. Saying goodbye to their beloved home on Quiver River, Kathleen, older by a couple of years left home first and Nelle followed a year or two later. Kathleen was soon established as a nurse in training at Baptist Hospital where she eventually gained an RN degree which afforded her a good job at one of the large hospitals in the big city (I'm thinking Veteran's Hospital). Nelle didn't realize her dream of becoming a coiffeuse but after a series of receptionist jobs (her good looks didn't hurt her opportunities) she met a dashing and charming young World War II veteran who had also relocated to the populous city from Bells, Tennessee after returning from the great war.

Not to brag, but both of my aunts were beautiful ladies, Kathleen a tall statuesque blond and Nelle, opposite in hair color but svelte in figure like her sister, they in combo were two very imposing femmes.

After a half year courtship, Nelle and Don were married in 1947 and set up housekeeping in the downtown area where

Don, in an energetic burst of entrepreneurial initiative, opened a drugstore in the business district. A son, Larry was born in 1948 and the family like many young families of the post WWII era slowly made their way upward in the pursuit of middle class prosperity.

In 1954, a move out to the suburbs past the Veteran's Hospital completed their temporary march to the second rung on the ladder of success. Of course that suburban location would have been east of downtown because that was the only way the large city could grow in those heady days of Memphis' housing expansion. It was near Audubon Park and Memphis State University.

I might add, Kathleen being career minded to a high degree, delayed her nuptials until the early 1950s at which time she wed Calvin Snyder, a civil engineer.

By the time of my visit in the summer of 1958, Don had gotten out of the drugstore business and had taken up a vocation in insurance sales, to which he was well suited… to wit: with his high spirited outgoing personality and his peppery line of uninterrupted gab, he was a "can't miss" candidate for success. In the burgeoning insurance trade, Don now worked for a company called "Bankers Life". Nelle continued to work a variety of jobs supplementing their income but unknown to me at the time of my visit, she was not working. Don's insurance job required a lot of travel; therefore, the family existed as a two car family like most families in that era where the wife and husband held down separate jobs, and my Aunt had a car at her disposal but at this juncture in 1958 she was in between jobs. Add to that, her need to be at home to look after a ten year old son, Larry, who was out of school on summer break. Obviously, one could easily see why she was idling in this summer of 1958. That was fortunate for me because she showed me around some interesting places that more than likely I would have missed had she been employed.

Nelle and Don came south to the Delta quite frequently, usually in the company of Kathleen, and we, the farm family always welcomed them excitedly. They always arrived in a big shiny new Oldsmobile or Buick sedan and naturally that impressed the heck out of the hoe bothers. We had no concept of the realities of city life and the expenses incurred to sustain a big city lifestyle. We all thought it was a piece of cake and we conjured up visions of being able to eat ice cream cones at will in that big brightly lit Sundries Store shaded by mythical skyscrapers. Actually I never saw the store or the fountain where ice cream was dispensed but in my imaginary world it was a pretty impressive place and invariably I could taste that unlimited scrumptious strawberry ice cream if I closed my eyes and turned on the thought machine.

One thing I can say about my aunts is they never forgot about their brothers and sisters who were left behind, especially the children. Their altruism had always stuck in my mind as being admirable. As an example, Kathleen gave all of her nieces and nephews in the Delta, toothbrushes, tooth powder and charts to hang by the lavatories. Every time we brushed our teeth, we were encouraged to place a tiny shiny star on the daily chart signifying our adherence to the teeth cleaning schedule so posted.

On her next visit to farm country, my aunt would check the charts for compliance and issue gifts accordingly. It was a small thing…her efforts to motivate us in carrying out hygienic necessities is still remembered by the writer to this day. By the way I still have most of my teeth, although I've spent a fortune over the years to keep them anchored but I'm sure my aunt's little scheme contributed measurably to my still possessing those ivories that still sit between my sunken cheeks.

But anyway, due to the solicitude of our Memphis aunts, they became our favorite relatives to a whole gaggle of nieces and nephews living in that isolated bucolic world. In effect, my first grains of thought about "hitting the road" immediately centered on Memphis as a first stop. My second destination, looming large in my brain's planning center was St Louis, Mo., home of my older brother Stan and his new wife, Frances.

And there I was at the Greyhound Bus Station in downtown Memphis waiting for my good aunt, Nelle and her husband to come by and rescue me from my somber desolation in the center of this big clamorous car-honking city. Darn it, some pangs of homesickness were starting to set in. Could it be ole Billy Ray was not cut out for this bright light venue?

They were surprised and at the same time glad to see me or at least from all indications they appeared to be happy to see Nelle's older brother's third son. However, if they weren't glad to see me, they put on a good show and I was made to feel well received. They accepted the fact that country folk sometimes made unannounced visits.

I was soon unpacking my unpretentious suit case in one of Nelle's spare bedrooms. This nice room would be my sleeping quarter for a couple of weeks. In my debriefing, I told my aunt and uncle that I was interested in seeking employment, intimating that their help and job expertise would be valuable in my search for work in these hard times. I'm sure in the privacy of their thoughts; their eyes were rolling back in their head. The country was in the pits of a severe recession and jobs were hard to come by especially for farm boys with no experience.

After inquiring about my future plans regarding college, I revealed the junior college basketball scholarship offer and acceptance…additionally I made them aware of my long range aspiration of becoming a football and basketball coach at the high school level. Because they were not sports enthusiasts, I could detect an undertow of doubt in their digestion of their young nephew's career selection. Inasmuch as I was always blessed with an ability to read minds, I quickly ascertained that my board masters were not that taken with my choice of careers. But what the heck, I was no longer a minor and could make my own decisions but because they were big city dwellers with the trappings of prosperity, this country bumpkin from Moorhead had a deep respect for their opinions.

My aunt and uncle came quickly to the conclusion that any job that could be procured in the remaining weeks of summer would be menial and I could do just as well in my hometown at Lamb's grocery store. So, almost immediately they resisted the idea of my getting a job. Nelle was thinking she could show me around Memphis and give me some exposure to city life that would certainly cultivate my cultural development if not a lot, maybe a smidgen. Coming from the same background and area, she knew I had missed out on the finer things in life owing to too much time spent in the cotton fields. In other words, a little city living could only help my maturation and benefit my chances of becoming a successful student at the Princeton of two year colleges, Sunflower Junior College in Moorhead, Mississippi, smack dab in the middle of the Yazoo Delta.

As I learned later, my Uncle Don was hatching an occupational proposition in his noggin that would be sprung on me later in the week. We'll get to that permutation later.

Part Twelve

The Memphis adventure was in its infancy. The next morning, my insurance salesman uncle hit the road early to sell his policies, so consequently that left Nelle to take me by the nape of my neck and haul my lanky body in her new Oldsmobile out to see the attractions of the city. And guess where the first place of interest I was so exposed. Yep, it was Elvis Presley's home which was only a *hop skip and jump* from the Broadmoor address where my suitcase was planted. The Presley house was located in the "Audubon Park" area where there was a plentiful array of upscale houses which in comparison to houses of today, the structures would have to be considered modest.

No glimpses of the "King" were in the offing but by and large we got a good look at the house which was larger than my hosts but, in my humble opinion, the place was not pretentious … it was just a regular three bed roomer with a moderate size swimming pool. Later the Presley family moved to Graceland and I believe it was slightly over the top insofar as gaudiness goes, but the smallish ranch style house we saw that day was in no way what one would think a big star would be holding court in. In actuality, the house was unoccupied at the time because of his army service in Germany. But then again it was only 1958 and Elvis' star would only explode into the superstar icon that he would become in the 1960s and 1970s.

With Nelle chauffeuring and Larry, my young fidgety cousin sitting in the back seat and yours truly sitting on the passenger side of the big winged Oldsmobile, we toured the grand city of Memphis from one end to the other. We rode down Beale Street, which I believe in those days was not a big deal...perhaps that was a day before it became famous for its restaurants and night spots. This was a time before the street became and was an object of urban renewal. I don't know why she took me down Beale Street that day...maybe she was lost...maybe it was a luck of the draw. I can't say I even remembered the event. In later years when the street became a tourist magnet, I dug deep into the recesses of my recall and pulled out a trace of remembrance and affixed it to my "ready" file. It's possible my recollection is a complete fabrication. You know, sometimes the ole brain plays tricks on our imbedded Kodak.

The zoo and Memphis Chicks baseball stadium were also on the parade route of attractions that I remember...we made a day of just looking over the Memphis landscape...it was without qualification a notable day in the life of a young Mississippi sodbuster. Oh yes, I almost forgot, we drove by the Veterans Hospital and I got to see my striking Aunt Kathleen who was on duty as a nurse in the vast facility. I'm sure all the old soldiers got a lift in spirit and regeneration when they comprehended that this tall classy blond was tending their ails.

Later in my stay, I would spend a day with my flaxen haired aunt in the confines of her home near the airport. She treated me to a cookout and it was a treat to eat as many hamburgers as one wished. I must say I took advantage of that offer…it was a rarity to be offered more than one delicacy in a sitting. Yes, I made a pig of myself but my aunt understood and didn't hold it against me. She looked at my thin frame and being learned in dietetics knew I could stand some fattening up. Nope…she didn't mind at all…she was ever more concerned about her kindred children who were springing from the same humble origins as was her station many years past. I may have been raw and rough around the edges but she looked past the babe in the woods exterior and saw potential in this young man who arrived in town riding the proverbial turnip truck. She had reconciled many years ago that if she could break the shackles of poverty and make something of herself, so could her sibling's children for they were constructed of the same genetic matter.

Part Thirteen

On my third day in Memphis, my uncle insisted that I go with him to collect overdue premiums from some of his delinquent insurance customers inside the Memphis city limits. In particular, I think he wanted to "size me up" at close range, inside his 1954 Ford sedan. It was hot and the sweat flowed in torrents from our foreheads but we were persistent or should I say he was persistent. The collections were met with the most pitiful and evasive stories one could imagine, but Don was aggressive and he knew how to deal with the "poor mouthing". Later than sooner, most of his short paying clientele reluctantly coughed up payment or partial payment. I was amazed...in my Delta frame of reference I was unaccustomed to seeing and dealing with such deceptive miscreants. But my Uncle was undeterred in listening to all the misdirection...he had the skill of an attorney, i.e. every distortion of the truth was handled with an instantaneous rebuke. He was glib. He was good. There was no thwarting his resolve to go home with those monthly premiums tucked snuggly in his brief case. Boy I thought to myself, I wish I could think on my feet that fast. He went home that evening knowing full well that he had had a very productive hot summer's day...in fact the extra push that he had given himself that day was for my benefit. He had put on a show, absent any ifs, ands, & buts; I was completely impressed with his grasp of salesmanship.

To further advance his budding scheme, that evening, he asked that I take his "Bankers Life" loose leaf sales manual and memorize the content of the sales procedure which was outlined on about ten laminated pages. I took the binder out to the patio and started cramming as the bright sunset lit up the back of the house where I sat in a lounge chair. I knew what Don had up his sleeve. He had a business plan stirring in his mind, but the time was not right to make a pronouncement to his protégé in waiting or to his wife.

It struck me that he was testing me to see if I had it in me to be an insurance salesman. He had hinted that tomorrow the two of us would head up to Dyersburg, Tennessee to make several sales calls in that city and a few on the way up. I memorized a couple of the pages and could recite most of the material on those two pages. Hopefully he would allow me a few days to commit the presentation to memory and I didn't let on that I was aware of his grand scheme.

In the meantime, Nelle had prepared a big supper and I was starved as usual. Larry was ripping and snorting around the back yard and had worked up a sweat (he was endowed with a hyper abundance of energy). Nelle grabbed him and sent him inside for a shower, but before she went back inside to finish the food preparation she informed me that she had asked the next door neighbor's teenage daughter to come over to meet me after supper was finished. I nodded in the affirmative "Yes that's fine with me" but in the back of my brain a little caution light clicked on and it was flashing yellow.

My luck with anonymous girls as far as them turning out to be winsome had a low batting average. How does an average of about 100 grab you...with an average like that in baseball you sit on the bench... but in the game of girl assessment, normally an avg. of 100 pretty much allows you to sit on the sidelines too. Oh well, what the heck...I was a trooper and who knows, the law of averages may be in for a correction on this very evening. Also, knowing my aunts penchant for all things stylish, I didn't think she would be so obliging if the young girl next door had been anything less than eye catching. At the time I didn't know the girl was only fourteen.

"Son of a Gun", was that a good tasting supper... being as famished as I was, a second helping of every food item on the table including dessert was automatic. I believe Don was right behind me in an encore performance of ladling up another go round of the tasty victuals. In answer to the assumption one might pose that we were a couple of gluttons, I would dutifully submit in our defense, that Don was such an intense hustler that he forgot to stop for lunch or perhaps that was his M.O. Anyway as a result of his energetic canvassing, the two insurance gumshoes (I know gumshoe is not the appropriate word but we were acting like detectives in pursuit of premiums) had gone all day without a meal. I couldn't vouch for Don but I rarely ate breakfast and that was the case on this day.

Now that the hunger pangs were in remission, the kitchen cleanup seemed to zip by as quickly as the food slipped down my esophagus…with Nelle and me forming a tandem of washing and drying, we quickly worked off the dishes, utensils and pans and shortly retired to the den. Don settled at the kitchen table and proceeded to process stacks of insurance papers, money and checks.

The den was not large but it was furnished with a sofa, chairs, side tables and a television set, but its main attraction and centerpiece…was a jukebox loaded with current hit parade records and some oldies for the middle age crowd. A very appealing stage for a seasoned "bopper" like myself …I must say I was impressed with the jukebox and the ambiance and even the music. My Aunts taste in music was eclectic but most of the Pop records that she had installed in the jukebox were to my liking.

Just as I settled into a big soft chair, Aunt Nelle clicked on a slow piece and the two of us did a snappy two step slow dance around the miniscule dance floor. Then she told me a little about the fourteen year old kid next door to which I didn't pay much attention. I figured she was some nondescript, pimply faced, flat chested pre-adolescent junior high school girlie. Realizing that my aunt was mostly interested in seeing some live bopping action, she had enlisted **Donna,** her next door neighbor as a pairing manikin in the performance of some ***American Bandstand*** type hoofing entertainment.

At this point in my life, my confidence in my dancing had reached its apex, so I was feeling pretty good about a bop workout despite the anticipated letdown of having an unaccomplished minor for my dance partner.

At this juncture, Nelle phoned Donna and told her to come on over to meet her sod busting nephew who had arrived in Memphis a couple of days back. Actually she didn't say "sodbuster"...to be honest, she said "world traveler". Naw, wrong again...I think she just said "nephew. I seriously doubted this city girl would know what a sodbuster was anyway. If she did, she wouldn't be impressed.

Even though I was not optimistic about my soon to be dancing partner's odds of being anything special, still I was curious but my expectations were not exactly primetime. The doorbell rang and my young cousin met Donna at the front door and brought her into the den where Nelle and I were sitting and toe tapping to the reverberations of the jukebox.

When she walked in, I must say I was completely overcome with shock. Here standing before my 20 – 20 line of vision was this very mature looking "beauty" dressed in white shorts and sleeveless blouse. I gazed at her in mute wonder, my lower jaw lost its rigidity and the resulting look on my face must have made her laugh to herself. She was not shy and she looked this older guy straight in the eye without giggling. Doing a quick study in my left brain or maybe it was the right side; I surmised she looked as if she could easily be seventeen years old and not a day less. Nelle had given me no indication that this girl was special but at first glance I discerned this little gal was extraordinary. But sometimes, initial appearances can be deceiving, but on the other hand, only after a few minutes of introductory remarks and small talk I came to the conclusion that my first impression of the young lady was right on. She was stunning. I was unaccustomed to being blindsided by anything that closely resembled stunning.

I didn't know what thoughts ran through Donna's mind but my prevailing ambivalence quickly dissolved into …hey, let's see what kind of dancing moves she has…if her bop steps are as good as she looks, I may have to invent some advanced dance routines.

Nelle stepped out to the kitchen to get some cokes. Left to ourselves the two young strangers chatted reservedly for a while, exchanging details of my home town, High School, her school and things that would interest a couple of teenagers. When Nelle returned, the three of us talked about our music preferences, artists that we liked and the records that were loaded in the jukebox.

After lighting up the commercial sized jukebox Nelle punched in some of the popular music that we had said we liked and in quick succession, I grabbed Donna's hand and we were off to the races. We bopped to Carl Perkins' *Blue Suede Shoes*,

Elvis' *Hound Dog and Don't be Cruel*, Fats Domino's *Blueberry Hill* and an assortment of Rock & Roll music including some slow pieces by the Platters, Sam Cook and of course, Elvis to name a few of the popular ditties of the time. We took a couple of coke breaks and probably danced all tolled an hour and a half. Nelle enjoyed every minute of our production.

Donna was an excellent dancer and I hoped I'd upheld my part of the partnership. It was true, the action on my end was equal to my partners but the question to be answered was... how about quality and style? Her dancing was in top form and I guess mine was passable since no complaints came from Donna or our host. All in all it was a fun night. I actually walked her home and shook her hand. I didn't want her to think I was a cradle robber.

Part Fourteen

Dyersburg was almost straight northward of Memphis and Don and I headed out bright and early the next morning aiming to make landfall there by mid-morning (no, we weren't in a boat). My mentor was in complete automotive control as he queried me about the Bankers Life sales pitch and procedures. I thought I did pretty good answering his probes and he seemed pleased but he continued to blister me with questions all the way to the rural city to our north. Mingled with my thoughts between his unrelenting questions were fleeting thoughts of that next door neighbor kid. If Don had known my concentration was being compromised, he probably would have reached over and swatted me with a copy of the

Memphis Commercial Appeal newspaper lying on the seat next to his coffee cup holder.

At this juncture instead of focusing on the here and now, my mind had relapsed to the early morning hours and I mean real early hours. At daybreak, my uncle had stopped by the Bankers Life office building to pick up his daily *leads* list. *Leads* were written inquiries furnished by potential customers responding to newspaper ads. These *leads* were hugely beneficial to sales people because it gave them the structure to call on people who had expressed an interest in their product. The system of developing leads was vastly superior to *cold call selling* which was a tough row to hoe even for the best of drummers. To me, this insurance selling business was starting to make some sense after all.

Don already had a stack of leads from which the Dyersburg trip was planned but he informed his understudy that he always mopped up the last minute inquiries in case some came from the area of the day's destination.

A common denominator between the two of us was our tendency to want to get done with a task as quickly as possible and move to the next target. Otherwise, we had virtually nothing in common as far as our personalities compared. Well maybe that's not correct, because he was a very amiable, sincere and warm person or so it seemed. Like I have stated before, as a young uncomplicated person, I lacked an ability to see below the surface of an individual. I knew in my mind that I was sincere and amiable in dealings with people; therefore Don and I were alike in that vein. But as far as unbounded energy and verbosity, I stacked up to him not at all. He was the supreme extrovert and I was congenitally introverted. But the pundits say opposites sometime make good teams. Hopefully we would make a compatible team. Actually I was an unknown commodity to Don…he didn't know me at all but he did have age on his side as an enabling factor to help size me up. He was testing this young recruit under fire.

On a couple of occasions, Don asked his binder bearer to clarify a point relative to a clause in the sales pitch and I responded promptly with the appropriate answer. Thank God it was material from the first two pages which I had memorized. Half way to Dyersburg, the car pulled onto a dusty gravel road and snaked its way two or three miles in the direction of the Mississippi River to a dilapidated house that was under severe attack from weeds and vine. Apparently Nelle's husband knew this country well, because left to me; I would have never found this place based on the sketchy information logged on the *lead* flyer. I found out later that my uncle was from Bells, Tennessee, a small community not far from our current location.

Before a knock on the screen door could be initiated, an old man stepped out and courteously welcomed us in the normal southern way. It was like we were long lost relatives showing up for a family reunion. Before long Don and the grandpawish septuagenarian were backslapping and carrying on like they were war buddies. Once inside the house, I could see the gleam in Don's eyes that spoke loud and clear "this sale is a done deal". We had gotten our foot in the door and there was no turning back Mr. Smooth. As we settled into an old couch that reeked essence of dog and cat, I was the caretaker of the Sales Binder and I had it firmly gripped in my palms.

The old man and his wife were interested in medical insurance …remember these were the days before Medicare but at their ages the premiums would be tough to make but Don worked out a plan to accommodate a meager budget funded by welfare and some rent income the couple received from farm land they owned adjacent to the old house we were sitting in. They could afford just the minimalist of coverage.

Off to a favorable start, the super salesman with his spiffily dressed sidekick with dog hair clinging to the seat of his black rayon pants parted company and was soon directing the Ford sedan back onto concrete pavement. Chalk up one sale and we hadn't even made it to Dyersburg.

Before the day was finished, four policies had been sold coming from about ten calls. Not a bad day…in fact it was an excellent day and Don was grinning from ear to ear. He felt so good around noontime he stopped for lunch and treated me to a big hamburger at one of the Dyersburg diners.

On the way home, I committed page three to memory and we reviewed the day's successes as I hung on to Don's every word accenting the highlights and giving reasons why certain sales maneuvers worked and others didn't. My education was in full throttle…balls to the wall…if you will. Hey," don't turn up your nose --- that term is not salacious, its airplane pilot jargon for full speed ahead …it means push the balls atop the control levers all the way until they reach the instrument panel, in other words "full bore".

Nelle and Don were both good cooks but with her husband out beating the bushes, the culinary duties fell to Nelle and she delivered a lip smacking dinner for us that evening. She indicated she had a positive feeling about our run up to Dyersburg and figured we'd want to celebrate our success with a good meal. As a testament to that toast, I was able to mutter "Amen" under my breath. Never before had I eaten this high on the hog...and incidentally I think if memory serves me, pork chops were the evening's main course. But let me hesitate just a moment before making that assertion, my remembrance is probably inaccurate because Nelle was always extremely health conscious. So as I sit here putting my thoughts on paper 53 years later, I'm thinking maybe it was chicken we dined on that evening in late July, 1958 in the suburbs of Memphis, Tennessee. Regardless of the main course that night, my memory is still lucid enough to tell me it was a fine meal. Too, I remember Don, his appetite quieted was beaming because he had made a bundle of money that day and he reared back in his easy chair ...it was time for some soulful relaxation.

I slipped away and called Donna from the den phone to let her know in an indirect way that I was interested in her without being too forward. I was still vacillating in my approach to this delicate situation concerning an eighteen year old making overtures to a fourteen year old girl (soon to be a fifteen year old). From where I came, boys and girls pretty much coupled romantically within a couple of years of their own age group. Actually Donna was closer to fifteen than fourteen years of age, but still... a three year gap in age was a stretch in my principled mind. It was easy to rationalize a solution to the predicament by acceding to the logic that she was so mature for such a young age. From what I had discerned the night before, the young lady was probably more socially developed than me owing to my rural environment. No doubt, in her urban surroundings she had ample opportunity to interact with numerous people at will, whereas in comparing my face to face activity, I was more than likely spending more time in the fields holding dialogue with soy bean bushes and cotton plants.

But sometimes when the old brain is introduced to a conflict in principles, usually in a short period of time, it (the brain) will spit out an acceptable resolution, or at least, an idea that can be reconciled within the framework of that person's conscience. Although my brain was working through other problematic issues like finding a temporary job, going to college, career options, and my family's crop situation, the computing organ sitting on my neck casually signaled for me to proceed with my absorption with "that comely girl next door".

Yes, I took time out from my insurance education to converse with the attractive soon to be ninth grader next door. It didn't diminish my confidence a lick when she reciprocated in kind.

Part Fifteen

As a matter of policy, Banker's Life management insisted the field agents submit paperwork for contacts the following day of closure unless it was a Friday. The sale of the four policies on Thursday meant that Don would need to take an office day on the following day, a Friday. Understandably, my presence at the office would be a distraction, so a suggestion that I idle on Friday, enjoy the day and study the insurance manual was right up my alley.

Don was in an expansive mood that bright Friday morning as he backed out of the driveway. He had intentionally slept a little late that morning, the choice being his prerogative inasmuch as he didn't punch a clock besides on the previous day he was on the road before the first slivers of light awakened the roosters and the Wrens. He was looking forward to finishing up the volumes of paperwork by midafternoon which would allow an early quitting time, making a return to the Matthews hacienda in time for a barbecue of which he was to be the chief chef.

Not to belittle my family's mundane lifestyle in Mississippi, yours truly was beginning to acclimate to this upscale suburban way of life at my aunt's trendy and cozy home. Enjoying myself to the fullest, I tackled the binder with vigor and was pouring over the text when Nelle interrupted to say we were going to a couple of department stores in the business district, to more or less, window shop and stroll the streets. I knew I would not be in the market for any merchandise because of my limited cash reserves but I was game to look.

This shopping exercise was not totally alien to my familiarity because my mother used to take us boys to Greenville's Sears store in the fall to buy Levi jeans and a couple of shirts for the ensuing school session.

Nelle, always one interested in fashion headed straight to a Gentleman's Clothier or maybe it was a Penneys Men's Department. We must have spent a good hour trying on classy looking sport coats. I think her motive was to get a look at her strapping nephew in some threads that would enhance his unpolished presence. And maybe as a secondary motive… if she saw a jacket that jumped out at her, she would take Don back later and have him outfitted in a new coat. I think Nelle was having the time of her life attempting to get a fix on my future potential. I don't know what she was seeing via her advanced vision but her apparent belief in my promising prospects served to uplift my self-esteem.

Once we were back on Broadmoor Street and safely inside Nelle's sunny brick house, out came the insurance orientation kit and the visitor from Sunflower County started cramming again. My Uncle would be proud of his nephew i.e. by the end of the weekend, I was convinced I would have this packet mastered and then it would be only a matter of being able to project the text into a vocally presentable form. With his speaking skills and oratory, Don could be my speech coach to tutor me in speaking skills up to a level that would make the client feel at ease and receptive to the pitch. A couple of concerns that I knew Don would bring up were my country drawl and monotone way of speaking not to mention a lack of full enunciation on key action verbs. But being realistic, I was not too naïve to think he could correct my bad speech habits in a matter of hours or days. With a lot of practice, it would take months and possibly years to effect a noticeable improvement but that's not to say I was not willing to try. At least once the teaching set in, I would have a grasp of the rules and could practice. One thing about it, although Don had not revealed his business plan for my development, I suspected it would involve a sales job in the Greenville, Mississippi area. With that said, the issue of my drawl would not be a problem in the Delta, given that everyone down that way speaks with a drawl anyway. On the contrary, a drawl could be a plus for an agent in that slow talking region. As I mulled over the ins & outs of selling and presenting, I thought about my traveling partner Thomas Blansett over in West Memphis or wherever he was at that point in time.

I left him with my Aunt's telephone number when we parted company on Monday but I had not heard from him since. I was sure he was out scratching but was not sure if he would be lucky enough to snag a job. For all I knew, he had gone back to Moorhead but I thought surely he would have called me before making such a rash departure. Today was Friday and noting our arrival in the city was Monday, that was only four days for Thomas to make something happen. Unknown to me at this time, his uncle had failed to deliver on his promise to have a job waiting for Thomas once he hit Memphis.

As that thought diversion was circulating in my brain, I heard Don pull into the driveway, exit the car and in full stride, whistling a happy tune, burst through the kitchen door, primed to launch his chef duties for the evening. Glancing over at me at the kitchen table, I could detect a look of satisfaction gleaming from his face at finding his young protégé with his nose in the Bankers Life manual. In rapid succession, he drilled me with a couple of insurance related questions to which I responded without hesitation. He seemed amused and I was pleased with my cleverness. I could picture him entering his bedroom, massaging his hands, saying under his breath, "trust me, this old country boy from the Delta may have it in him to make a good living selling insurance". "He may have the stuff to pull it off." But that was me thinking …not him talking. I'd have to wait on what he really thought. We were just in the first quarter of this life game called "mentoring."

In short order, the patio grill was loaded with charcoal and flames were shooting skyward. In a few minutes, the coals were glowing bright red, likewise Don was not glowing but he was enjoying a relaxed state of mind from ingesting a couple bottles of beer. I refused an offer of beer because I didn't want my aunt to think unfavorably about my acquired social habits. Hopefully she thought…a nice boy like me did not resort to drink to have a good time.

To celebrate the rewards of the week, steaks were grilled, potatoes were baked and corn on the cob was wrapped in foil and steamed in butter while the other "sides" completed their cooking. As befits most seasoned chefs, Don orchestrated the timing of the steaks grilling and completion to coincide with every item finishing at the same time. I believe this was my first exposure to the terms; rare, medium rare, medium well and well or no pink. I selected "medium well" and have pretty much stuck with that grilling preference throughout the years.

It's funny how old country boys can remember in acute detail some of those feasts they gobbled up 60 years ago. Yes it is amazing and that was one troughing I still remember.

And to cap off a fine evening, I went out and talked to Donna across the backyard fence and yes, she was still looking good, decked out in her fully appreciated sun dress.

Part Sixteen

What a wonderful weekend. That Saturday morning, I got a taste of golf or rather observing up close the game of golf. I quasi caddied for my uncle at the **Audubon Golf Course** near where they lived… in other words I supplied the brawn to carry a bag. Accompanying us was Aunt Kathleen's husband Calvin. Both he and Don were avid golfers and of course I knew nothing about the game but was willing to carry one of their bags. It was sweltering but everyone had a great time, although by the time we finished at mid-day we were soaked with sweat and spent for the most part. I was allowed to hit a couple of balls but was perplexed at my inability to strike the balls with any force. The shots were glancing blows and I soon realized that the game of golf was complex and not easily mastered. That summation of reality applies to the status of my golf game to this day. In reflection, I couldn't tell you if the two uncles were good golfers or not, I plainly don't remember and no one mentioned a handicap. But we all had a big time…the foursome behind us probably thought the young man caddying in front of them was out of his element scurrying around like a lost possum in a potato patch. And they were absolutely right…I didn't know a thing about golf rules or decorum…primarily I just toted the bag and let Don select his own clubs and balls. If someone had shouted "Fore", I would not have known to drop to my knees with my head tucked. In all likelihood my reaction to turn around to look would have gotten me clobbered with a 125 mph latex missile.

As we headed home from the golf outing, it dawned on me that this was a lifestyle that I could get used to in a hurry. Let me enumerate: good job without backbreaking work, good comfortable home with all the amenities, good food and available public recreation all rolled into one were some ingredients that pleased my druthers. I made a vow to make the best of my opportunities to insure fate gave me a chance to achieve some of this good life in the future.

At the conclusion of that brilliant weekend, the uncle and visitor found themselves on the hawking trail again but this time it was not up to Dyersburg. We were up northeast of Memphis a far piece but still out in the hinterlands of farm country. Several calls were made on a variety of farm families, some middle aged but most were in the "autumn of their years" category. Don thought it about time for me to "walk my talk" as a sales person trainee. He wanted to test my presentation moxie, knowing that I had memorized the Bankers Life sales brochure. As we drove out to the country in the early hours, he had fired off dozens of questions pertaining to the manual and I had given a passable accounting of my knowledge. Now it was a matter of being able to present the material in a convincing way.

In the process of staging my very first sales presentation, Don pulled out a well scripted "lead" that contained lots of information, a sure and significant indicator that the older couple we were about to see, was seriously interested in buying a life insurance policy.

Affirming the correct address, Don pulled into their gravel driveway alongside a well-manicured farm house and we were warmly invited into the living room. After a preliminary chat up, Don explained that I was a sales trainee and he was asking their permission if they would agree to listen to my presentation. Their reply was reassuring …"Oh yes, absolutely… the young man is such a clean-cut nice looking boy …we would be happy to hear him out." It was obvious, the woman was more conciliatory towards me than the old man (for some reason old women tended to always embrace my humble non-threatening persona).

Admittedly, I was nervous as a thief in church or maybe more descriptive, anxious as an illegitimate city cousin at a family reunion. Never had I done any public speaking to speak of. Except one time as an officer of the *Future Farmers of America* at an annual banquet I made a two minute speech. Even that attempt at public speaking turned into a disaster when my chair flipped over as I stood up to commence my speech. As I opened my mouth in Patrick Henry fashion, the clang of the chair hitting the floor echoed like a cymbal dropped from a 12 foot ladder in the Sistine chapel. How I mustered the strength to start and finish that speech, after the shell shocked audience had the wax knocked out of their ears, I've never been able to comprehend to this day.

To assuage my doubt, it was impossible to fall back on memories of warm subconscious allusions to speeches with applauding audiences, because there were none. I couldn't back out now, I was on my own…I'd have to wing it.

I did it! But Don was sweating more than I was. I stumbled my way through it. Don stepped in with several clarifiers and polished off a knock' em dead closing. The old couple bought the policy…the only one sold that day. What a relief.

Hopefully my contribution helped? Did they feel sorry for the boy? Probably.

Later, between calls, the maestro critiqued my sales pitch calling my examination grade fair but inadequate which certainly didn't surprise me one iota. What would one expect…first time out …not much… and that's pretty much what I delivered…not much. Nodding in agreement, Don seconded my personal assessment. But he was careful not to discourage me…he pointed out that that he thought I started off too fast…my speaking pace didn't match my natural pace therefore my articulation of words was jerky and disjointed. Although my start was fast paced, it slowed as I started to grope for words. To tell the truth, my mind was racing ahead of my slow talking mouth and I didn't have the experience to rein in the brain waves which were literally overwhelming me. How does one manage that affliction?

To further his analysis, he was not particularly enamored of the way I haltingly verbalized my pitch. He told me "you've got to smooth out your delivery and that takes practice and time".

I didn't get riled or down on myself. As a matter of note, I hitched up my pants and looked at my shortcomings and reasoned as all students of the life process realize… natural born phenoms are rare… to be good at something, practice is the elbow grease that paves the way to improvement. Realistically, I knew intuitively that one could not expect to do well on the first trial. I had proven that in my sport endeavors, especially in basketball where it took a lengthy fifteen moons to develop a jump shot that would repeat with any accuracy. So, yes…my uncle hit the bull's-eye squarely when he said my sales pitch offering was at best mediocre. He didn't have to tell me because I knew I was lousy.

I think he, somehow, had been hopeful that I would knock their socks off on opening day like a highly touted blue chipper but the old boy from Mississippi didn't have it in him to pull off a showstopper. Don acknowledged to himself that it would take a lot of work to shape the kid who was shaving every other day into a confident pitchman. And that was the end of the analysis for the time being.

After all the "leads" were exhausted, Don called it a day we headed home to Memphis but since we were close my uncle's home town, he decided to pass through Bells, Tennessee to visit his mother who still lived in the small town. As the car entered the main street and proceeded across a railroad crossing, Don related the sad event of his father being hit and killed by a train at that very intersection in 1947, a few days after his marriage to Nelle. He didn't elaborate and I didn't ask any questions. That mention was the end of any reference to the tragic accident.

His mother, who appeared to be quite young, I would guess in her mid-fifties and well preserved, welcomed us to her immaculate home situated on a well-kept street in the little Tennessee town. After introductions and family talk, we sat down to enjoy coffee and pie. As the conversation waxed and waned, it seems information surfaced to the effect that she had a new man friend and I remember Don became upset with some aspect of the relationship to which I had no clue or desire to be in the middle of, so I stepped outside. I certainly didn't want to get caught in the crossfire of a family dispute. There was one thing about my uncle that I admired and that was... he did not bite his tongue to hold back his opinions, no sir, he didn't, but to his credit he spoke softly and quietly with all due respect to his mother. Sorry to say, but the sales crew from Memphis parted company with the family homestead in an unpleasant mood or should I say half the crew...yours truly was an impartial bystander in the matter. After we left, the driver of the Ford headed south, simmered for a while but soon calmed down and resumed his normal cordial bearing before arriving at the pretty bungalow on Broadmoor Drive.

We had had a long day but even though tired I was looking forward to an evening accompanying Donna to a skating rink. Although I didn't skate, Nelle was driving us to a roller rink that night. It wasn't like it was a date...I was mostly along for the ride. Nelle was serving double duty as chauffeur and chaperon.

Actually I had not seen much of Donna since that night of dancing the previous week. I had talked to her a couple of times but most of my time had been spent on my mushrooming insurance job but after today's debacle perhaps it was just as well that I spend more time on fun. I think Don had reached the point of not having a lot of confidence in his nephew's selling acumen at this stage of development. The nephew, no doubt needed a gross amount of priming before he could be turned loose in a territory. A tentative plan of setting me up with a Bankers Life Sales territory in and around Greenville, Mississippi had provided Don with the adrenaline to aggressively mentor me but now after seeing me in action he had concluded: what's the rush? To that end, he had suggested that when I started college in the fall taking a "Speech" class should be one of my top curricula priorities.

But anyway, so much for careermongering...it was time for some hair loosening. We went to the rink that night and Donna skated and I watched from the sidelines. After watching her graceful glides around the floor, my opinion of her prettiness multiplied and I must say I was smitten with this wholesome teenage ninth grader. I knew this dalliance was an exercise in futility but there was an aura about this girl that made me sit upright not to mention her seventeen year old sized body loaded with curves made my neck crane every time she skated by. This "crush" thing was probably a dead end street but my thought process told me it could be fun while it lasted.

Several times during the evening, Donna doubled with what appeared to be a fifteen year old kid in a skating routine that involved arm in arm maneuvers. For all I knew he could have been her high school fellow...it made me wish I could skate. But that was the way it was, I didn't skate, so the young peach fuzzed dude had his hormone glands stimulated that night while mine remained moderately dysfunctional. Never the less, it was an enjoyable night of girl watching...yes it was a treat after a stressful day of insurance hawking.

I think I can safely say that that ride home was the last time I saw the girl next door. The night turned out to be our "sayonara". I talked to her a couple of times on the phone after that night but that skating affair was pretty much the culmination of our short affection. Given that Donna must have been devastated when I pulled the parachute ripcord to St. Louis a few days later, I could sympathize with her anguish, because I felt a similar glum especially when my train chugged north to the Lewis and Clark expedition jumping off point.

Not intentionally, but I've jumped ahead of myself in the storyline, so please bear with me as I reset the date and time on my Timex watch.

Part Seventeen

My eighth day in Memphis was spent at my other aunt's house where we enjoyed a cookout as touched on earlier in the story.

She came over to Nelle's place about mid-morning and picked up her home town nephew. She had a small son, Mark, but for the life of me, I don't remember if he was with us or if he was at a nursery.

I don't remember my uncle being there at any time during the visit so it was assumed he was at work since this was a week day. He was a civil engineer by trade and now that my memory brightens, it comes to me now…yes, he was at his day job with the Memphis Department of Public Works.

In line with her husband's employment, another piece of information that sticks in my memory is Kathleen's airing of Calvin's dream to open a fast food diner with drive through service. He never did take the leap but he was way ahead of the curve in his thinking. Remember these were the years before fast food cornered the dining market and if he had jumped on his idea in 1958, who knows, his venture may have been another McDonald's or Burger King.

Kathleen, a nurse, was enjoying a rare off day. As I said before, we had a jolly good time and talked the day away, mostly about my future. At my asking, she indicated her work history included stints at Baptist Hospital, the Red Cross and Veterans Hospital.

At the mention of my insurance selling exploits with my mentor, Don, her favorite brother in law, she expressed amusement but didn't comment at first report. Reading her reaction, I don't think she thought much of my professed path as a fledging salesman, inasmuch as she tactfully "implied that I should stick with the teaching and coaching dream." Having a good understanding of the Griffin clan's introverted tendencies; she put two and two together and concluded, correctly "that it would take a change in personality for me to succeed in the sales field." Concurring that Don was a natural born public relations artist, she offered that "I should stick to a career more in tune with my inherent likes and dislikes." Furthermore... she expounded "Being in the public arena was not a good fit for a boy with my lack of persuasiveness." "Selling demands a thick skin and an attitude of boldness, imposition and stepping on toes." Her belief that those "imbedded tendencies were not part of my genetic makeup" was met with my unconscious agreement. I caught myself physically nodding my head in agreement without knowing it. Her advice to me was to go with something that I could enjoy. It would be much easier to school oneself in a pleasurable line of work rather than jumping into a vocation of chance.

Before that day rolled into history, and after two giant hamburgers had been socked away, my recurring uncertainty toward a sales career was replaced with a firm resolve to pursue an education centered on teaching and coaching. But how was

I going to break the news to my good uncle and career advisor? Would it disappoint him if I jumped ship?

Then it occurred to me that I need not tell him of my mind change at all. It was really his idea in the first place…I just sort of went along with his plan to make him happy. I had been willing to the give the insurance game my best shot and I did just that. So why worry about it.

It's funny how adults figure things out much quicker than young sprouts. As it turned out, Don was way ahead of me in the game of taking stock, because he was struggling much the same as me with the question: "how am I going to break the news to my trusting nephew that his Salesmanship Suitability grade falls in the lower quartile of poor.

So as it turned out, we both let the issue pretty much die a death of neglect. I only went out selling with Don one more day in those final days and he instructed me to passively observe him in action and take mental notes of which I concurred with a sigh of relief.

Later on that day, which was a Thursday, I told Don of my intention to move on up the line to St. Louis where my older brother and another uncle lived. I had already announced my plan to Nelle the previous day. I'm sure they we elated to see me go since I had screwed up their routine …I know they wanted to get back to a state of normalcy. Moreover, both my esteemed next of kin had run out of places to show and tell. Let me see, taking inventory…I had seen the main attractions of downtown Memphis, I had experienced several working trips in Memphis and up to Dyersburg and Bells, Tennessee and had learned the rudiments of insurance salesmanship, I had met a fine looking next door neighbor girl, I had gone on a golf outing, I had had a good visit with my other aunt, I had enjoyed an evening of watching a skating exhibition performed by a lovely athlete and I had enjoyed good food that a normal country boy would not have access to. Yes, I could maintain fervently that this Memphis trip had been highly informative and enriching. I had already stored a variety of experiences in my brain archives for later reference and withdrawal. Those mental pictures would remain intact throughout my 71 years and are still intact to this day as I sit here writing, knowing that that cornucopia of information is readily available at an instant beckoning.

On the previous Tuesday night, a phone call came to me from my traveling buddy, Thomas. Having split from his uncle after a short stay, he was rooming in a boarding house in the downtown area of Memphis and was working at a nearby Kroger's Supermarket. Imposing on my aunt the next day, I asked if she could taxi me over to see my friend over in the bowels of metropolitan Memphis.

I found him in the produce section of the big store in white apron and with heads of lettuce in his hands. I felt a little jolt of guilt, knowing Thomas was hard at work and I was having the time of my life, traveling the back roads of Tennessee, living in middleclass trappings and consorting with pretty women...well not so fast...make that one pretty girl. Really, I felt bad that Thomas was working hard and I was mostly loafing, I really did.

We quickly got down to the mundane...he, briefing me on his whereabouts and state of affairs and me telling him of my plan to take a train to St Louis, not to work, but to soak up some more culture. I could now understand why rich folks traveled to broaden their cultural portfolios…I felt the same way. However maybe it was different for the rich, while they probably went to museums to view expensive artwork by Masters, I was out looking at baboons in a zoo. Nothing ventured, no culture gained was my motto. Of course, the previous thought was just a joke. I was really anxious to visit my brother in the big city of St Louis.

Once again, within a time frame of a couple of weeks, Thomas and I parted company, but consumed with the understanding that Sunflower Junior College was our exit strategy. This bite of life had turned out to be hard work for Thomas and almost the opposite for me. But nonetheless, we both came to the same conclusion…more education was a must if we expected more out of life than just a nibble. Understandably, the two of us were probably unfit for steady employment at that stage in our lives, at least I was. He was proving he could handle a steady job but working in a Super Market was not a career either of us wanted to pursue. I told Thomas I'd see him back in Moorhead in early September before Sunflower Junior College started its fall session. For the record, Thomas did return to SJC and attended for the duration of the 1958 – 1959 school year. After completing a year of college, he joined the Army and eventually ended up in Germany.

I spent one last day with Don on the road and we had a relaxed and entertaining day. A nice lunch at a cafeteria and some down to earth joking and joshing set the tone for our final outing. I don't remember selling any policies that day but Don said he didn't care since he had already exceeded his sales quota for that week. As always, in his company, I got to hear some of his war stories and tales of other adventures and I might add… the stories were not repeaters, thankfully. He was a sincere guy and I believe he had my best interest in mind when he tried his little development experiment with me on the dusty roads of east central Tennessee. A psychologist, he was not …and yes, I would utterly agree and I think he would concur, that he totally miscalculated my behavioral bent. You know the old saying "it's impossible to make a silk purse out of a sow's ear."

Although his grand plan of making a sales rep out of me had hit the skids so to speak, he still had faith that I had the tools to be a success in any endeavor I was willing to tackle. He so much as told me so. It made my day knowing that I had not totally disappointed him even though I was not cut out to be the Dale Carnegie inspired super salesman.

My Memphis saga was drawing to a close and on Saturday, the thirteenth day of my visit, I started my wrap up duties in preparation for my journey up to St. Louis. I called the train station for the Sunday schedules and determined the Missouri Pacific passenger train would leave at 8:00 AM, make a few stops up the line, and then proceed north to arrive in St Louis at 5:30 PM. After confirming the schedule, Don said he would be glad to take his city hopping nephew to the train station and in the same breath, no less, hinted at the likelihood he could still get in a round of golf after dropping me off. That made me smile because I knew both he and Nelle were ready for a return to their regular schedule.

I had washed and ironed my clothes and packed my little suitcase. My shoes were shined...no not really...but the dust had been brushed off...you see they were actually leather suede moccasins with no luster. Before I went to bed that Saturday night I laid out my black khaki pants with the fashionable miniature buckle in back and a nice cross striped shirt that Mrs. Durrett had given me for a graduation present. And of course my white socks were placed near the shoes. I wanted to look spiffy in the coach car during my chase up to Saint Louie in the Oriental Express.

I called Donna and told her my mission in Memphis was finished and I was headed to St Louis and last but not least, I moved into the den to let Nelle hold court in the Rock and Roll pavilion. The subject of college and vocation had been beaten to death; therefore those topics were ignored in favor of possible lurking snafus associated with this intermediate trip and the return to Moorhead. She was concerned about my going to St Louis by my old lonesome but I assured her there was virtually no risk of getting off track (no pun intended). I would go straight to St Louis Union Station located in downtown, call Stan and he would pick me up...it was simple as that. I was advised to stay away from unsavory stragglers at the Union Station (largest railroad terminal in the USA). Her unease arose from her fear strangers would bamboozle an old country boy and perhaps take advantage of his trusting nature.

Ole Billy boy was the intrepid traveler...yep, fearless, feckless and naïve...or better yet, dumb as a paperweight. I thought I had my act together but as the story unfolds, it came to past that my complacency was ill founded since, as it turned out, my best laid preparations didn't go according to plan.

I went over my mental checklist with Nelle and everything seemed to be in order. Premature hugs and goodbyes followed, and then it was early to bed. I slept soundly knowing I would see my older brother the next day. How little did I know what surprises lay ahead in the day to come?

Part Eighteen

As I watched Don's Ford Fairlane get smaller and smaller in the distance as it disappeared from view as sighted from the steps of the Memphis Union Station, I gulped, swallowed hard and sighed uncomfortably. My sudden loneliness was conspicuous for the first time when it dawned on me that for the first time in my life I was standing there at the entrance to the Memphis Union Station, suitcase in hand and nobody standing beside me. Not a brother, not a running buddy nor a butcher friend was to be found. Nil..., zilch...zero. I was absolutely on my own with no one to lean on for encouragement, advice or consultation. I was now a solo act and my survival meant I would have to make it with self-reliance and with dependence on the wits provided by my Maker.

After the purchase of a ticket which I remember as being around $10, I made entry to my assigned passenger car and took a seat next to an open window. Looking around I saw that all the windows were open because there were no air conditioned conveyances in those days. It was August and it was hot and it was stifling inside the car. The seats were more like benches in a church and the padding was spare...not very accommodating for my hatchet derriere but I wasn't complaining, it seemed nice enough for the ride up north. Looking around after everyone boarded, I was surprised there were not many boarders, most were families of three or four. I was hoping there would be some nice looking girls sitting around that would add some spice to the wood paneled décor but under the circumstances I gathered no such luck like I had had with the serendipitous appearance of Donna at Nelle's house. Certainly the odds were against an encore encounter.

Soon the train was on its way but its top speed of 50 miles per hour didn't show promise for an early arrival in the river city. Although the speed was boring, it generated some air movement within the car and provided a minimum of breezy comfort. The train engine was a steam locomotive and it could be heard chugging away as it crossed the Mississippi River Bridge and coasted down into the western flat land and leveled out on a never ending stair case that paralleled the massive river. Then in a short while the track took leave of the river but stayed close enough that landmarks belied the fact that the giant muddy river was just over yonder across them cotton fields and willow thickets.

I tried to sleep but was too wound up to persuade my body to produce a state of lethargy that even closely resembled slumber. I talked to an older man sitting with his wife and a little boy who was his grandson. He was not very talkative but I got it out of him that he and his wife had been in northwestern Alabama visiting a divorced daughter who had fallen on hard times and they were taking her only child back to live with them in Rolla, Missouri.

He was an educator and taught at a college located in the city of Rolla. At that pronouncement, I warmed up and told him about my quandary of trying to decide on college or going to work of which he opined boldly "go to college and you will never regret it". Ummm, seems like I'd heard that reproach before.

The little fat cheeked boy was not dressed very well causing me to guess his mother was probably bad off financially, and too, if the grandparents were taking the boy away, certainly the child's mother must have been incapable of providing for him. I felt sorry for the four year old and talked to him for a few minutes and gave him a dime to buy a cola. He smiled broadly and buried his head in a pillow resting in the grandfather's lap, acting embarrassed. I slid away and resumed my previous position and stared out at the telephone and power poles zipping by hoping they would hypnotize me. The time passed slowly and boringly but sitting on a train counting poles was a better option than chopping cotton or hacking coffee weeds on a searing day like today. Finally, yes finally I dozed off but it was nothing more than a cat nap with one eye open.

Around lunchtime a waiter came through the car and took orders for lunch and drinks. I decided to have a ham sandwich and coke. That was it. I figured Stan would take me out to dinner that evening after he picked me up.

The screeching and screaming of the metal wheels making contact with the steel rails periodically jolted me out of my rubberneck drowsiness. For sure I was developing a crick in my neck if I didn't straighten up, but the pull of sleep was hard to defy. I kept dropping off and couldn't keep my eyes open. The seat didn't facilitate lying down, so it was necessary for me to sit in a slumped position which only exacerbated the sleepiness wracking my body.

Occasionally a trip up and down the aisle relieved the bogginess in my legs and brought me back to my senses, but as soon as I sat down again, the nodding would reengage. I thought to myself "man this is painful…at least on a Greyhound bus you can recline the seat and sleep."

I thought the train would never get there but finally around 5:00 PM the old steamroller pulled into St Louis Union Station, a mammoth stone castle with a towered façade and tracks running every which way. Out of the gate with suitcase in hand I worked my way from the engine house to the main building. Moving into the terminal part of the building I was taken aback by what looked like a huge aircraft hangar appointed with architectural refinements that established its historical vintage based from the late 1800s, I felt like a lone bee trapped in a one hectare arboretum. The architectural provenance supported its foremost credential of being the largest train station in the Americas and I willingly consented to the accuracy of the claim. In the spring of 1958, I had seen Union Station in the nation's capital and it was not as big as this place.

Enough of this gawking, the first order of business was to contact my brother Stan.

Part Nineteen

The middle brother's destination on that August day in 1958 was Stan's apartment on St. Charles Rock Road on the outskirts of St Louis, Missouri. Stan's full name was Stansel but no one could confirm where the origination of that name came from…it was rumored not from his mother but from a relative that Stansel's name was fished out of a newspaper article about an itinerant but never successful politician, named Stansel from up around Drew, Mississippi. Jo saw the article, liked the name and put it in her memory bank. When the stork visited in 1937, she popped out with that name and applied it to the birth certificate, omitting a second name in the process. Throughout his youth Stan was just "Stansel" and that was it, no nicknames, only Stansel. After he left home and got out into the world his friends and associates started calling him Stan and the name stuck.

In the fall of 1955 Stan left Moorhead and went to his Uncle Gene's home in St Louis seeking a job at which point employment was found at his uncle's place of employment, Hussmann Refrigeration. The job on an assembly line didn't pay outstanding wages but the money was impressive compared to the Delta. By the way, as a matter of information, the factory manufactured large commercial type coolers found in large food supermarkets.

Uncle Eugene Moore, Stan's mother's kid brother had found work there right after World War II when he and his wife Verma visited a relative and by chance obtained a job at the big plant. He had accompanied the person with whom he was visiting to a job interview and the job counselor saw him sitting there and ended up hiring the handsome war hero instead of the in- law. Eugene had been a combat veteran decorated with two Purple Hearts and a Distinguished Service Medal in Europe during the Battle of the Bulge and the march to Berlin. He returned to Moorhead and tried his hand at farming but was not content with the prospects.

In addition to his good luck, Verma found employment in a shoe factory on the same day and they hastily checked out to Moorhead, loaded up their domestic stuff, returned to the city of Lindbergh and set up housekeeping. And now twelve years later they welcomed Jo's son Stan to live with them until he could afford a vehicle and a place to live. The couple had no children, so they were happy to have Stan as a guest and boarder. They treated him like a son.

Stan settled into his job and after a three month probationary period, Hussmann Management, acknowledging his farm boy work ethic set him up with a permanent assembly line post. The permanency of the new post gave him confidence to buy a car, but he still was reluctant to rent an apartment. He paid his Uncle Gene for room & board and stayed on for a while. Now with transportation, Stan made infrequent trips back to Moorhead to see his parents and brothers and he always remembered his brothers at Christmastime. The first watch that Bill ever owned was a Christmas gift from Stan and he proudly wore it everywhere.

Although he dated some Missouri women, he pined for a girl from Gould, Arkansas who he had met while visiting an aunt and uncle who had bought a farm in the Alluvial Plains around Gould. They corresponded via letter and Stan was soon making trips down to Gould to see the attractive Miss Frances Heflin, a petite and bubbly brunette.

By this time in 1957, Stan had a one bedroom apartment and soon padded the occupancy of the little flat with a new bride from the beleaguered Governor Faubus' neck of the woods. Frances moved in and got a job. Stan bought a 1955 Chevrolet Belair hardtop… a fine looking car it was…but maybe the V-8 was not as hot as he wished. At Christmas 1957 he and his new wife came home from St Louis in the Chevy and he and Sonny Boy Matthews in his 1955 Ford Vic duked it out in some drag races out on Highway 3. Sonny held his own and his 1955 Victoria won as many of the races as a disappointed Stan did. Call it a "wash". Sonny went home that evening with a grin on his chin.

Meanwhile down in Moorhead, the year of 1957, saw the Griffin family still bringing in cotton and soybean crops and Stan's brothers were growing up--- Bill was a senior in high school and Bud had opted to go to college and was matriculating as a freshman at Sunflower Junior college pursuing a 2 year degree in Building Technology. Benny was in the seventh grade and knocking them stiff in football at Moorhead Grammar School. His coach was Bill Hood, Cousin Carolyn's new husband. The mention of football here may seem stilted but its importance to Benny's later life and prominence is worth including in this piece. He used football and his own determination as a means to break the chains of poverty to become well known in Baton Rouge and he used his football prowess to gain a college education.

Concurrently, 600 miles to the north as the crow flies, the oldest son was doing well in St Louis. He had a decent paying job and his wife was working also. Their income was sufficient to enable Stan to indulge his love of flying, i.e. the extra money allowed him to take flying lessons from a licensed flight instructor. His dream of obtaining a piloting license would not be a short term goal; it would take persistence and many hours of training not to mention substantial cost.

In the spring of 1958, Jo and Troy received news that they would be grandparents later in the year. Stan's wife was pregnant and was expecting in October. They still lived in a small flat out in the St Louis suburbs which adequately accommodated their housing requirement for the time being. They would consider renting a larger apartment after the baby arrived in the fall. This scenario pretty much set the stage as far as Stan's current living arrangement played in this globetrotting tale of Billy Ray's surprise "meeting up" with his unwary brother at the St Louis Union Station.

The Missouri Pacific railway coach carrying brother Bill to a rendezvous with Stan was in route on this August 10th, 1958 date but there was one main ingredient missing from Bill's well-oiled plan. From a preparatory standpoint, the same mistake that Troy had made in the trip to the Carolinas in 1955 reared its ugly head again in 1958. Even though Bill had Stan's address and phone number, he had not taken the time to call his host and alert him to his intentions of coming for a visit. He thought he would surprise him much like country folk do when they show up at a relative's place for Sunday Dinner.

Ummm, needless to say, these series of events were adding up to an interesting conjunction of paths or lack thereof.

Part Twenty

Hallelujah! The Missouri Pacific choo - choo has arrived in the big city of St Louis!

In a few minutes, I was in control of my sea legs and had found a coin operated phone booth and dialed Stan's phone number. There was no answer. On the third try and no answer, I decided to kill a little time, thinking he and his wife may be outside or had run an errand or any other number of activities that could have taken them away from the apartment. I didn't have my Uncle Gene's phone number so I scanned the huge phone book for his name but found nothing in the listings close to his name of Jessie Eugene Moore. To add insult to injury, his address was not packed in my wallet like I had for Stan's place, once again a dastardly oversight on my part. But at this point in time, it was useless to dwell on the matter.

In the process of killing time before my next call, a large map of the city posted on a wall near the phone booth caught my attention and I proceeded to locate the general vicinity of Stan's apartment. I thought to myself "Wow, that's a far piece from where I'm standing in this depot (marked by a star on the map), it may take them a while to get over here to pick me up." At the end of a thirty minute wait, I called again and fifteen minutes later, again no answer. A dash of anxiety started to set in but I rationalized their absence would be only temporary.

At the end of two hours, as it was starting to darken outside, I decided to take matters into my own hands and work my way west from Market Street using the city transit system. Making my way out of the building, I cast my eyes down the street in both directions but didn't see any signs indicating a bus stop. Next to me stood a black man in a porter's uniform, so in violation of my aunt's caveat not to make eye contact with strangers, I asked the man for directions. In a cordial response, he told me to follow him and he would take me to the spot. Uh oh, have I screwed up royally and I haven't gotten out of the train station? Apprehensively, I followed the guy for about a block and a half and voila there was the city transit boarding spot. I confessed to the gentleman... and I "repeat" he was a gentleman that, I was new to the city and had not used the transit system. He quickly gave me an overview of the lines and asked me where I needed to go. I knew I was going out on a limb by giving him the St Charles Rock Road address but his instructions to me were to catch the next bus and proceed to an intersection that I don't remember. "Get on the next bus heading north and ask the driver where to get off...keep at it until you work your way through the city and sooner than later you'll be on St Charles Rock Road. From there it's a straight shot up to where you are headed."

I thanked the man generously and he turned on his heel and promptly returned to Union Station. I thought to myself "that guy could have led me down a dark alley, knocked me in the head and taken what small amount of money I had on me and nobody would have found me until the next morning." Wouldn't that have been something if Stan had opened the next morning's paper and read about a Mississippi victim named

Billy Ray Griffin being found in an alley near Union Station. Yep, that would have been a jarring surprise for all concerned.

At this juncture, I had met no harm but I was hardly out of the shadows of Union Station. The next couple of hours would be a passage into the unknown but for some irrational reason, I was not nervous ...I guess my naiveté consumed me to the extent that I thought all people would react decently to me if I treated them with decency. At this late hour, my suitcase was a dead giveaway if someone was looking for a victim to rob but I never hesitated to take stock of my vulnerable situation to consider the dangers. I just barreled ahead at full speed.

I caught the first bus and told the driver to let me know where I needed to get off to make a series of connections to get over to St Charles Rock Road... He was a good guy, friendly and patient...he told me to stand next to him and not take a seat. In a few minutes he brought the bus to a halt and as passengers were filing off he took a look at the paper with Stan's address. He told me to get off and wait for the next bus which would be by in about 10 minutes heading north. I was told to look for a particular street name on the bus headliner, get on that bus and ask the driver for help. Actually the route was checkered, move up, and then move over a street or two working toward the well-known Rock Road. I followed that procedure for a couple more connections but it was a painstaking procedure and each exchange took time. I missed a couple of buses because of poor timing and it was soon 11:00 PM and the groups hanging around the stops grew seedier and more threatening (at least in appearance). My focus was so resolute to get to Stan's place, there was no fear factor in my thought process... calmness was the order of the day. I still did not know why Stan had not answered my phone calls but there was not time to stop and try to find pay booth.

All the drivers were super fine people...thank God it was in the 1950's, the age when people had character no matter their circumstance. They were black and white men who without fail acted like they were genuinely concerned about this young plowboy struggling in his attempt to find a needle in a haystack and doing it in the middle of a hot summer night in a million peopled mega city. In reflection, I suspect the drivers were probably southerners from small towns who migrated to St Louis in the hard years.

It was my last exchange before reaching St Charles Rock and the bus stop location was in a run down, garbage infested stinking alcove of a place with poor lighting. Standing around were four bad looking customers in their early twenties. I kept my distance, didn't speak or make eye contact. Since there were just the four characters and I cornered in this dilapidated pit hole, for the first time that night I started feeling a little uneasy especially when they started nudging one another with their gazes trained on my suitcase. Should they make a move on my luggage, a vision of the lanky greasy looking one wearing my rear buckled khaki pants flashed in my disconcerting mind? How dare he think he was gonna steal my only brown breeches. I didn't have many and dadgummit if I was going to give up my suitcase lying down. What an irrational thought...me against a gang of four. How crazy to think I could have escaped. Where to...a dead end alley?

I believe my G.A. interceded that night and stepped between the boy from Mississippi and the rough looking culprits from a St Louis ghetto. *Sammie Ray* had a history of saving me through the years and I was not surprised when the toughs elected to be good guys and leave the boy alone. They had a sure thing but didn't take advantage of it. Thank you very much, *Sammie Ray* and also thank you Mr. Bus driver for pulling into that spot at the right moment.

I'm sure I probably over dramatized this event but I didn't want the readers to think I sailed through this crisis without breaking a sweat. For someone who had hardly been out of the cotton patch, this erratic trip through the city and beyond went pretty smoothly all said and done. After a myriad of interruptions, I found myself on a bus headed up St Charles Rock Road and a benevolent bus driver close by keeping an eye on me. I asked him if his name was Sammy Ray. He shook his head and smiled a big toothy grin without looking my way.

Out on the far reaches of the road that connected St Louis and St Charles, Missouri, my kind and blessed friend, the bus driver, stopped his sparsely loaded transit bus in the middle of the road and pointed across the street telling me there was the address written on that piece of paper I had given him when I boarded. Yes he stopped in the middle of the road just to accommodate me. Wow I was overwhelmed with gratitude. I hope to meet that fine man on the other side of the pearly gates one of these days.

As I trudged across the road to the little apartment, I looked at my watch and it was midnight. Stan and Fran would be flabbergasted for sure especially at this late hour but a knock on the door yielded not a soul. After knocking several times with no luck, I noticed an attached building and door that seemed to be part of the same complex. Reluctantly, I hammered on the door and finally an old lady spoke to me through a locked screen door. After telling her who I was, she informed me that Stan had gone to Arkansas with his wife to check on the wife's sick father and they would not return for a couple of days. Since she was the landlord, she grudgingly decided to let me stay in Stan's apartment until morning accepting the fact that I was his brother. She was an acquaintance of my Uncle Gene, had his telephone number and would call him first thing the next morning to see if he would come over and pick up the stranger standing at her doorstep.

If she had not seen fit to let me in Stan's apartment, I don't know what I would have done...more than likely I would have slept on the doorstep. But fortune was with me once again and after raiding the refrigerator, I settled down on a little sofa in the den of the apartment. It was 01:00 AM and black as pitch.

Early the next morning there was a knock at the door and there stood my Uncle Gene with the biggest grin on his face one couldn't imagine. After a big bear hug, he backed away and looked me in the eye and laughingly exclaimed "you rascal you I can't believe this". He was wholly amused at my audacity to come to St Louis without advance notice and he was doubly incredulous that I had bus hopped through the crime ridden precincts of downtown St Louis in the middle of the night.

He just shook his head and with his arm around my shoulders, we walked in tandem next door to the old lady's house. Not surprising, she was peering out the screen door observing my homecoming since obviously she had notified Gene about the unfamiliar occupant sleeping in Stan's apartment. After apologizing to the lady for upsetting her, he commenced to tell me that when the she called him in the early hours of morning and had asked him if he knew Stan's brother "Bill"? Apparently in response, Gene hesitatingly told the sweet lady **"No! Stan does not have a brother named Bill."** From the lady at the other end of the line, there came a gasp and a startled refrain "Oh my God what have I done?" In Gene's knee jerk response, he was subconsciously counting off the brothers...Bud, Billy Ray, Benny and Bishop. The name "Bill" did not register since he always called me "Billy Ray". It did not immediately occur to him that Bill was Billy Ray.

Yep, my patroness, the gracious landlady was aghast at her apparent error in judgment. Her first impulse was to call the police but by that time Gene had collected his wits to determine this "Bill fellow" was the third brother Billy Ray. As a consequence he quickly back tracked, assuring the woman she was safe. She was much relieved at the turn of events. Thereupon, I took my turn to step up and apologize too and the old lady quickly warmed up to me like most old women were inclined to do. I don't know why. Nevertheless, I was glad to see her raw nerves were salved.

Gene informed her that he would accommodate my room and board until Stan returned, leaving her to lock up the apartment. I was soon parked in my uncle's house, alone, but with a television to keep me company. Both he and my aunt had to go to work.

Sitting there passing time and bored with game shows on TV (the set was located in the basement) I decided to shower and shave. As a general practice, I only shaved every other day but here lately I saw the need to remove those black whiskers every day. I had reached the point in my young life, for whatever reason; maybe it was due to elevated hormones, five o'clock shadow was starting to jump on me at three o'clock in the evening. No, in another vein, I would venture to guess my coal black hair had something to do with the swarthy facial hair…those quarter coin size patches of ebony stubble that had suddenly appeared at age fifteen had now consumed my face from the ears down to the folds of the neck, level with the Adams apple.

I had used my last razor blade at Nelle's house, so I searched for blades in the medicine cabinet but found none. Then I saw it… my uncle was old timey I guess…a straight razor sat on the lavatory in a case and a leather strap hung from a nail on the wall. Ummm, I'd never tried this before but it looked simple enough. In 15 minutes, I had raked off the topical whiskers but by no stretch of the imagination could one call me clean shaven. Too, there were more than a couple of nicks on my face that required a styptic application to stop the bleeding. Looking in the mirror I was hard pressed to find anything in my reflection that looked decent enough to show to the general public. My hair was wet and wild, my five o'clock shadow was more advanced than ever and I had wounds of every shape and form all over my face. Man, methinks "I should have left well enough alone". You've heard that old saying haven't you? Despite my fractured body, I was about ready to implode from pent up energy.

For the second day in a row I was a cornered rabbit...yesterday I was in solitary confinement in a train car and today I was hogtied in a four walled basement, although television programming had kept me moderately entertained but my restrained vigor was busting the seams. I combed my wet hair, went outside and walked around the block hoping to find a Mom & Pop grocery store where I could purchase an RC Cola and some peanuts. My preferred way of drinking soda and eating peanuts was called a combo which in definition meant the RC was swigged down 4 or 5 ounces and the peanuts dumped in on top of the liquid left in the bottle. With every ensuing swig from the RC a proportionate number of peanuts entered the palate along with a drizzle of sweet cola to satisfy the taste buds for that particular craving. I believe that concoction was invented down in Moorhead by some of the black friends we knew like Frank, Willie Junior, Tattersall and Eustis. For them and us alike, that was an infrequent treat akin to eating ambrosia at Christmastime. Well, not exactly but RC & peanuts in combination was good stuff.

I returned to my basement haven with my craving for RC and goobers unabated but temporarily forgotten. I plopped back down in the master of the house's easy chair and my thoughts turned to the previous day and night. I really had not thought about the events of yesterday but now that I had time to deliberate, I was overcome with a feeling of wellbeing. Under duress, I had performed commendably if I say so myself. It was like I had another engine in the pit of my chest that kicked in and sheparded me through the ordeal. An absence of fear and my ability to clearly focus on the objective was calming to contemplate. In my mind, I chalked up last night's experience as an added rung in the growth of my self-esteem and character. I knew now for all time that I possessed a reserve that I could count on for such occasions as last night. Its positive effect so mollified me… I dropped off to sleep in my uncle's chair.

As I sit here today in the year 2011, writing this story at age 71, I can rightfully say that that streak of "reserve that I spoke of in my eighteenth year" continued to assert itself in times of necessity throughout my life. That little reservoir of "adrenaline fueled overdrive" has never deserted me to this day. Also, I acknowledge with absolute straightness … those bus drivers that I encountered that night in St. Louis taught me the meaning of kindness, humility and a real concern for his fellow man. Not one of those men expressed any impatience with me even though I'm sure they were tired and jaded. I have never forgotten those good men.

Part Twenty-one

I awoke from my nap with a start. Owing to my severe fatigue, a deep REM sleep had enveloped my body for a couple of hours and produced a pleasurable dream juicing my unconscious senses with foggy apparitions of my parents displayed in the front yard of our home on Sheffield Road. They were clothed in their Sunday best and Dad was pointing to the cotton field nearest the house and expounding about the best crop he had ever witnessed in all his years of farming. Sure enough, a glossy scene of humongous cotton plants loaded with hundreds of maturing bolls and blooms materialized for a second or two before disappearing from my memory. Dad seemed to be saying the crop would yield 50 bales of cotton which would put the family on easy street for the rest of 1958. As I shook my head trying to wake up in this strange place and with the dream still fresh in my mind, I laughed out loud at the absurdity of the vanishing hallucination. Although the dream was farfetched, my heart warmed at the sight of my parents. I felt some guilt for having not thought of them in my whirlwind travel quest for the last two weeks.

With the dream dissipating, my mind focused on Stan and his current whereabouts. I rationalized that he and his wife would return that Monday. He did but she didn't. Mr. Heflin's health was still uncertain, so Frances decided to stay in Arkansas for the week and Stan would return that weekend to bring her home.

At about 04:00 pm he pulled into my uncle's driveway in his shiny red & white 1955 Chevy Belair Hardtop. I was impressed but what eighteen year old springer wouldn't be. I thought to myself…if I had those wheels I could challenge old Hervey for some of those girls that drooled over his fine cars.

Post handshakes and a hug, Stan, much like my uncle's reaction, grinned like a Cheshire cat at my antics of coming north without letting them know. Arriving home from Arkansas that afternoon, his landlady came hotfooting it over to tell him about the brother Bill saga of the previous night. After repeating himself for the third time telling me how crazy I was, I got in his car and we returned to his place. Later that afternoon after work, I called my uncle to tell him of Stan's return and that I'd be staying over at his place for the remainder of my sojourn.

Stan's wife Fran was getting along pretty well in her pregnancy and Stan indicated she was big as a baby hippo. A son, Bryan would enter the world in October but at this juncture his mother was a couple hundred miles away so that meant my only host, Stan would be out of pocket in the daytime hours. I slept on the little sofa and spent the next couple of days watching daytime television which was pretty dull stuff but in those early years of picture tube entertainment all the programs held some interest strictly because of its novelty.

My favorite program, as one might suppose, was **American Bandstand,** a program that hit the airways at around 16:00 hours in the afternoon. Dick Clark was the host and of course he was the personification of youth…he looked about my age although in actuality he was probably in his late twenties. I remember **Bandstand** had entertainers making cameo appearances just about every day attended by a crowd of Philadelphia teenagers dancing to records and the entertainer's songs. I didn't know it at the time, but in 20-20 hindsight, the performers lip sync'ed their pieces because I don't remember any accompanying bands or orchestras to speak of. Some of the songs were backed by strings but there were no stringed instruments in view. In those days it was easy to fake out an innocent audience.

The record "Sixteen Candles" was the number one song and it was played every day on **Bandstand**. Some of the performers that I remember seeing on the screen that week were Fabian, Bobby Rydell, Frankie Avalon and Leslie Gore, all natives of the Philadelphia area, so it made sense why they were live entertainment on an everyday basis. Actually I preferred many of the other artists who were never showcased, e.g. Bing Crosby, Frank Sinatra, Perry Como, Lawrence Welk and Hank Snow. Gotcha on that one didn't I! No in 1958 my favorites were Elvis, Gene Vincent, Roy Orbison, Chuck Berry and Sam Cook to name a few.

In the evening after getting off work, Stan and I toured some interesting historical places and he even took me to the zoo. Wow, my cultural standing was elevated another notch with that eventful viewing…yep; adding those Baboons and Bandicoots to my repertoire of applied animal observation raised my intellectual license to almost doctoral status. My ego was not getting any bigger but my resume was enlarging. If I didn't watch it, Sunflower Junior College would be beneath me and I'd have to opt out of that basketball scholarship and consider furthering my education at Emory or one of those elite southern universities over yonder in Georgia. With Stan serving as my tour guide, I got a cursory overview of the Washington University campus…it was really fine. I was thinking perhaps if I did well in junior college, I could possibly come to St Louis and finish my studies at that beautiful university campus. However, as we rode around the metropolitan area, for those few days, it became apparent that Stan was not in love with his assembly line job and had a dream of moving back south to pursue a career more suitable to his liking. Without a college education he was limited on the what, ifs and where his desires would take him but it became obvious that his roots in St Louis were not that firmly planted, certainly not to his complete satisfaction. It would do in the interim. Little did I know at that time that the lack of a college education never stymied Stan in later life as he in fact would become the owner of a corporation in south Alabama worth seven figures.

Since Stan was working the dayshift, our sightseeing activities were restricted to the late afternoon and early night hours. We saw the Busch beer distillery but didn't tour the place because of the late hour. I think we did look in on the Botanical Gardens but I don't remember much about that cultural event. I was particularly hyped when he informed me that we would attend a Wednesday night major league baseball game between the St Louis Cardinals and the reigning 1957 world champion, the Milwaukee Braves at Busch Stadium.

America's favorite past time, baseball, or more precisely, Major League Baseball was a particularly and keenly partisan sport of mine along with college and NFL football. At any and every opportunity I had to read a newspaper sports section or a Sports Illustrated Magazine I would have my nose between the pages in a New York second. During school sessions, the SAHS/SJC library provided this student of sports trivia with those daily and weekly editions of literary bonanza. In the summer months I would scrounge my uncle's old newspapers to keep abreast of baseball standings and stats. Owing to the low number of major league teams in the 1950s compared to now, I was able to keep up with all the teams and their stars' statistics whether the items of interest were batting averages, home runs, RBIs and pitcher won / lost records, etc.

I professed an allegiance to the Pittsburg Pirates...I don't know why...they were perennial losers always settling in last place after the first five games of the season and ending the year 40 games back of the league leader. They were terrible, but as much as I liked the underdog they never failed my distrustful outlook that somehow they would surprise me with a good season. At this time in 1958, hope for the Pirates had faded to "no comment" by July, thus I had given up on them completely for the year 1958. Having never seen a major league game in my life, I jumped at the opportunity to go to a game in St Louis. My devout fanship of the unmighty Pirates would have to be put on hold while I pulled for the Cardinals. Stan was not a sports enthusiast per se but he was willing to take me to Busch Stadium and sit through a game. He liked car racing and hunting, two sports that I cared diddly sqwat about but being the good host, he knew I liked spectator sports so he was willing to take me out to the ballpark that sat spread-eagled close to the banks of the Mississippi River.

On Wednesday as I sat around the apartment and vegetated -- my thoughts kept compassing on the game that evening. I was so much looking forward to seeing those legendary athletes and "the House that Dizzy Dean built", Busch stadium.

As the scene morphed into reality later that evening, I sat staring in disbelief at the beautiful manicured playing surface and the far reaching stands that encircled the field. From our vantage point high in the outfield bleachers, one could see everything even though the players looked like dwarves apart from the outfielders who were closer to us than the diamond positioned infielders, pitcher, catcher and batters. My young eyes, then better than normal 20-20 vision, soaked up the carnival atmosphere and the sight of 31,000 attendees and mind you this was a Wednesday night.

For you old timer readers sopping up this nostalgia, do you remember Warren Spahn? He was the starting pitcher for the Braves that night, a 20 game winner for about 15 consecutive years...with that said, I figured to be in for a treat that night. The Braves were the defending World Champions and they were loaded with stars in addition to pitchers, Spahn and Lew Burdette, they had Eddie Mathews, Hank Aaron, Joe Adcock and Red Schoendienst. In 1958 it appeared the Braves were headed for a second pennant in a row based on their standing at the time of this game. They were in first place in the National League and led the Cardinals by ten games or more.

The St Louis Cardinals were not as illustrious as the Braves but they had some big name stars with the likes of Ken Boyer and Curt Flood but their drawing power was piddling compared to their mega star first baseman, Stan "the man" Musial. At that time he was a giant in the sport and pulled down an annual salary of $50,000, an amount unheard of in the penny pinching 1950s. Compare his salary to Warren Spahn's $37,500 and one can readily see where Musial ranked in drawing power. Every time he came up to bat, the crowd would go wild and he responded with two hits that night in four times at bat.

The Braves won that night and went on to win the National league title in a breeze. However they got their comeuppance in the 1958 World Series where they lost to the hated New York Yankees, 4 games to 3. With all said and done, the Cardinals were at best a mediocre team and finished the year battling the Pirates for the not so coveted cellar position.

At game's end, as Stan and his guest fought their way through the exodus of sweating fans, I savored the thought that I had chanced on another improbable yet memorable event that would be engraved in my cranium's memory cells. It seemed every way I turned I was being bombarded with special comings and goings that could best be chalked up as uncommon. Who would have thought my fateful arrival in St Louis would dovetail with my attending my very first Major league baseball game featuring the World Champions. I guess it was a given that I was in the right place at the right time one more time. "*Thanks again* ***Sammie Ray****, but you can take your hand off my bunched collar... or better yet, maybe I should consider buying you a leash to help you stay in control of this erratic kid.*"

Earlier in the day on Wednesday, I had had the honor of receiving a Thursday night dinner invitation from my Aunt Verma ...a meal that would be served the evening preceding my departure for home on Friday. Given that Stan had weekend plans of returning to Gould, Arkansas starting out early Saturday morning. With that development, I figured my best departure day would be Friday. I planned to catch a Greyhound bus in the dew settling hours of the morning. Taking me to the bus station that early would be an imposition on Stan but he said he didn't mind. The trip back to Moorhead, Mississippi "where the Southern crosses the Yellow Dog" would require a full day of travel. The bus would pretty much follow the same route as the Yazoo Railroad track as it headed south into the Delta and crossed paths with the Southern Railroad in my hometown. The bus known for its many stops would be a full day affair. I'd be lucky to get home before sundown on Friday.

Here it is Thursday afternoon and my time in St Louie is almost up but in a fit of preparation, I packed my suitcase and dusted off my loafers. I watched **American Bandstand** on a St Louis TV station for the last time and welcomed Stan home from work at Hussmann's. After taking a cool shower, he was ready to roll and we jumped into his red hardtop and sped over to Uncle Gene's nice comfortable home on the other side of St Charles Rock Road.

Aunt Verma placed a fabulous dinner in front of Stan and me that night. We were ready for some tasty and filling food. It would be an exaggeration to say we had been eating well, having deferred to pot luck dining since my arrival. That mode of hunger abatement equated to a lot of bologna and goose liver sandwiches. Fast food had not reached its heyday in 1958, so we had to fend for ourselves in the culinary realm and for us that meant cold cuts and little else.

If anyone remembers "My Christmas Story" in the early part of this book, there were several references to **Adams Grocery Store** in Moorhead. The proprietor of that store was Mr. Clyde Adams, the father of Aunt Verma…who at this very moment, was pouring gravy on my mashed potatoes and refilling my iced tea glass. At that time in 1958, my nice looking aunt was probably 36 or 37 years old and dressed in a fashionable outfit. I know it sounds like a broken record with my singing the praises of classy aunts but it was the truth. It always amazed me that all these finely clothed aunts of mine with origins in Moorhead, as to where they got their sense of style and fashion. The same went for my mother...in her younger days in pictures I have observed, she was invariably dressed in the latest fashions of the 1930s and 1940s. Even today in the late 1950s she would not think of going to Moorhead without "dressing up".

As we sat eating and talking that last evening, my uncle was still laughing and shaking his head in disbelief that I had traipsed through the Hell's Kitchen of inner city St Louis in the middle of the night. He intimated to the round table dessert eaters that he had fought several World War II battles in Germany and he didn't think he had the guts to drive into the St Louis ghetto areas at night without fearing for his life. I chuckled to myself upon hearing that remark and thought out loud "yeah, but you don't realize who's sitting next to me as you speak...*Sammie Ray,* my benevolent protector". He probably thought I was being a smart aleck sitting over there with a smug look on my face but I meant no disrespect. I truly loved all of my mother's brothers and sister and their spouses...they were fine people. And I didn't want to leave out my aunts and uncles in Memphis; my fondness for them was just as well meant. I respected all of them greatly and still do to this day. With the exception of Don, all of them are still living.

Over the years since that August night in 1958, my Uncle Gene has told and retold the story of my adventure in St Louis. My uncle still lives at age 90 in St Louis and he still marvels at my super survival instincts, but like I've always said, he doesn't comprehend the fact that I have an invisible companion parked with me at all times.

Part Twenty-two

And thus, as the dust settled, the St Louis trip came to a gentle termination that next morning after supping with my wonderful kinfolks, Stan included, who had been a generous host with his time and money. The bus station was back in the downtown area near Union Station, so that meant he would have to go in the opposite direction of the Hussmann factory but he didn't mind the inconvenience. He hated to see me go and I hated to leave his company although I knew I needed to be getting on down the road. We shook hands intensely and I turned and entered the station with a tear or two in my eye. I was such a sentimental slob.

The next time I saw Stan and Fran, it was later in the year around early November and they had their brand new son, Bryan with them…he was only a few weeks old. By that time I was well ensconced in collegial ambiance surrounded by the whitewashed halls of SJC, a pre-eminent institute of higher learning. Also of entirely more significance was the occurrence about a week later of Troy, my father, in desperation, going south to Baton Rouge in search of a job. To everyone's baffled surprise, he returned to Moorhead with a job in hand despite his herniated groin which in the past always eliminated any chance of employment. I had to do a retake and look into my aura, to insure *Sammy Ray* had not shirked her allegiance to the old country boy and jumped ship to my Dad. Nope, although I couldn't make out her image, I was confident she was still there holding her leash and patting me on my shoulder. For sure I felt the interminable warm caress.

The reason my Father was able to get that job without a physical exam owed to the influence of Marvin Reeves, another uncle of mine, who was married to Troy's oldest sister. I told you this Griffin clan was a big far reaching family. Uncle Marvin had worked at **Jack's Cookie Company** for many years, knew the owner well and convinced him to waive the physical for Dad, which he did as a favor to Marvin.

Before we could catch our breath, the Troy Griffin family had loaded up a trailer with clothes and personal items and took off back to Baton Rouge. Bud was now the sole occupant of the Griffin homestead out on Sheffield Road. His only means of income was provided by the Sunflower County School Board in payment for driving a school bus and that job would play out in May.

Hey, wait a minute I'm getting ahead of this splendid story.

Back to the bus station, I paid my bus fare of about $15 (Stan had slipped a few dollars into my back pocket as I pretended I didn't notice). His charity certainly helped my state of mind because my funds were just short of running out. Soon as I got back to Moorhead, I'd need to high tail it to Lamb's Grocery and see if he would reinstate his fair haired boy in a butcher position with high pay. Then I thought about Thomas Blansett...now that he had all that big city experience at Kroger's in Memphis, he would probably be Lamb's first choice as Jones Wong's replacement. For all I knew, experienced Thomas was already back in Moorhead filling that job. Well, I hoped not.

The big Greyhound bus was soon making good time on the highway to Cape Girardeau. I sat next to a middle aged fellow who dozed off to sleep as soon as we took off. Later he awoke and we conversed about his and my destination. He lived in Jonesboro, Arkansas and made a living as a farm implement salesman. What a coincidence… it seemed we had something in common. He was a salesman and I had tried my hand at the same profession, if that short term attempt with Don is what you could call it. Relating my insurance sales debacle, he laughed heartily and told me not to be disheartened if I still wanted to pursue that line of work. He pointed out, that when he started out as a young car salesman; he couldn't sell a car if his life depended on it, but he stuck it out, gained confidence and eventually became a half way decent salesman. In a little while, he got off the bus and I settled back to kill time until we reached Memphis where a 45 minute layover was scheduled. As far as seeing any landscapes worth looking at, there was nothing to hold my interest, inasmuch as the terrain featured nothing but flat bottom land and row crops, an exact replica of what I had seen coming up on the train. As a matter of comparison, the scenes outside the window looked depressingly the same as farm land south of Clarksdale, Mississippi. With nothing to interest me, the roaring bus tires making contact with the concrete highway exerted a numbing effect on my snooze mechanism and I was soon fast asleep.

After disembarking from the bus, inside the Memphis bus station, I found a phone booth and talked to Don for a while.

I was surprised he was home on a Friday and not out beating the bushes. It dawned on me he was surely thinking out loud, "dang it, I just got rid of this ploughboy...what's he doing back in town bothering me again." I made sure I cleared that matter up in short order by telling him I was passing through Memphis on my way home from St Louis. He seemed to be in a rush, so not wanting to hinder him I let him go and without missing a beat I immediately called Donna. She seemed happy to hear from me, which really made my day. I asked for her address, wrote it down and stayed on the phone for another 5 minutes giving her a quick recap of my St. Louis trip. At the completion of that short telephone call, I lowered the back of my head so that it rested comfortably on the glass enclosure, took a deep swooning breathe and muttered to myself "me, too". It was an unintelligible response to a loaded question but I fully understood what it meant since I was the originator of the question. Donna and I exchanged letters after I had settled back into a routine in Utopia but the impracticality of my affection for the attractive young lady soon dissipated into a "moving on" chapter.

That pretty much ended the highlights of my so called 1958 travel spree ...because in short order the Greyhound attendants herded the black and white riders, back onto the refueled bus. In clarification, the ridership consisted of mostly white folks because a majority of the blacks riding a bus that day were headed in the opposite direction on a northbound bus. To Chicago and Detroit no doubt but who could blame them. After the passengers settled in their seats, the big vehicle continued its trek southward on that dusty highway that ran through Delta Blues Country.

I had much to mull as the bus roared away from its Memphis landing. I thought about my buddy Thomas Blansett, I thought about Stan and my St Louis relatives, I thought about Nelle and Kathleen, I thought about my parents and lastly I thought about Donna…the one slowly vanishing image I would think about for the longest time.

"Yazoo Delta, here I come…the wandering, prodigal son is about to show his face to the local natives after a three week absence. Did you miss me"? I'm positive their reply would have been "no way, Billy Ray, we really had no idea you were gone."

In fact, while I was gone, I had reaped an Associate's Degree in a condensed study of life's lessons in three short weeks…but wait a second, it was more like six weeks if the planning stage were included. With the high intensity of that six weeks and the unusual level of energy expended on logistical and itinerary planning, adult discussions of career paths, discussions of college, practicing the rudiments of selling insurance, crisis management, money management and just outright exposure to urban life and activities all added up to make an upward impact on my maturity level. I was not the same air headed boy that got on that bus to Memphis three weeks ago.

Homeward bound with colors flying, there was little left on this trip that would interest the weary traveler or the cynical reader of this story. All the platitudes that I could dream up to close this carefree story would be a waste of poor writing.

So that ended another inconsequential chapter in the history of the middle Griffin boy who lived and wandered Sheffield Road, you know, not far from Moorhead, Mississippi where "the Southern Crosses the Yellow Dog" located right smack dab in the middle of the Delta.

CHAPTER THREE

Part One

It was a remarkable morning. The sun had risen --- appearing as a big luminous disc levitating above the Southern Railroad track to the east of the homestead's back forty, positioned just barely above the horizon. It was absolutely clear. No smog, no dancing mirages, no haze and no pall as far as the eye could see.

During the night a strong cold front had born down on the Delta flatland and in a broad sweep of cool wind, its visitation had wrung most of the heat searing humidity from the air that had held the area hostage through yesterday's oppressive weather. The cool air, instantly soothing, dislodged the malaise that had settled into the bodies of the locals and replaced it with an attitudinal uplift.

Yesterday, one certainly may have thought their malaise was a permanent malady. But, my, oh my, how the spirits had soared in all the collective members of our family on this incomparable day. It was almost like everyone was high on a palliative but, no way… it was a natural high brought on by high barometric pressure and cool air. It was a much needed purgative but not in the sense of a colonic… it was more analogous to a cleansing of the spirit like a baptism. In short, it was rejuvenation…that is…in the lexicon of the planter, it was the balm that would ease the injuries made by backbreaking labor and a vicious sun. The human energy that had almost petered out save maybe the reserve to crawl into bed at sunset each night to try to somehow negate twelve hours of energy sapping toil with twelve hours of restful sleep. The hard working farmers and their hard working helpers were pretty much worn out from unabated overwork. The resurgence of strength would prevail for a few days until the cold front washed out, but thankfully the temporary relief was a Godsend for the Delta masses.

Not only were the effects on the disposition bracing, the effect on physical phenomena was just as impressive. The air was free of miasma, smog and haze leaving in its wake a brightness pervading the ether that allowed the eyes to see objects with great clarity for long distances. The likenesses of people seemed to be improved, their hair looked silky, their teeth were whiter, the color of their eyes shone brighter, their smiles were more radiant and their moodiness had disappeared over night. Even looking at one's countenance in a mirror reflected back to the gazer a higher state of attractiveness that the night before looked like "death warmed over". It was grand and everybody wanted to sing and whistle. What an amazing transformation of the human spirit and the environs to which the humans were affixed. The coolness and the brightness made the sky bluer and the leafy plants and trees greener, the earth's black soil, not so black but a mix of brown and loam, the feathers of birds reflective and dazzling, the textures of the farm house and barn less drab, the odor of the farm animals less offensive and the mosquitoes and gnats less numerous. The world as it appeared after a long awaited cold front encompassed the region was a vast improvement over yesterday's world that so grudgingly gave way to the pleasant turnaround.

We all looked forward to this weather event that always came in September and a majority of the time it came around about the time we started back to school, so in our minds there was this correlation of superior feeling and school starting up. So in a way, "school and the fall season" equated to elevated moods in the minds of the Delta's children.

It always happened this way; this cold front in the last days of summer invariably blew in at about the same time that fall classes were starting in the schools.

For those who have never lived in the Yazoo Delta, and never lived through a hot humid summer in that part of the country will find it difficult to grasp the debilitating effects the unhealthy oppressive heat has on its inhabitants, especially if the caste are field workers. And back in the days of 1958, to be sure there were a lot of farm workers sweating their socks off who could not imagine a climate any other way. And if you add to that, a lack of air conditioning, one can readily see why the misery index always rose to unbearable levels in the Dog Days of summer in that place called the Yazoo Delta.

Because the Delta plains are virtually sub sea level and because its physicality is like a recessed empty dinner plate, the resulting stagnant air trapped between the hills that lie to the west and south makes the hundred and fifty mile caldera-like lowland nearly intolerable during the months of July and August.

Hard to imagine but if one has lived in the alluvial plains they know what I mean. Nonetheless, as bad as it was in those sultry months, the anticipation of a soothing cold front always lingered in the psyches of the adults and the children this time of year. And I was not exempt from this same expectancy. Over the last four or five years I had become conscious of its habitual coming.

And true to its inevitability, a cool blast emerging from the Midwestern prairies overtook the Yazoo Delta in early September 1958.

Despite the simmering heat, the cotton plants were thriving. That's to say, the plants were growing vigorously without producing squares, blooms and bolls ... in other words, the plants were not fruiting. Yes the stalks were amassing great height and size but it was easy to see the natural photosynthetic process was only creating legginess and pulp. Of course, all farmers of the region had seen this before and they acknowledged that the late replanting in May and June had taken its toll. It was an accepted certainty the cotton crop of 1958 was poor, very poor. It would be a late harvest with puny yields and everyone knew what that meant...yes for certain, it meant hard times, for the coming winter, it presaged a gray season of imminent despair.

The hand writing was on the wall, but even though all the grownups were indulging in gloom, the youngsters wouldn't and did not let the bad news get them down. After a three month interruption from school, they were ready to see their friends again in a school setting... the cotton crop be damned. They had a life to live and something as insignificant as making a living was not about to distress the youngsters from enjoying activities and companionship provided by their school and their fellow students. These revered schools as they were, were all grounded in the little township of Moorhead, Mississippi smack dab in the middle of the Yazoo Delta in the year 1958 Anno Domini.

Part Two

Moorhead, carved out of the hard wood, cane and vinery jungles of the central Delta in the early 1900s was not the prettiest of jewels even in its glory days. And most certainly in 1958 it was past its prime. Pejoratively, it was referred to as a one light town much like most of the small farm communities in the central Yazoo valley.

However, Moorhead, even with its neglected appearance, was a mega-town compared to some of the black earth Delta villages that didn't even have one red light...all they could hazard was an inconspicuous "Slow" sign on the side of a narrow highway in an effort to slightly deter speeders who raced through their lint saturated crossroads. And yes the lint came from cotton ...thousands and thousands of acres of the fluffy stuff. A majority of the lint snows was deposited in September, October and November but its dusting of the settlement's few dilapidated buildings and streets lasted until it rotted from the effects of numerous winter and spring rains. For a person with a cultured eye, the little towns were nothing to write home about even in the best of conditions. Most travelers just looked straight ahead not caring to absorb the vantage of witnessing poverty and decline up close and in person. As far as speeding, who really cared because the little settlements had no law enforcement unless it was a night watchman who only cared about getting a few winks of sleep during his midnight shift so he would be alert for a day job that was in no way related to tracking speeders.

And Speaking of Moorhead.

It was a megatown alright and it certainly had the rare distinction of having a big changing traffic light at Washington and Olive but the fact was not flaunted. The business district had one main street running east and west, which served to split the downtown area approximately in half. Three intersecting streets and a railroad track running north and south for a couple of blocks on either side of Washington Street (Main) pretty much delineated the entirety of the shopping district. In those days, there were five grocery stores, all but one owned by Chinese merchants, two dry goods stores owned by Jewish merchants subtracted by one (I believe a store owned by Mrs. Gray had burned to the ground by that time), one dime store, two barber shops, one white café, one black café, one bank, one movie theater, Post Office, one defunct Chrysler –

Plymouth dealership, one dry cleaner, one hotel (not sure it was still in business in 1958) , four service stations, two Drug Stores, three juke joints owned by black entrepreneurs and one non-operational train depot that in earlier times had serviced the "Southern" railway company. Slightly down rail from the depot, another railway company track called "The Yellow Dog" intersected the "Southern" line thereby giving Moorhead the distinction of having the only common elevation railroad crossing in the USA. As a consequence of this oddity and safety concern, the little town was known throughout the region as the place "Where the Southern crosses The Dog". Strange as it seems ...in the hundred years of the crossing's existence, there had never been a head on train collision.

Names of businesses worth mentioning were the Moorhead Cotton Gin, the Oil Mill, Tyner's Mini-grocery and Foot long Hotdog Stand, a Freezer Locker, a Pool Hall and Domino Parlor, the Gayloe Movie Theater, the Hervey Lumber yard and a couple of Mechanic Shops.

Incidentally, Tyner's foot long hotdogs were no less than 15 inches in length which pooh poohed the notion that a customer always gets short changed if he is foolish enough to believe a food joint's advertising. Those humdingers were everything they were cracked up to be, plus they were loaded with a ½ pound of chili, one whole chopped onion, ¼ pound grated cheese and a big squirt of mustard, all encased in a Wonder Bread bun almost the size of a sliced loaf, then wrapped in wax paper all for one silver quarter. What a bargain...for such a delicacy. Never once do I ever recall having acid reflux from such a delicate entrée. Prime ingredients I guess… or maybe in those days I had an iron stomach hardened from ingesting too many collards.

In addition to all those aforementioned business establishments, I believe at one time Moorhead had a cobbler but at the time of this setting the shop had closed due to Moorhead's uptick in affluence. Most of the Moorheadians now owned two pairs of shoes instead of the obligatory one pair, which generally rested under the bed only during the dark hours. The rest of the time they were wrapped around the lower digits doing manual work. One good thing about the Shoe Shop guy was his instant service…one could enter the shop, remove his one pair of hoofers and 10 minutes later walk out with new rubber heels and leather soles, good as new. The cobbler would even add a little shoe polish to the deal and slicked the shoes up with a rotary brush on his motorized fly wheel. With that quickie in one's rear pocket, the satisfied customer was good for another year of pounding gravel, asphalt, concrete and cobblestones. How nice it was…and most people think we had it bad in those Neanderthal days. The nicest part of all was the cost of those hammertoe covers…if I remember correctly it was only a buck and change and from a "snow-cone stand" on wheels in front of and under the store overhang, for another nickel, a big heaping cone of shaved ice covered with one's pick of fruit flavors could be enjoyed during the wait. Strawberry and banana were my favorite lip stainers dished up by the Wright boy who owned the thriving enterprise. He always gave me a little extra extract on my cones and I always made it plain that I appreciated his generosity.

Historically, Moorhead's only established car dealership, which existed in the 30s, 40s and early 50s, had a big impact on the automobile brands that the people of the town wheeled around in. Yes, in that era there were a lot of Chryslers and Plymouths running the streets and parked in the front of the major establishments like Lamb's Grocery, Diamond's and Himelstein's dry goods stores, the former on the corner of Olive and the latter about midway down Washington. The Chrysler/Plymouth dealership owned by Mack Shaw went out of business in the early 50s and the building was converted to a service station and a café. Harrison's Moorhead Café was actually a relocation of one from the south side of Washington Street.

And last but not least there was the Sunflower Junior College campus situated at the southernmost part of town. It was an institution before I knew what the word meant. All I knew was it was called "**the college**" and it was an integral part of the place called Moorhead.

Part Three

The Sunflower Junior College campus situated in the southern part of this small town of Moorhead, Mississippi on Hwy 3 enhanced by an attractive backdrop, consumed at least five city blocks, and the grounds were adorned with a grassy lawn containing a labyrinth of sidewalks forking to the various buildings including two main flagship edifices made of brick and masonry. A two story main building called Stansel Hall fronting Hwy 3 was primarily a clutch of classrooms but the Administration Building connected by a roofed walkway on the east side, contained offices, an auditorium, biology labs, a museum and classrooms. A brand new glass & metal library was shoehorned catawampus in between these buildings off to the north.

To the south in the same general area of the flagships sat an old abandoned concrete fish pond whose heyday was long past. Its yearly painting was still maintained but the campus capstone housed only algae and absolutely no golden carp. Its biggest attraction was for resting student's backsides between classes.

To the south of the aforementioned buildings on another block sat the cafeteria, girl's dormitory and canteen. Farther south behind those buildings could be found the gymnasium, football stadium, field house and a teacher's apartment house. I believe the bottom floor of the apartment also served as a Home Economics classroom. In my high school days I dated a girl who lived on the upper floor of that building ...her parents were instructors at the college so I distinctly remember that building...it actually fronted Hwy 3 and sat adjacent to the girl's dorm. The field house upper floor also facing Hwy 3 served as the location for the school Band and its institutional center.

On the backside of the campus...that would be the east side, across the street from the Administration Building and Auditorium there were at least two or three men's dormitories with the one nearest the Admin building being the athletic dorm where the football and basketball players resided. Further south & east, down a street that accessed a vocational shop and classroom, another teacher and married student apartment accommodated a majority of the college staff. That was pretty much the layout of the Sunflower Junior College campus in 1958.

Oh, yes as an afterthought…across from the vocational shop was located an old gym that housed the Moorhead National Guard unit. The unit commanded by Mr. Pete Wood, my high school Agriculture teacher, had been called up during the Korean War and sent to the Far East to serve in that police action. Police action, my foot…what a joke to call it that…that 1950 war was nothing short of bloody mayhem between American soldiers and Asian communists. I'm not aware of any of our National Guard boys getting killed in that war, thank God. They all returned to the area and resumed their lives at the conclusion of the cease fire and armistice.

The football stadium had stands only on the north side of a crowned lush football field. The crown of the gridiron was so severe, at ground level, one could hardly see over the rise to the other sidelines. Constructed of thick wooden planks, the bleachers stretched out between the 20 yard lines and at best would have only accommodated maybe a thousand fans. The seating planks were not solid below the foot rest kick plate and anything in the way of concession debris fell through the cracks down to an open space below the stands. As kids we would go to the Stadium on Sundays after a Saturday night game and scratch for coinage under the stands. Every now and then, we would be rewarded with a couple of nickels or maybe a quarter. Eureka!…pay dirt and away we would dash to a downtown store to purchase a Double Cola and a Baby Ruth candy bar or maybe a Butterfinger which at that time in history, both the cola and the candy bar were large…very large in size and once eaten exacted an instant gratification as the combination of sugary delights hit the digestive tract.

The SJC Trojans always seemed to have excellent football teams under the direction of Jim Randall, Jimmy Bellipanni and J.D. Stonestreet. I had been a fan since 1953 after I started playing peewee football and realized there was a college in Moorhead that had a football team. To demonstrate how naïve the Griffin boys were in the early 1950s, my brother, Bud likes to relate the story that when he was in the sixth grade, one of the Armstrong boys at Moorhead Grammar School asked him one day "hey Bud, let's go down to the college and watch football practice". Bud's vacant response was "What's a college?" He was totally oblivious that Moorhead was a college town. That goes to show that we, the Griffin boys and probably some of our country buddies lived in a small innocent corner of the universe in those days. Our view of the world was doubtlessly tunneled within the constraints of Moorhead Grammar School, downtown Moorhead and the roads that led to our house on Sheffield Road and the country corridor that we lived in.

Starting in 1954, I never missed a home football game in Trojan Stadium, college or high school. As I said, the Trojans had good teams and went to a couple of bowl games between 1954 and 1956. In those days, Hinds Junior College was a powerhouse and captured the State and National Championships two or three years running. In 1954, Hinds sported a team that had Jimmy Taylor and Earl Leggett, two world class players who went on to NFL fame and All Pro recognition. Needless to say with that illustrious fire power, SJC lost handily to Hinds in those years.

Mississippi had the strongest junior college Athletic Conference in the USA and the eventual winner normally claimed the national championship after winning a bowl game over some California or Texas team. Although not always, were the Mississippi teams the winner. I recall one of those years; a California team, Compton Junior College took the trophy.

Because my world was so narrow in 1958 owing to the reality that I'd never been anywhere to speak of … yes I had been to DC, Memphis and St Louis but those ventures had been so fleeting it was almost like viewing a newsreel. With everything considered, I thought the SJC campus was impressive from a provincial viewpoint. Granted, provincial was not part of my vocabulary at that time. Although my world was a world of simplicity I didn't connect the two words. Indeed, I would guess a sophisticate from Saratoga, New York would not find my college digs very eye popping but what the heck, in my view it was pretty cool.

In my previous synopsis of the school's campus appeal, I failed to mention that the grassy lawns of the campus were dotted with large oak and poplar trees which enhanced its pastoral appeal. Ivy League it was not, but the large brick buildings built in the 1920s and 1930's added character to the overall beauty of the landscape. By and large, I had no problem with the excellence of my educational setting. The town of Moorhead was not the most spotless of places especially the areas around the juke joints in the vicinity of the Moorhead Gin but the college situated in the southern part of town was surrounded by some older fine houses which softened its appearance of being just an average small town high school campus. Without SJC, Moorhead would have been just another nondescript run down crossroads in the Delta; but the addition of the college campus dignified the town with its presence.

Lots of jobs were generated by the upkeep and running of the educational institutions known as SJC and SAHS. The educational facilities bore a lifeline to many of the locals who depended on the school for employment.

Most of the kids attending Sunflower Junior College were residents of the central Delta, namely the students came from Indianola, Leland, Greenville, Benoit, Rosedale, Shaw, Shelby, Ruleville, Clarksdale, Inverness, Belzoni, Isola, Louise, Greenwood, Tchula, Itta Bena, Minter City, and Cleveland to list a few of the feeder towns. Of course Moorhead, Blaine and Sunflower contributed quite heavily to the student body with their busloads of post high school neophytes coming in every day along with the elementary and high school kids. The college kids from these locales could easily stay at home and have transportation provided by the county at no charge. In essence, for these lucky locals, it was like having a scholarship with room and board at home and no transportation cost. Their only out of pocket costs were for tuition, books and lunch fees. It was quite a deal.

And then there was a segment of the student body that came from out of state and out of country. If seems the few out of country students were from Puerto Rico…I'm not sure how that connection came about unless possibly some alums of SJC settled as teachers in the Caribbean and steered some of their students to the Mississippi/Yazoo Delta.

Adding some pizzazz to the local color of the student mix was the out of state group. Most were student athletes who had been recruited by the SJC coaches through their contacts with former players who were now high school coaches themselves. Typically there would be about ten football players and maybe five basketball players who would show up on campus in the early Fall from out of state.

It was a bad omen for the local males, but this cadre of out-of-state beefcake provided a perk for a lot of the high school girls enrolled at SAHS owing to the eventuality that most of the athletes ended up dating the local girls including the college ones. Consequently, the outcome of these liaisons left the local boys without much of a selection for pretty girls ...seeing as most of them (attractive girls) gravitated to the muscular college jocks. Left without a hefty stock of available squeeze stock, a lot of the Moorhead boys found Greenwood and Indianola the better hunting grounds for the opposite sex. Such was the case of Sonny, Billy and me in the pursuit of eager women. Actually "eager" is not the adequate word...maybe "lukewarm" is more appropriate. In that decade, the 1950s, there didn't exist a girl that could be typed as eager...there was no such creature that I was aware of. If there were, they were able to suppress their mating proclivities without a hint of expression. They certainly fooled me in those growing up years.

This magnificent day was no different...the football players had arrived a couple of weeks prior to today's registration for preseason practice and the girls were mulling around and checking them out as they feigned interest in the collegiate courses they would be taking. Noticeably, the girls had a knack for checking out the boys without giving a hint of obvious interest? Amazing how they did it but, the guys, me included, were always at a loss in ascertaining whether or not a girl was interested in them. It's like…" oh, she must be eyeing that flower arrangement behind me."

The campus was abuzz with activity, students registering and moving into the dorms and apartments. The opening football game would be played that coming Saturday night and the band was already practicing for an opening night performance. In the vanguard, beautiful majorettes were prancing their routines and flinging batons twenty feet into the air and catching them with hands behind their backs. There was much anticipation of the coming game. Because there was always a quick turnover of players in the two year junior college programs, it was hard to get a fix on the quality of a team on any given year. 1958 was an unknown.

In a nutshell this was my OLD SKULE, this place called SJC. The beauty of the campus, the back drop, the people, the dialects, the poverty, the innocence, the friendliness, and the downright goodness of all the attributes melded together to make the place a happy place, at least for me. In my search to know about the history of this institution, in my high school days, I would slip off to a corner room in the old library and pull out the old "Retrospects" which were the school annuals going back to the establishment of the school plant in the early 1920s. Perusing every page, I saw the likes of old familiar faces and characters that I knew currently in their almost unrecognizable youth. I saw relatives, I saw classmate's parents, I saw old teachers, I saw football and basketball heroes, I saw politicians, I saw Delta luminaries…what an education it was. All those handsome youngsters were now older and not so handsome…it was eye opening and it gave me a perspective of where the people came from and where they ended up in current time, this era of the mid-1950s. It was a history of personalities. Some I knew, most I didn't. To me, it was a fascinating venture into the past.

Very interestingly, I ran across a picture of Mr. Melvin, a poor farmer and the patriarch of a family of fine boys that had lived close to us in my grammar school days. There he was in one of the 1930 annuals all decked out in a football uniform and looking at the camera in a menacing way that belied his easy-going demeanor that I was so familiar with. Here was a college man and a football star and I had no idea that Mr. Melvin had such status in his youth.

And so it was, this gloriously sparkling day was my time to register for the fall semester at Sunflower Junior College in Moorhead, Mississippi, smack dab in the middle of the Yazoo Delta. My mood was buoyed by the autumn like weather and I was not deterred by the portents of a bad cotton crop…my main focus was on my future as an incoming freshman college student. The college faculty had set up various classrooms for the students to register and I got in line for the class selection process in Mr. Herman Thigpen's home room. Because he was so friendly and personable, Mr. Thigpen was one of my favorite teachers. I know this is a bit quirky but I liked the way he wrote his script and I plagiarized his penmanship style which was a straight up rendering of characters as opposed to a standard right slant adopted by most practitioners of script. I liked it but most of my teachers didn't care for the way some of my letters were less than cipherable.

Not only was Mr. Thigpen suggesting an individual curriculum for each student in the line, he was serving as counselor/advisor and very quickly with his help; I had my subjects picked for the first semester 1958. If I recall, one elective was the extent of my choice for a class...the rest of my classes were required. So it didn't take long for me to shoehorn *College Algebra, Western Civilization, English, Psychology and Physical Ed* studies into the allotted time slots for the Monday through Friday schedule.

Sonny Matthews accompanied me in the registering process and filled out his schedule which almost replicated my program. He was not aspiring to be a football & basketball coach, so that made Phys Ed a non-requirement for him. Taking from the previous story, Sonny was a year ahead of me in school but he had opted to work at the Ludlow Textile plant in Indianola during my senior year in high school which was 1957 and to date 1958. He had decided that working shift work in a textile mill was not his ticket to a future. Still living at home close to where I lived, he chose to give college a try with his parent's blessing and resigned from Ludlow prior to the start of the fall semester. My good friend Roy did the same thing. There is nothing like the reality of a shift work job to make a person's dreams turn from bringing home a paycheck to seeking college credits at an institution of higher learning. A straight day college career was much more appealing than a grimy assembly line job…just ask Sonny and Roy.

Sonny was enjoying his new found freedom from the isolation created by his job. Back in the mode of a care free high school student, he was once again enjoying life to its fullest. He had a nice car and had found a part time job at a service station in Moorhead. Along with Billy Tyner, who was now a sophomore in college and some of the other regulars, Greenwood was still attracting our utmost attention as a fertile girl haven. As stated before, Roy had enrolled at SJC and given up his Ludlow job but his participation in our group was limited because he was in love with a lovely girl from Blaine. His focus was naturally in the right place considering the couple had started discussions of marriage.

Upon completion of our time with the registrar, Sonny suggested that we go over to the Trojan Canteen and get a soda. Arriving inside the two story building that housed the student "watering hole" known as the Canteen we went to the counter and ordered Barq Orange sodas, not necessarily our favorite drink but its large size overrode our druthers over quality and taste. We were forever the pragmatic country boys. Of course that didn't count Billy Tyner because he normally had enough change in his pockets to get whatever he wanted…he went along with our choices just to be hospitable.

Usually a "Watering Hole" implies a place where beer is served but no way would an educational setting in Mississippi in 1958 promote the use of alcoholic beverages. As a matter of fact, the Canteen was a place on campus where a student could go to get refreshments, play ping pong and listen and bop to a great sounding jukebox and socialize with other students. Sandwiches of all sorts (mainly bologna and lunch meat) could be purchased for $.15, thus in lieu of a lunch in the main cafeteria at a cost of $.40, most of my compatriots and me opted for the Canteen style of daytime troughing. A sandwich, a drink and a bag of potato chips cost only a quarter, so once again, one can see why we opted for the canteen scene. Illustrative of the times, in those days there were no free government lunch programs. If one didn't have ready cash to pay, he or she went hungry until they got home and grabbed a cold biscuit.

In the halls of the Administration Building, we had bumped into several of our former high school classmates who had their sights set on advancing their educations and four or five had drifted into the Trojan Shield for the same reason we had gone in that direction. I greeted Thomas Blansett, who was back in town after spending August working in Memphis ... remember I had left him when I made my journey up to St Louis. He was looking fit and it was obvious he was happy to be back in Moorhead...yes...he was back living with his parents in the house down from the Oil Mill. When we parted company in Memphis back in August we had agreed to meet again at Sunflower Junior College and here we were just like in our high school days. I was glad to see him and we talked about our Memphis adventures as we ate our bologna sandwiches and sipped orange soda.

Playing ping pong over in a corner were several guys who were strangers to me and my cohorts. We assumed they were football players as they seemed to be relaxed in the confines of the campus watering hole. Since the football players had arrived several weeks in advance of the school session, they were already familiar with the only place on campus that one could realize any recreation, unless it was down town at the city Pool Hall. One can imagine, they were bored stiff coming from larger towns and cities in the South, stuck in a lazy town like Moorhead. Of course, Moorhead did have a nice movie theater and a lot of student athletes combated the doldrums by taking in the latest movie releases. Too, some of the athletes had cars which opened up access to Indianola, Greenville and Greenwood, cities much larger than Moorhead, thus their boredom could be abated more liberally than the students in residence who didn't have transportation of which there were many.

But my clique was made up of local bodies... Sonny, Billy and yours truly were not bored, inasmuch as our schedules were fully chocked with chores at home (at this point in time we all lived with our parents) which entailed some farm work for the two country boys and store clerking for Billy, the city boy. Sonny and I both worked at the two prominent service stations in town too, he at **Tehnet's** and me at **Bill Colliers**. Usually I worked on weekends at **Colliers** and Sonny worked various hours at **Tehnet's** like he had in his high school days. Bill Collier, the proprietor of the station where I worked had a routine that included going to college football games on weekends, therefore, due to his absence, my services to help pump gas was needed on Saturdays and Sundays. He was a devout SJC football fan and followed them all over the state of Mississippi taking in all their "away" games. Ole Miss was another favorite of his and he occasionally went up to Oxford and Memphis to view the Rebel games. In those days, Ole Miss was a Division I collegiate powerhouse, so it was a big deal to go to one or several of their games.

As we sat around a table in the canteen and jawed at this early September noontime siesta, the subject of football came up. We were all curious about the Trojan football team's prospects for the coming 1958 season. We knew they played their first game on the road up at Northwest Junior College located in Senatobia, MS but at this time no one had given any thought to going up near Oxford to see the game. Not one to practice frugality like his broke buddies, Billy Tyner's face lit up as he blurted out "heck you bunch of rednecks, let's go to the game, I'll drive my car". Being in a state of denial because I had just spent $20 on three used class books, I couldn't see spending more money to buy a ticket to the game even though it was probably only a dollar. But on second thought, the idea of going to see the Trojans play was intensely appealing to my thought process, however; my immediate acceptance was rebuffed by my responsibility to cover for Mr. Bill Collier at his Service Station on Saturday to allow him to go to the same game. With my participation receding into oblivion at that moment, Sonny quickly fell in line with Billy's bright idea and said he was good to go ...count him in.

As a fourth rider, even though he wasn't present nor engaged in our conversation, Cokie could be elected to fill out Billy's 1952 Chevrolet sedan's ridership. Cokie was a few years our senior and had a job with the Mississippi State Highway Department; therefore he always had money and would be a choice candidate to be a fourth passenger in the ride up to the Northwest Jr. College campus. Being a little bit on the crazy side, Cokie could add a little atmospheric spice to the group's flamboyance for the two hour stage show that would surely eventuate on this coming Saturday afternoon. The inference to craziness was not meant literally...in fact maybe shortsightedness or fearlessness would better define his actions especially if he had a beer or two under his belt. To add credence to Cokie's reputation of atypical behavior, he was known around town as the hardheaded guy who always slammed his empty beer cans into his forehead to flatten them out for neat stacking and he was also known for his ability to clean out his car's glove compartment while tooling down Hwy 82 at 70 miles per hour...mind you, with his head up under the dashboard for 2 or 3 minutes at a time. That and a few other behavioral abnormalities could be attributed to Cokie's personal catalogue of idiosyncrasies but let's not get carried away into a prolonged litany at this particular moment since its divulgence could take a dozen minutes or so away from this priceless story being recorded as I speak.

Thank God, Cokie would not be driving. For the sake of our own mortality or lack thereof, harnessing his body to a rear passenger seat for this trip was of the utmost importance. You know, a "loose cannon" can sometimes be discharged if one positions it aim into barren cotton fields. That was Billy's intention...shackle him in the back seat to prevent his lighting the fuse or in case it was lit, making sure the projectile became a harmless misdirected dud. That was Cokie, our lovable "loose cannon".

With my mind racing with thoughts of reconciliation, my brother Bud popped into my realm of consideration… hmmm…I'm wondering if he would fill in for me at Colliers Service Station Saturday afternoon. I could work the morning shift because the trip's departure would not proceed until after high noon…assuming the trip was only a couple of hours driving time to Senatobia. Yes, that was my solution…Bud would work for me. Almost in the same millisecond that my brain spit out the solution to my dilemma, I tapped Billy on the shoulder as he was downing a big bite of ham sandwich and told him to count me in for the Northwest Mississippi Junior College trip.

Nobody mentioned sharing the gasoline expense with Billy so I didn't dare bring up the subject. Usually Billy furnished the gas for these quickly organized sorties so it was prudent for me to keep my mouth shut. I'm sure Sonny was thinking the same thing. The fewer dollars we spent the better…we certainly didn't have any loose change to spare. Too, Cokie was a generous soul with ready cash and we were convinced he would cram a few dollars into Billy's fist as a token of appreciation for asking him along. Regardless of help from his penniless cohorts, Billy was willing to foot the entire transportation cost, no matter.

With the Senatobia trip plan all but settled and a time of departure fixed, we rolled out of the canteen in a file with Sonny and yours truly splitting off in the direction of the tan 1954 Ford Fairlane that was my cousin Sonny's pride and joy. In the distance behind us, we could hear the Jukebox in the canteen wafting out a Tommy Edward's song "It's all in the game" a melodic ode that was a favorite slow dancing piece in the fall of 1958. Several couples had moved to the dance area and were sharing a two-step embrace as we made our exit across the sycamore laced campus to my good cousin's car.

Part Four

As we torpedoed through lingering clouds of dust on the gravel road called Sheffield Road, Sonny slowed his Ford Fairlane to a crawl to let the gray airborne particles blow and settle away from the road. It appeared the car ahead of us was Aunt Beulah Sheffield and the tail wind generated by her vehicle was really stirring up the dust on this gorgeously warm but not hot dry day. Even at the slow pace we were going, agonizingly soon, my house came into view and Sonny dropped me off at our mailbox located on the main road near our gravel driveway.

Taking leave of Sonny's car, walking with an arm load of books toward the gray clapboarded house set 150 feet off the road, my thoughts drifted to the not too distant past. It is strange how the mind produces these little dribs and drabs of past experiences without any encouragement from the conscious mind. Maybe the eternity of our last mile in Sonny's car before he dropped me off had triggered a random thought that was large in my mind at the moment "heck I could have walked home in the time it took us to get home today".

Our house was exactly three miles from the town of Moorhead and it was nothing for the Griffin brothers to walk to town on a whim. Sometimes if we had a dime, we would hoof it to Moorhead to soothe our cravings for treats…like…

to buy a soda pop and a candy bar, loiter around town and then walk home before darkness overtook the Negro cemetery that we had to walk past to get home. Yeah, we always made sure light was still visible when we headed back home in the dusky hours.

Please excuse the intermission but it was hard for me to forget the time when I was fourteen and got caught in Moorhead after an afternoon of swimming in the Moorhead Public Swimming Pool. Usually it was easy to catch a ride home with an aunt, uncle or someone who lived out in the corridor but on this particular day my luck ran out...nobody showed up on the streets of metropolitan Moorhead to give me a ride home. I hung around the vacant streets and pool hall with a couple of my city buddies until darkness overcame the little borough and still there was not a ride home for Billy Ray. As in singular...yes just Billy Ray, absent his normal hanger-on buddy or two from the corridor.

Then reality dawned on me...by now it was pitch black...the only way to make it to my house was to walk the three miles in awkward darkness. With much hesitation, and a deep breath, I lit out for the Griffin homestead up the road that entered Moorhead from the northwest, forking from Hwy 82 at the barn that had the **Chattanooga Lookout Mountain** advertisement painted on its roof. Once I got past the glow of the city lights, I could hardly see my hands in front of me but I could feel the gravel under my shoes. As I approached the area of the aforementioned cemetery I felt the urge to pick up the pace and I did so with determined urgency. At first it was a jog, then a stride and finally a sprint. At age fourteen, a boy's energy level is boundless and true to form, after jettisoning the cemetery in my wake, I never downshifted and continued to stride frenetically. I guess I must have gotten my second wind (in this day and age, they call it a runner's high), back then; track coaches called it a second wind. If only Coach Bellipani, our high school track coach, knew I could run like that he would have had this lanky freshman running the mile on the track team.

At the conclusion of a mile, I allowed myself to resume the pace of a hurried walk. Although my eyes had adjusted to the darkness, it was a moonless night and I still could only make out the lightness of the gravel roadway. That's really all the navigational guidance I needed to get home, so my eyes were trained on the middle of the road with my feet offset in the right tire lane.

I crossed Hwy 82 and proceeded up Sheffield Road, across the Moorhead Bayou Bridge, being careful not to step off the edges of the barrierless bridge; I groped my way across the middle of the bridge and reached the other side safely. As I breathed a sigh of relief at mastering the crossing of the bridge, out of nowhere, an invisible wayward cow just off the side of the road (no I didn't see it), rustled heartily in the bushes and bellowed the loudest ear splitting exhalation I had ever heard. I almost dropped to my knees with alarm as the penetrating "Moooo" pelted my super sensitive sound receptors. What the hell? Then I realized it was a harmless and shepherdless bovine but it took a minute for my heart to cease racing. Thank the Almighty, I had a strong heart.

After doing a reactionary pirouette in the middle of the road, I gathered my wits and quickly aimed my human carcass straight north up Sheffield Road, scratching gravel as I took off. Why waste all that adrenalin that just got pumped into my bloodstream. As a result of that logical thought, I commenced to run the rest of the way to my house which should have ended the story, but my adventure was by no means finished.

In full stride I turned into our driveway but slowed to a walk and looked around. In the dim light it occurred to me the old 1952 Chevy was not parked in front of the house and then I remembered, my parents and two younger brothers had gone to Lake Providence, Louisiana to visit an aunt and uncle that day and would not be back until tomorrow. My older brothers were out with friends and probably they would not be home until midnight. When I realized I was the sole occupant of that unlocked black spooky house, my poise became a bit unzipped. In those days, nobody locked their doors and all that stood between a prospective night time prowler and the occupants of a dwelling was a latched screen door. That was it. In our situation, with teenage boys coming home in the middle of the night, there was no need to even latch a screen door. So in effect, there was no such thing as home security.

The only times anyone in our neck of the woods ever remotely showed any apprehension about home safety came when reports of an escaped convict got reported. It would usually involve an escaped killer from Parchman Penitentiary, and then everyone would lock up at night for a few days.

I wasn't used to being at home at night by my ole lonesome but that night I killed some time reading on the sofa and then went to bed around10:00 PM. Just as I was dozing off, I heard a sound like someone plucking a stringed musical instrument in the other room. Immediately I sat upright and strained my eyes, peering into the darkness of the adjacent room. With my heart pounding, my imagination ran wild with thoughts of some mysterious stranger roaming around the house and here I was in my bed, a sitting duck for a crazed ax murderer. The bedroom that I was in, afforded no outside egress unless one exited through the room from which the audible chimes emanated. I was hemmed in …frozen to my bed.

By now my ears were flared like radar receivers and the signals entering my auditory system were being interpreted as every conceivable noise associated with stealthy footsteps and human breathing. Then a quickly oiled idea arose from a sea of brainwaves that were brought on by my heightened anxiety…I could escape through one of the bedroom windows…all I had to do was lift the latch on a window screen and drop to the ground outside the big window. But then what…I didn't care, I would be free to flee in my underwear in any direction.

As I threw off the sheets to make my escape, through a window of the Griffin boy's bedroom I saw car lights in the distance and very soon, a car pulled into our driveway and my brother Bud jumped from his friend's car and made his way into our house.

On the verge of abandoning ship, I immediately relaxed and fell back into bed as lights came on in the kitchen, relieved that a jump through the window would not be necessary. I figured the mysterious interloper in the next room would be nixed by Bud's clamorous activity in the kitchen but with ears cocked I could detect no hint of shocked bustling from the inner room. Perhaps the mystery man high tailed it through the unlocked back door when he saw the car lights emerging in the driveway. Either that or poor Bud was going to get the surprise of his life as he made his way to our bedroom through the room that contained the stealthy intruder. As I held my breath and the lights went off in the kitchen, Bud made his entrance into the bedroom and commenced to take off his clothes and get into the double bed next to my bed. He had no idea I was camped in the same room. Since there had been no raucous interception of either party, perceived or otherwise, in the intermediate room, I assumed my imagination had gotten the best of me. I remained silent for a couple of minutes, and then expelled a cough to let Bud know he had company. Bud, slightly taken aback, interjected into a black and silent room "what the hell are you doing here…I thought you went to Lake Providence with the folks?" I didn't answer and pulled up the sheets.

After contemplating the situation for a few minutes, my nerves calmed and my physical body by this time, overcome with fatigue, I rolled over and eventually dropped off to sleep.

After arising the next morning at daybreak, I noticed my older brother Stan had made it in during the night sans me hearing him come in. The morning light outside accompanied by roosters crowing had awakened me from a most restful sleep. It had left me confident and energized after the previous evening's imagined dangers. Nothing like daylight to wash away fears of night time creeps.

Taking care to not awaken my brothers, I stepped into and impulsively reconnoitered my parent's bedroom which was the location of the sounds that had unnerved me during my entry to bed the previous night. Almost immediately I found the source of the sounds that had scared the wits out of me.

Next to a dresser and near a window, sat my brother Stan's guitar where it was assumed he had placed it in haste when his buddy picked him up the night before. Normally the treasured Gibson guitar would be placed in its case after a practice session but in all likelihood Stan had quickly deposited the instrument against the dresser when his friend arrived in the driveway.

Well, I'll be dog gone…it hit me like a sucker punch…putting two and two together upon observing the position of the Gibson close to an open window I figured it out. Combined with a slight breeze puffing through the window I could visualize the window curtains rippling across the guitar strings generating the musical sounds that my finely tuned ears had picked up during my solitary confinement the night before.

How **embarrassing**…the thought of my getting "worked up" over such a harmless fluke was hard to swallow. I chided myself for being such a weenie and made a mental note not to divulge my previous night's experiences to my older brothers and I never did. They would have laughed themselves silly I do believe.

Thanking the readers for their patience, I realize the preceding story was a bit sappy but maybe my children and my brothers can get a kick out of its telling. Sorry to bore the rest of you.

Part Five

Intercepting me as I entered the house after getting off the school bus on my first day of college classes, and before my handful of books could be placed on a table; my mother announced to me directly that my father needed my services at the back of the blacksmith shop where his International Harvester Combine was parked. He was performing maintenance to get the big red machine ready for soy bean threshing expected to take place in mid-October.

After changing out of my school duds into some work rags, I grudgingly moped out to the site of the combine and helped with the annual maintenance tune-up although my heart wasn't in it. I tried to sustain some feigned interest because I knew my Dad was killing himself working, trying to provide food and supplies for a farm family in a year that was destined for failure. The soy bean crop showed some promise to bring in a few dollars but the cash crop, cotton, was an abysmal failure. In an attempt to offset some of the shortfall, Dad had gotten a night time job at the Oil Mill in Moorhead. After working all night, he would sleep in the mornings and tend to his farm in the evening hours. It was tough sledding for him but he was holding up quite well although the strain was obvious. Acknowledging his sacrifice, I was making damn sure I didn't let him down with a halfhearted attitude even though I couldn't muster much interest in his project of the moment. Certainly mechanical objects and their workings was not my cup of tea but like I said I put my best foot forward with the best of intentions and made every effort to engage in small talk and jokes to humor him for the afternoon. Without a doubt I was concerned about our family's livelihood prospects especially bank payments that would come due in the late months of the year. With all my heart I tried to empathize with my father but to be perfectly honest, my thoughts were more on the trip to Senatobia than they were on greasing pinion gears and sewing patches on canvas conveyor belts. It wasn't that I was insensitive...my lack of feeling for the family's impending dire straits owed basically to one thing... it all boiled down to my youth. A young man has the ability to worry but not to the depths that adults do. I was concerned about the financial situation but I was not paralyzed with despair. I could still function exactly as I did a year ago, which was a good crop year. This year is a bad crop year...I'm still on auto pilot and my internal engine hasn't missed a lick. Bring it on! I'm optimistic in my outlook...isn't that an integral part of the farmers creed. Never let a bad crop waylay you...if that were not true...there would be no farmers left in the Delta. I was good to "move on" but my father knew full well that the 1958 harvest was a bummer.

Since I was still depending on my family for room and board, my routine of chores and helping all I could on the farm was not diminished at that time. I was still a part of the labor force that made the old farm click or so I thought at the time. That's the way it would remain until I moved into the junior college athletic dorm in October.

I can safely say that this afternoon's job of helping my father with the "combine" was probably the last time the two of us engaged in a farm related job ...just him and me as a team. I had moved beyond picking cotton since the service station job took all my time on the weekends and unbeknownst to any of us at that juncture, the core family of four would soon pack up and move to Baton Rouge, Louisiana. Moreover, the cotton that year, what little there was, would be harvested with a one-row mechanical picker that belonged to my Uncle AP. He let my Dad borrow it and in a couple of weeks, the crop had been picked, loaded on trailers, trucked to Moorhead and ginned.

With that bit of ancient history rolled out as background, the stage was set for my college career to be launched from my home base and soon to be athletic dorm at Sunflower Junior College in Moorhead, Mississippi smack dab in the middle of the Yazoo Delta.

After catching up with Bud that evening, his initial reaction was that he had other plans involving his girlfriend from Sunflower but after some reconsideration decided the money would come in handy and he agreed to work for me at Collier's Service Station Saturday afternoon. Now I could conclude my plans for the trip up to Senatobia which was unfolding that coming weekend.

And so it was...September 1958... a good time to be alive...no wars going on at the moment and Dwight D. Eisenhower, our president seemed to be a good enough guy and Congress was exhibiting some semblance of fiscal respectability. The cold war with the Soviets was in full thrust but no one in our midst thought about the inevitability of an atomic holocaust...to tell the truth it was really beyond our comprehension...so we didn't worry about it. We were footloose and carefree. Yes we were.

Our trip to Northwest Junior College in Senatobia, Mississippi went as planned and we enjoyed the game which was won by Sunflower Junior College. We were all happy about the outcome but I must say, the Trojans just barely squeaked by a weak team that normally dwelled in the cellar of the Mississippi Junior College rankings. Based on the night's performance, I had my doubts that my team would be a power to reckon with in 1958. Another thing that disappointed was the smallness and ricketyness of the Northwest stadium but it's possible my remembrance of the facility was based on the visitor's side of the field and not the stadium as a whole. As I recall, my eight legged group was able to move along the sidelines observing the action with only a cable separating us from the playing field.

Being good boys that night, beer drinking remained verboten but Cokie acting to stay in shape bought a canned drink, emptied it in short fashion, then slammed it against his forehead to crush it. It was a ritual that he went through to toughen the skin on his head. Fortunately, that was about the extent of his zaniness that night.

One reason, this little insignificant trip was chronicled was to highlight a prominent event that occurred that same night in Atlantic Beach, New Jersey. At the conclusion of the game, our group stepped into the little college's social gathering place (canteen) to grab a soda prior to our hitting the road back to Moorhead and we all noticed a small TV screen showing the Miss America Pageant in its final moments. I was aware, via newspaper accounts but I don't think any of the other guys knew about the Miss America beauty pageant going on that night. What piqued my interest in the newspaper article was the selection of a Mississippi girl as one of the ten finalists. Never had a Mississippi participant won the crown in the illustrious history of this prestigious beauty contest.

As I stood watching I told my friends that a girl from Ole Miss was in the finals ...they immediately became interested in the television program, as did most of the people in the canteen. The Ole Miss campus was only a short distance from Senatobia, the point at which we stood with mouths agape.

Bert Parks, the Master of Ceremonies had just announced the final three and the southern belle from down Jackson way clung to one of those spots. The crowd watched and cheered as Mary Ann Mobley from Brandon, Mississippi was crowned Miss America of 1959 (even though the pageant was held in 1958).

I seriously doubt any of the other guys in our car pool remember that trip that night but by dovetailing the football game at Senatobia with Mary Ann Mobley winning the Miss America crown, I was able to recover that memory 53 years later. At that time in history, the state of Mississippi was looked down on as a backward state; therefore any positive accomplishments by any of its citizens were proudly hailed by most residents of the state. Amazingly, the following year another girl from Natchez, Mississippi, Lynda Leigh Meade won the 1960 Miss America title. The odds of that happening were probably a million to one but poor old Mississippi, the land of Faulkner and Bilbo, had upset the odds makers two years in a row.

Post football and beauty on display, it was time for Cokie and friends to go home...the long trip to the central Delta awaited us. The four sober travelers marched out of the Northwest Junior College canteen with the sounds of Bert Park's singing to the girl from Brandon with the refrain "There she goes Miss America...Miss America 1959." We still couldn't believe a girl from Mississippi had won. Our state may have been the most maligned state in the union, but when it came to good looking and fashionable women, it was no contest compared to the other states of the union. In passing, I thought to myself ... "yes, Mississippi is a dog in eyes of many but the Magnolia state is blessed with the most beautiful women in the world bar none". I didn't think anybody in their right mind could dispute that argument that night...and I still think it's a platitude that still holds water to this day.

Part Six

By now all the students who were staying on the SJC campus were settled in their assigned dormitory rooms and the stay at home kids were registered and ready to go. A day of orientation was under our belts and the first real day of actual classes was upon us. Living at home on this first day of college, I caught the Sunflower County school bus driven by my brother, Bud and was deposited at the entrance close to the SJC administration building. As I recall, I was probably the only college student on the bus...even though Sonny was now attending college, he drove his own car.

Bolting the yellow Bluebird bus, my attention was centered on getting to class and seeing some of my old high school classmates and some new faces. I was especially curious to see who my college basketball teammates would be and where they came from. I knew Tommy Edwards and Charles Boyer, ex SAHS players but other than those two guys I had not met the rest of the 8 or 9 other players who would be on scholarship.

At the conclusion of my Math and Psychology classes, the relaxed atmosphere and a sprinkling of old friends in my classes made me feel like I'd never left the halls of Sunflower Agricultural High School. In fact the facility housed both schools and some of the college teachers crossed over to teach high school subjects. JD Stonestreet was my Math instructor and I do believe he taught an Algebra class for the under classmen in the same class room as did his wife who taught English in both academic divisions.

It was time for lunch break on this fairly hot and clear Monday (the cool air that I spoke of last week had exited to the east and the mood was not as elevated as last week) ...with hunger pangs gnawing at my midsection, I crossed the campus to the Trojan canteen. Soon as I walked in, it was obvious the wait at the counter would be extended because a big line of students had queued up for service which amounted to the goods being almost exclusively cold cut sandwiches and soft drinks. Waiting in line, I struck up conversations with a couple of friends from Blaine and Sunflower...it was almost like old times...it appeared I knew just about everyone in the crowd. Out of the corner of my eye, I caught a glimpse of this large, very large young man sitting at a four chaired table in a corner of the dining area. The legs of the chair he was sitting in were bowing under his prodigious weight. The guy was huge, probably 280 pounds … I didn't recognize him…he was new to the campus but there was something about his facial features that made me take a second look. I said to myself "hey that boy looks familiar; I swear I believe I know him". After nudging my friends and asking them if that fellow was in any of the morning classes, one acknowledged that that particularly recognizable student was in his English class and the teacher had mentioned he was a long way from home…in fact his home state was reported to be California.

I went about my business, purchased a bologna sandwich and a soda and sat down with Thomas Blansett and Charles Boyer at a table near the side door having a western exposure (this particular door accessed student traffic arriving from the football stadium and the basketball gymnasium). As we chatted, the subject of the fat guy sitting across the room came up. They didn't know his name but his vague familiarity continued to haunt me. I could have accosted the big fellow but it was not in my mettle to do such a thing. My lack of social skills dissuaded me from taking that step. I soon forgot about the stranger and went about my afternoon classes with eager caution. I liked all my teachers and my classes were interesting. My college days had begun and I liked it.

Later in the day as I rode home in the school bus, my thoughts turned to the fat guy that I had seen in the canteen. I was sure I knew him from somewhere in my past but I couldn't put my finger on the exactness of my remembrance.

Part Seven

A couple of days later in our first week of junior college, Billy Tyner bumped into me in the library…while we were both scanning back to back issues of *Sports Illustrated.* When we started chatting in a lively exchange, Mrs. McInnis, the librarian gave us the "hush" salute which encouraged us to make a hasty retreat to the exit door. Granted, she was a pain in the butt but she was just doing her job. After deciding to go out and sit under one of the big leafy oak trees on a park bench, Billy commenced to tell me that "John Bright Russell," a former friend, had come from California, enrolled at SJC and was staying in the men's dormitory on campus. That pronouncement caught me by surprise. Yeah, I remember John Bright…he was in my grade at Moorhead Grammar School many years ago until he moved away in the sixth grade. As a matter of fact, he and I were the best of buddies and played pee wee football in the fall of 1952, the year that he moved to California. Fresno, I believe was the place out west that the family moved to in 1952. Of course Fresno didn't mean anything to me; California was California … you know… that foreign country out west. Yes, I remembered John Bright…a lot of us in those archaic days had two first names same as John Bright, like Billy Ray, Ed Wayne, Thomas Edgar, John Robert, etc. etc. as having a stocky and muscular physique which empowered him on the football field. In the sixth grade, owing to his solidness of bulk, he made the first team and I became a scrub under Coach Bellipanni.

Well I'll be dag gone; ole John Bright is back is he? Tyner nodded affirmatively and leaned over whispering in my ear like he didn't want anyone to hear him "yep he's here but you won't recognize him…he is big as a house".

And then it dawned on me --- that big guy who I had seen at the canteen on Monday was none other than John Bright Russell, my old grammar school friend from way back when.

I had seen him a couple of times waddling across campus since the canteen sighting, but I still had not approached the big fella.

Pointing in the direction of the large two story brick building next to the athletic dormitory across the street, Billy in his southern drawl droned "I've been to his room over at the men's dorm…do you want to go see if we can catch up with him?"

My response was immediate… "Let's go, I'd really like to see if ole John Bright remembers me after all these years." And away we went, cutting across the campus ignoring the sidewalks. We were soon bounding up a flight of stairs to get to the second floor where the 18 year old California expatriate was bedding down at night in an overstressed single bed with a wafer like mattress, which appeared to be so thin the bedbugs were dying of exposure. The webbing that kept the mattress supported above the oak floor appeared to be extruding mattress material through the small openings but it was just an illusion. Like I said, the mattress and webbing were stressed awfully close to its maximized specification due to John Bright's excessive gravitational exertion but so far, it (the mattress) was holding firm but the mattress surface on the underside was starting to assume the appearance of a big rectangular Belgian Waffle and that was no kidding.

Well so much for John Bright's dainty little bed...it was just an observation that I quickly made when I entered his room that first day of our re-acquaintance, but I'm getting ahead of the story. Let me reset the time frame...Billy and I entered his open door room and there sat John Bright sitting on a chair with a guitar in hand strumming a country piece I couldn't identify. I wasn't much on country music because I was a Rock & Roll aficionada at that time in history. Later in life, I grew to enjoy some of the less twangy country music but in this era, I didn't like it.

With me side by side with Billy Tyner, the singing émigré from Fresno recognized his old grammar school buddy, Billy Ray and grabbed him in a bear hug. The feet of this lanky 155 pound friend of earlier days was left dangling above the floor as the teenage Baby Huey swung him around his humongous body much like a wrestler twirls his opponent in a heavyweight "ras'ling match". Thank heavens I was only suspended a few inches off the floor.

As I connected the face of the current version of John Bright Russell with memories of the stocky 6th grade version in 1952, the resemblance was now clear as mud. Yep, it was John Bright alright, no doubt. His rotundity had faked me out temporarily but now it was time to rehash our growing up years.

Because Billy T and John Bright had had their homecoming reunion a couple of days before this meeting today, no bear hug came forth for my older cohort. I think he was glad. They had been friends for many years in John Bright's grammar school days due to the proximity of the Russell home located not far from the Tyner Mini-grocery. In the old days, John Bright hung out at the little store and he and Billy became friends over the long haul. To further cement the relationship, John Bright had also been in Billy's sister, Betty' class, so it was not like the boy from California was in the midst of strangers.

For the ensuing two hours, Billy and I paid rapt attention to John Bright as he regaled us with his life story post Moorhead. In a nutshell, the Russell family departed Moorhead in search of a new life in golden California, that land of plenty, in 1952. Because Fresno sat in the fertile soil of the San Joachim valley, its attraction to farm folks from Oklahoma and the south in the depression years had made it a Mecca for people down on their luck. The culture there rooted in bible belt traditions and lore was definitely suitable for newcomers from the south, so the Russell family felt like they could fit in from the start of their new life in Fresno or so that's what old John Bright told us. We had no clue what Fresno had or looked like…we thought it was another bright lighted metropolis in the California valley country near Yosemite National Park. In fact it was a major US city of 100,000 people in the early 1950s and a lot of the families living there depended on agriculture and its derivatives for their livelihoods…with cotton farming being a major influence in the central valley.

John Bright, himself, as far as I knew had never been a farm boy even in Mississippi considering his father's vocation as a mechanic. When they lived in Moorhead his father worked as a mechanic at the Chrysler/Plymouth dealership and the son was considered a city boy. That's how I knew him…he was a city slicker and I was a farm boy. We became close friends.

Spending the night with a buddy was the deal that sealed and solidified a school boy friendship in those days and we did that many times, probably much to the chagrin of our parents.

I remember spending the night at his place many times because invariably we would take in a picture show at night on those occasions, then retreat to his home which was across the street from the noisy Moorhead Gin. I can still remember a movie in particular that we went to one night, whose main character was a sinister limbless circus freak. The guy was all torso and a head, but how he managed a life I still don't know to this day but I do remember the freak was a clandestine murderer. How he was able to kill people without arms and legs remains a mystery but that black and white flick caught my attention and its fear stigma is still embedded in my memory. Scared and jumpy as a couple of rabbits, we ran all the way from the Strand Theater to his house on Olive Street.

He had two teenage sisters that were a little standoffish which could be expected…certainly these comely girls weren't overjoyed with the prospect of having to put up with another wet behind the ears kid at their family residence when in reality their attentions were primarily focused on college boys. I was excess baggage and a distraction but I didn't mind the snubbing …I hardly noticed that I was an imposition to the girls. Certainly Mrs. Russell was a hospitable lady and we got along just fine. As I recall, his dad was a silent man, but I may be wrong about that…perhaps his reserve may have been a result of fatigue.

John Bright would spend the night with me on occasion and he became one of the Griffin boys at my house. We would do our rural things and he enjoyed every bit of our country way of life especially the country cooking.

The Russell kid was Mr. Personality…never met a stranger in his life. As we pal'ed around all over the town of Moorhead, every person on the street knew John Bright. Our roving included the Junior College campus, where he knew all the football players by name and they knew him intimately and without fail he carried on a lengthy play of words every time a player was met. I was not nearly as outgoing as he was. I tended to speak only when spoken to, but my buddy would initiate conversation on sight. The college boys loved him and it didn't hurt that most of them knew he had two good looking sisters.

One football player in particular was crazy about John and would carry on with him for long periods of time. His last name was Dowdy… I've forgotten his first name, but nonetheless, he was an All-State and All-American junior college gridiron star from Florida. He was the best player on the SJC team in the early 1950s.

He kidded young John unmercifully every time we met up with him on the streets of Moorhead or on the SJC campus. One time, I distinctly remember him joshing John Bright about Moorhead's blight and ugliness to the extent that the youngster's ears reddened. Talking about how bad Moorhead looked was a subject that raised the good natured kid's dander and he argued nose to nose with the big muscular football player. Of course Dowdy was playing around with John but the kid took it seriously. He loved Moorhead and he was not about to let the big guy get away with putting down his hometown without raising a verbal rebuke. What really got

J.B's goat on this particular day was Dowdy's condescending assertion that in Jacksonville, FL where he came from, the city authorities didn't allow cats and dogs to defecate (I think he probably said "crap") on the downtown streets or common areas anywhere in the city. Pointing out a big pile of dog manure near where we were standing, which in all likelihood had probably been deposited by one of my classmate's Great Dane, ***Duke***? Old ***Duke*** had the run of the town and was big as a Shetland pony. Yes, by all means, ***Duke*** was capable of dumping prodigious amounts of unspeakable residue on city property with no regard to location.

Dowdy (man, I wish I could remember his first name) reinforced his contention that Moorhead was filthy and then expanded on his claim that Jacksonville had animal toilets set up throughout their fair city for domesticated animals, specifically dogs, to use in times of nature's calling. He followed: **"it was a city ordinance, that at an early age, all dogs and cats had to be toilet trained in the use of strategically located rest facilities, otherwise, pet owners were subject to fines if their animals were not in compliance."**

Noticeably incredulous, J. B. showed tempered restraint after the junior college All American let out a deep throated laugh that echoed off the brick wall of ***Diamonds Dry Goods Store*** and resonated down the street toward ***Collier's Service Station***, so guttural it had everyone turning their heads to see what was so funny. Starting to fume, the grammar school student told Dowdy he was full of that stuff he was just talking about and walked away. Dowdy continued to cackle as we headed down the street toward the Sunflower Junior College campus.

I think John knew his agitator well enough to know he was pulling our leg but being the country bumpkin that I was, I absorbed his story, hook, line and sinker. My main thought at that point if one cared to articulate it in a couple of words was "Boy, Jacksonville, Florida must be a heck of a clean place" compared to our little town "where the Southern crosses the Yellow Dog". And too, given the fact that Delta bred mongrels didn't have good sanitation manners or mating prudery made Dowdy's claim seem even more incredible. Shucks, I would guess in Jacksonville, the canines there probably didn't even slide their rear ends across the grass to scratch an itch like our poor old dogs were in the habit of doing without any hint of modesty. How embarrassing it must have been for Dowdy (gosh, I wish I could remember his first name) to constantly witness that bit of uncouthness in Moorhead's unchecked canine population.

Against this backdrop of something less than an antiseptic setting, the Griffin boy and the Russell boy roamed the far perimeters of the little country town without ever taking notice of the negative views seen by our out of state college age detractors. We thought Moorhead was just grand.

Despite the surface appearance of John Bright's feigned acrimony, this stout muscular boy of 12 years was still a favorite of the Trojan football heroes. They knew he was a Teddy bear. I don't think there was a single player who didn't know John Bright by name and character. Even when I was not with him, he habitually hung out at the SJC football facilities during the months of football season. At that time he aspired to be a football player and was a pretty good peewee player owing to his rock solid compactness and brawny build. At that stage in his development, he certainly would not have been considered to be fat by any means.

Part Eight

So we meet again after a six year interlude…this boy who left his childhood in Moorhead, Mississippi was now in our midst again, masquerading as an almost unrecognizable cherubic man-child but still grounded in an affable mien that we remembered from days long past. It was the same chummy John Bright Russell who lived on Olive Street way back when.

Shifting back to real time to mid-September of 1958, this triumvirate of former grammar school buddies sat in John Bright Russell's dorm room rehashing old times to the delight of our cloudy recalls.

John had given up his football antics and was now entrenched in the "country and western" music scene. Even though he had the weight to be a football tackle or guard growing to maturity in Fresno, he acknowledged his interest in pigskins waned as he grew bigger in girth and shirt size. His extra weight was not the kind an athlete could take to the bank. Sure… if the added bulk had been muscle, then football may have been in the cards for the big guy, but no, the kind of lipids that were settling around John's midsection were like those that a bear puts on to make it through a winter. The added weight and the effects of developing manhood had changed his voice to a deeper tone but it was by no means what one would think of as bass, it was probably more a mix between bass and tenor, if there is such a voice tone. How would I know…the rudiments of music were so foreign to me I didn't know a high note from a bank note. Anyway his singing was bouncy, happy and fast paced and it acoustied off the walls of the small dorm room, but as I said earlier, country music was not my cup of tea. Not only was he a singer, John informed Tyner and me that he was coming into his own as a songwriter and had written several pieces that he was trying to market in Bakersfield, a hotbed of country music, a city producing an assortment of young stars who would later become world class entertainers.

Little did I know at the time that John Bright Russell would become a star on the Grand Ole Opry in the 1980s? That's the reason I'm putting this addendum in this article. I'm more or less saying "hey, I knew Johnny Russell way before he became famous and well known on the Honky-Tonk circuit.

So, let me finish the story of the California boy's homecoming before getting back to my 1958 experiences as a junior college underclassman. I'll have to jump ahead in time from the day Tyner and "Yours Truly" were holed up in a tiny room listening to the Russell sound that didn't catch our fancy, i.e. by no means did his music make the hair stand up on the back of our necks. At that moment in time, any ideas of this guitar picker becoming a professional entertainer were about as far removed as us thinking he would become an NFL football player.

This continuum of the Johnny Russell saga follows without regard to the other events going on around us. Those events will be captured, not in sequence but randomly as I move forward in other subjects relative to my school experiences in 1958.

Our normal group including myself, Tyner and Thomas Matthews, welcomed Johnny Russell (that's the name he wanted to be called) back into our fold and we commenced to do our normal tomcatting activities that involved carpooling to Greenwood, drinking beer and chasing elusive women. Because we didn't fully appreciate our California buddy's talent, we didn't appeal to him to do any singing in the car during those forays to the city at the confluence of the Yazoo and Tallahatchie rivers. We were just a bunch of not very serious minded junior college matriculates living a nominal life of carefree tranquility.

After a few weeks of basking in a collegiate smorgasbord of fun and levity, one of the guys from our aggregate caught news of an impending "Talent Show" that was to be held down at the Inverness High School auditorium. Any and all types of performers were welcome to participate in the competition and Johnny wanted to go and be a contestant. With the exception of the Californian, most of our group preferred "Rock N' Roll" and didn't think he had a prayer of a chance winning the competition given his genre of music. However we were game to jump in Tyner's four-door Chevrolet to journey down to Inverness and enjoy a good talent show.

The exact date of the Talent Show has become indistinguishable in the cobwebs of my internal mainframe but I would venture to say it was probably the first week of October 1958. John had only been on campus for maybe three weeks... but what the heck, the time frame is relatively unimportant in the context of this recollection. For us hangers-on, the upcoming event was strictly a chance to go out for the evening and have some fun. As far as any expectations of big Johnny winning the competition, we just couldn't envision such a possibility.

Seemingly in the blink of an eye, before Moorhead's man about town, George Kelly, could enunciate the word "jujitsu" (he actually pronounced it "ju ju"), John Bright's entourage of backslappers were loaded up, on a beautiful autumnal evening heading down to Inverness to partake of all that untapped yet native talent that everyone knew resided in the central Delta. One could expect an array of pianists, southern belle singers with quaking high pitched voices, curvaceous twirlers & pretty dancers, teenage magicians and the usual fare of entertainers normally seen at local talent exhibitions of that era.

As our quartet entered the secondary school auditorium, the place was abuzz with chatter from a full house. All the locals from miles around had come to this little country backwater called Inverness for an evening of watching and hearing an uninterrupted sequence of variegated yet hopeful parade of rough around the edge performing artists.

At some stage during his registration and through the grapevine, John Bright heard the Talent Show organization had national ties and in line with the Inverness show, other localities throughout the USA would be holding the same kind of preliminary events. Much like the bracketing and pairings of a basketball tournament, the winners of the far ranging competitions would lead to larger cities in an act of elimination and progression. Basically, the winner of the Inverness program would next go to Memphis, TN in a semi-final faceoff with other event winners from the Deep South. Then, the survivor of the Memphis elimination match would then proceed to a national showdown of regional winners in New York City at a later date in the year of 1958.

In reality, Johnny had performed in talent contests in California in his high school days and he was confident he could win the Inverness turkey shoot. His three cohorts being totally ignorant of the potential outcomes didn't think much of his chances at this event or anything in the future. Like I said, we were in the fray only as bystanders and casual observers. No long range soothsayers were we. We figured our friend's audition was just a one night stand.

To make a long story short, we, the SJC college partisans settled amid the crowd of neck craners, twisting in our seats as the frontline pianists and singers enthralled us with their renditions of classical music and Broadway production "sing a longs". Not a contestant, up to this point had performed a Rock N Roll piece…yep we were getting antsy and we could only imagine what our buddy, Johnny Russell was going to come up with to embarrass us when he made his stage entrance. We made sure we didn't make any noise in the way of displaying loyalty to our friend from sunny California. If the truth be known, we, the Rock N Roll set didn't want to be thought of as a bunch of rednecks supporting a big heavyset comical hillbilly singer and guitar picker. We were quiet as titmice hiding in a French hedgerow and we all sort of instinctively slumped down in our auditorium seats, so as not to be seen supporting any of the contestants, especially the big one who was soon to make his grand entrance.

At this point in the program, the cascade of entrants had not made any deep seated impressions on the Moorhead threesome seated in the 4th aisle about half way down the chair row near the center of the large room. To use a figure of exactness, our view was from the fifty yard line. Tyner and Thomas wanted to go outside for a smoke but they were not about to stumble through the legs of seated occupants between our chairs and the location of the aisle. Good thing they didn't because our good buddy, Johnny Russell was introduced to the crowd at that very moment and the multitudes never flinched…there was no response whatsoever…the audience looked askance at the corpulent cowboy, expecting mediocrity and they reacted accordingly.

And then true to his nature, the outsized performer started a lively banter with the audience and was soon strumming his guitar and singing a tune that I don't remember. As I sit here writing 56 years later, reflecting back on that night, I wonder if his performance included, "***In a Mansion stands my Love***", a piece of work that he purportedly wrote in 1958 and was later recorded by Jim Reeves? I don't know…maybe the other guys can remember if that was his signature entrée that evening in tiny Inverness.

I would say the audience as a whole responded warmly to his performance but it was in no way earth shattering. They clapped reverently but nobody whistled or hooted at the conclusion of his singing. He took leave of the stage and several more performers followed his act to round out the program.

And then for the finale, the judges announced the winner and guess who...yep, to his entourage's shocked disbelief, Johnny was "the man" who took home the bacon that night five decades ago.

With the winner's check in hand, Johnny gently placed his revered guitar in the trunk of Tyner's automobile and plopped down on the passenger side of the tilting vehicle all abeam with relief and pride. And we were with him all the way...we were hoping some of the limelight shining on the big winner would somehow deflect some sprites of luminance over our obscure smiley faces ☺.

Back in Moorhead, we went straight to the pool hall and Tyner, the money man, bought Johnny a Pabst Blue Ribbon beer and we (with our Cokes) all toasted him for his winning performance. Lack of legal tender was the reason we had Cokes and not beer. As we sat around discussing the next step in our star's march to fame (that would take place in Memphis in a couple of weeks), we were all gung-ho to make the trip and give Johnny our loyal support. We were not accustomed to associations with accomplished folk, so it made the adventure more surreal and tempting, in essence; we all felt a surge in ego as we basked in Johnny's good fortune and the benefits that went with it. It was brainless to assume that attitude but we did.

The planning of the trip to Memphis was in full bloom when out of the blue Johnny's bubble of destiny got busted or so it seemed at the time. To our dismay and sadness, word came from California that Johnny's father was critically ill, necessitating Johnny Russell's return to his home in Fresno. He never said goodbye and he never returned to the Moorhead campus. I think he intended to come back but the severity of his father's sickness forbade his return to a school located 2000 miles away.

Without being redundant, I can safely say I never laid physical eyes on John Bright's sizeable frame again. After he left Moorhead in despondency on that October night in 1958, and as I moved on with my life away from Moorhead, his memory faded into oblivion. I didn't know what became of him in that far off land of California. Then in the late 1970s I caught sight of him on a Country and Western themed television show and proudly announced to my wife "hey that's ole John Bright Russell...he and I were good buddies in my younger days in grammar school and junior college." Well I'll be dog gone, now I can say I know a big-time celebrity to which I can put an actual real life face to (as in flesh and blood), a person whom I actually arm wrestled, played football, camped out and spent the night with.

Later in the 1980s he was a frequent guest of Ralph Emory on TNN and I watched him perform on those occasions and took great pleasure in his success. I thought it would be appropriate to imbed this remembrance in a passage of this total story since the memory of its occurrence is still keen in my mind. In capturing the events of my college days at SJC, any references to the march of time would be incomplete if I were to omit the Johnny Russell story. Johnny is now dead but the following bio sheds some light on where his trail led after his short-lived college days in 1958 came to a poignant close.

John Bright Russell was born in ***Sunflower County, Mississippi****, January 23, 1940. Russell's family moved to Fresno,*

California from his hometown of Moorhead, Mississippi, when he was twelve years old. Even then his goals were centered on country music. He was both a songwriter and performer as he sang and played the guitar. Jim Reeves heard his first record, '"In A Mansion Stands My Love" (for Radio Records when he was 18), and recorded the song as the back side of "He'll Have To Go." Other early Russell compositions included Loretta Lynn's' "Two Mules Pull This Wagon" and the Wilburn Brothers' "Hurt Her Once For Me." Russell was working on a song about Hollywood but a chance remark," They're gonna put me in the movies", enabled him to complete it as "Act Naturally." Russell's co-writer, Vonnie Morrison, placed the song with Buck Owens and it became a number one US country hit.

"Act Naturally" was recorded by the Beatles with Ringo Starr on lead vocals for their ***"Help"!*** *Album, and was also the backside of their US number one hit, "Yesterday". Russell, who had recorded as a sideline for MGM and ABC-Paramount, took his own career seriously when he signed with Chet Atkins for RCA in 1971. He had US country hits with "Catfish John", "The Baptism of Jesse Taylor", "She's In Love with A Rodeo Man" and, most significantly, "Rednecks, White Socks and Blue Ribbon Beer", which became an anthem in the South. "I was appearing on Charley Pride's road show", said Russell, "and he wouldn't let me sing the song cause he thought it was racial". Russell did not write his biggest RCA singles. He explains, "I like singing people songs and as I tend to write hurting love songs, I never wrote the kind of songs that were right for me." Russell's 1977 single "Obscene Phone Call" was banned by several US radio stations. In 1978 he moved to Mercury and his singles included "While the Choir Sang the*

Hymn, I Thought Of Her", "You'll Be Back Every Night In My Dreams" and"Song Of The South".

George Strait had a US country number one hit in 1984 with Russell's "Let's Fall to Pieces Together" and Gene Watson did well with "I Got No Reason Now For Going Home". Although Johnny Russell's name was known only to die-hard fans in England, he was a showstopper at the 1985 Wembley country music festival with his Burl Ives-styled personality and humor (Ives did, in fact, record a Russell song, "Mean Mean Man"). Russell, a heavy man, made this opening remark," can you all see me at the back"? which was a winner; a successful tour in the United Kingdom with Boxcar Willie followed. A heart attack put Russell out of action for some time, but he returned to Nashville as a songwriter and singer.

In 1985 Russell became a member of the Grand Ole Opry. Hal Durham of the Opry, once said, "Johnny consistently delights the Grand Ole Opry audiences with his unique style of singing and comedy. He is an outstanding showman who carries on our tradition of quality entertainment here at the Opry."

Johnny Russell died on July 3rd, 2001 at the age of 61.

Awards

- *Grammy Nomination-"Male Vocalist of the Year"*
- *BMI Achievement Awards*
- *Nashville Song Writers Association-2 of the top 15 Songs of the Year*
- *RCA Records-"Golden Boot Award"*
- *ASCAP-Awards of Merit*
- *R.O.P.E.-"Lifetime Achievement as an Entertainer" 1995*

As a footnote, I am compelled to add that John Bright proved to be an altruistic and caring soul who never forgot his home town as demonstrated by his later in life charity to Moorhead and its residents. Over many years in the late Twentieth Century, John Bright and many of his friends from Nashville came back to Moorhead on an annual basis and held concerts for the people of the Delta. He also established a college scholarship foundation at Mississippi Delta Community College (remembered as SJC) to facilitate a means to provide educations for needy students of the region.

Earlier in this story I said John Bright left SJC in 1958 and never returned. But I stand to be corrected on that misrepresentation because in actuality, John Bright did in fact come back to his old college town in the Delta, albeit not to acquire an education but to deliver educations. To reward his good works, the community of Moorhead installed a large sign at the town's northern entrance on Highway 3, claiming John as a native son. The sign remained there for a good many years but in the current time, if my last visit to Moorhead is correctly recalled; I believe the sign no longer stands.

Part Nine

In 1958, the interminable heat of summer and early fall had now dissipated into a refreshing coolness that spanked the nights of late September and early October. The sparsely dotting of trees in the Delta slowly took on the elegance of muted yellow, orange and red. The color distinction of leaves affixed to the indigenous poplar, oak and sweet gum trees was not as perfect as one would see in pictures of upstate foliage in the hills of northern Mississippi or northern Alabama but in its own right, the Delta arbors and Sumacs held their own subtle form of perfection painted by nature's own handless brush strokes. You know…sometimes one has to fabricate their own sense of beauty from lowly surroundings which topically may not have exacted worthy praise from strangers up north. In my humble opinion, in the transition from summer to fall, our Delta village and countryside had gradually metamorphosed into a veritable pumpkinpatchland of straw and ocher. In my view, there was no other way to describe it. I'm sure a lot of the Moorhead natives didn't see it that way and I'm definitely sure Dowdy, the football player from Florida could find no redemption in the appeal of leaf pigments on the SJC campus during this time of year in the deep south. But the prettiness was there if one had the inclination to acknowledge it.

Despite living with my family out on Sheffield Road, my college experience was rolling along substantively. I was attending classes every day and sweeping up style points afforded by the accoutrements of academia. Add a little Greenwood carousing to that mix and one could easily see why a country schoolboy of eighteen lunar rotations multiplied by twelve was enjoying a most auspicious jumpstart in his race to acquire a higher education. Even though I was not a devotee of concentrated study and the burning of midnight oil, I nevertheless was broadening my perspective by busying myself with ample classroom participation, notwithstanding the fact that most of my knowledge assimilation came, not from elbow grease, but by osmosis and by rubbing elbows with smart people.

Our **Western Civilization** class was a son of a gun. Taught by Mr. McCarty, any student who let his mind wander and who failed to take notes was a lost goose from day one. That was me, that guy, Mr. Who, just referred to. But let me explain…I did enjoy History and made various feeble attempts to absorb as much of the professor's discourse as my ADD would allow. Mr. McCarty's credentials were impressive (his wall held diplomas taken from Tulane, University of Texas & University of Georgia). He lectured his forty pupil sized classes in a rapid fire of erudite terminology and phraseology that sailed over my head like a homerun hit over a pecan tree in a cow pasture baseball game. I struggled enormously but I was able to maintain a C average which I thought was pretty darn good for a hoemeister whose vocabulary could be distinguished as mostly monosyllabic. Customary words of my ilk, for example; "suppertime", "betcha", "molasses", "cornpone", "lespedeza", "red-vines" and the like, rarely issued from McCarty's stern voice box… instead uncommon ten dollar words like Cro-Magnum, primogeniture, regency, Hapsburgs, Armada, etc. glided off the high stucco ceilings like a football yell resonating through a megaphone. At the close of each lecture, it was necessary for the confused sodbusters to beat a path to the school library and thumb through a big pedestaled Webster to relieve some of their ignorance relating to those natty historical catchwords.

But I wasn't alone in my classroom deficiency…my cohort, Thomas M. was in the same class with me and he suffered too. My ADD was probably classified as a chronic case and my cousin's an acute one. In reality, neither of us had the disease…we were just lazy and undisciplined when it came to schooling. Our efforts to learn a course of study was flawed from the get go. There were just too many other distractions to occupy our undeveloped and peanut sized brains. In the realm of "isms"…upon closer examination, one could also diagnose the likelihood and presence of hormonal hyperactivity as being a causal factor in our inability to be good students. For proof of that assertion, one only had to look closely at our densely extruded whiskers which by that time had proliferated to coarseness in the extreme.

On the other hand there was one subject that I found I could excel in and that was a Physical Education class taught by Coach Randall, SJC's head football coach. Football was the science he taught and he was brilliant. He had a beautiful handwriting style and his diagrams of Xs and Os were always perfectly aligned and his accompanying lectures, loaded with wit, were attention grabbing, at least to me, they were.

Coach Randall had one of the most profound southern drawls that I have ever heard to that day and since. He could wax poetically in football jargon and the random witticisms thrown into his dissertations were uncommonly hilarious although I'm not sure he meant them to be. He caught my attention on the very first day and I was hooked on the science of football. Too, this funny man had a Bear Bryant/Woody Hayes personae and he didn't put up with any bull crap…period. That style of teaching back in the 1950s was very effective and I latched on to every word that Coach Randall spouted. He was intimidating but he talked my language.

Remember, I had a yearning to be a coach and Physical Education was my main course of study to be. As circumstances started to stack up in the fall semester of 1958, the next chapter of my Junior College experience unfolded thusly:

My younger brother, Benny, a Moorhead Grammar School eighth grade student had reported for Peewee football practice on this day in mid to late September of that eventful year. Being fairly large for his age and having played organized football since fifth grade, he was expected to be one of the stalwarts of the team. After their first practice, he came home and informed me that Mr. Bishop, the school principal was trying to coach the team by himself. Consumed with the thought that here... on a serving platter was an opportunity for me to pick up some experience as a coach at the Peewee level and to further my objective of becoming a coach, I vowed to go to Mr. Bishop the next day and offer my services. True to form, the next day after my last class let out at SJC, outfitted with my normal mode of transport, I hoofed the mile and a quarter over to the grammar school playground, accosted Mr. Bishop in his coat and tie and servantly asked him if I could help him coach the team.

He accepted my offer and in no time at all, in fact, that same day I got down in the trenches with the young 12, 13 and 14 year old players and made an attempt to organize the ragtag bunch into some semblance of a team. Unfortunately, Mr. Bishop was an intellectual and knew practically nothing about football, therefore other than running the youngsters through calisthenics (side straddle hop, knee bends & pushups) and some tackling/blocking drills...standard team concepts..., like having a playbook and determining who were the best boys at what positions was missing from the school principal's practice scheme. As a carryover from the previous season when the team was coached by a Coach Randall protégée, Bill Hood, a well versed ex-football player, the current batch of players had resumed their positions from the previous year. So, all in all, the team was pretty much set based on the remnants left from the year before.

Because I had followed the team closely due to my brother's participation the year before, I knew all the players and had a good estimation of their capabilities at the various positions. With some minor tweaking, two teams with backups were quickly constructed from a selection of about 30 kids of assorted size and age.

God bless him --- Mr. Bishop gave me full rein in this aspect of coaching the team and I reveled in his trust. I had always prided myself on being an original thinker and I put my inventive mind to work dreaming up creative plays that Coach Randall would have been proud of.

Armed with a little knowledge, a creative mind and a slop jar full of enthusiasm, using a combination of plays that I remembered from high school and plays of my own design based on Coach Randall's diagrams and logic in Phys ED, a playbook was put together and printed on lithographic paper. Soon thereafter, the teams had learned their plays and scrimmaging was the menu of the day. The key to a good team was good material, which we had and refinement of our few plays through execution, execution, execution. Usually by the time I walked from the SJC campus to the grammar school playground, Mr. Bishop had the preliminary warm-ups already completed and I would walk the boys through the plays and then through live scrimmages. We ran our plays from a winged - T formation and Roger Dale Reeves was our quarterback (makes me wonder where he is today). Benny was our ace running back and he was a workhorse. Not one to brag but I'll have to admit the team was sound and structured. Good athletes prevailed and we went through a six game schedule, including Indianola, Ruleville, Linn, Sunflower, Belzoni and Inverness and didn't lose a game, however one tie blemished a perfect season. The intoxication of success offered by the chance to mold these young athletes into a well-oiled football machine solidified my desire to be a coach at the high school level even more than I imagined. I could hardly wait to get over to the grammar school every day.

Man, I had a lot on my plate. I was still living at home, helping with farm chores, going to school, trying to study a little at night, working at **Colliers** gas station on weekends, coaching peewee football, taking in all the SJC and SAHS football games at home and away and serving in John Bright Russell's retinue of handlers. My head was dizzy with options and staring me in the face, I would have to move into the SJC athletic dorm. As a scholarship requirement, all the basketball players had to be housed in the athletic dorm prior to starting basketball practice in late October. This turn of events would compromise my ability to coach my adolescent gridiron upstarts every school day. On the other hand, with the cooperation of Coach Jimmy Bellipanni, I was given permission to miss basketball practice on the dates of our final two peewee games which allowed me to be on the sidelines with the team for the season's wrap up. My absences only pertained to games and not every day practice. At that point in the season, the boys on the peewee team as a unit were regimented enough to practice the whole of the play book under the older educator's supervision.

In lieu of missing basketball practice, Coach Jimmy required that I report to the gym during a couple of study hall hours to run wind sprints in solo to make up for the conditioning exercises that were skipped. That was my just compensation for helping develop future recruits for SAHS and SJC. But I didn't mind, I loved coaching and I loved playing basketball...it was well worth the time and effort. I look back on those days with warmth and affection. I presume that's why, at my current age of doddery...my remembrances of those events are still so clear and firmly rooted.

Part Ten

Sometime in mid to late October, the SJC athletic department sent out a letter to the (half scholarship) basketball recruits informing them to go by the Dean of Men's office to pick up their room assignments at the athletic dorm. I believe there were only two local student athletes who fell in that category. Besides me and myself, the other guy was Charles Boyer, an ex-teammate on my home town basketball team from 1956 -1958. He lived up at Blaine and as destiny would have it, we ended up roommates in that fall of 1958. As a consequence of Boyer's father being a salaried plantation manager, we tended to have something in common or at least in the likeness that we lived in an agricultural setting, we both could relate to the other's rural circumstances and agrarian life style.

All the rooms in the old athletic dorm were small, dark, and austere. Each room was equipped with (2) single (chigger infested) beds, one table, two straight back chairs, a doorless closet and a single overhead light. The amenities were Spartan but we didn't notice. From where we came from or I should say, where I came from, these newly found accommodations were an improvement over my own residential digs out on Sheffield road. I think Boyer's home boudoir, was a little more upscale than mine, so I assumed he was not as taken with his new digs as I was but he didn't complain.

It didn't take us a long time to move in...a few clothes, underwear, socks, toiletries, towels, books, bed sheets, pillows and blankets and that was about it. Our only shoes were on our feet so that eliminated the need for a shoe rack. All said, it was obvious to prying eyes that we travelled lightly. Heat was provided via steam radiator and cooling by a medium sized window. Nope, there was no air conditioning...ha, are you kidding? The room had a door but no lock...thievery and privacy was a zero concern.

In the middle of each dorm floor sat a large ceramic bath house and latrine that accommodated showering, shaving and grooming for the occupants of the hall. That was well and good but in the early morning hours the place was a madhouse.

I don't remember but there must have been laundry rooms in the dormitory housing units but I do recall that my mother took care of my dirty clothes on my weekend visits. At least I left the soiled stuff with her and picked up the laundried garb on my next visit to the home front.

Once Boyer and I got settled in, we discovered the locations of the other basketball player's rooms and we made visitation rounds as soon as we learned all the Bob Cousy wannabees were housed on the first and second floors. As the fall semester started and progressed into October, we had made prior connections with the boys on the team by means of class co-attendance and participation in pickup games at the gymnasium. Several of the Mississippi natives were already familiar to us because we had played against them in high school. The out of state guys were lesser known but at least we knew them on sight and knew where they came from.

The Registrar, Mrs. Scroggins had given us meal tickets that allowed us to take all three meals every school day and on weekends at the large School Cafeteria situated next to the Girl's dormitory. The meal ticket was of great value to me because up to that time, I had to dine in the canteen at noon on a measly $.25 allowance which didn't provide adequate nourishment for a high octane sodbuster, student, coach, carouser and athlete. My weight had plateaued at a gangly 155 pounds, but as I said before in a previous episode, when I got that meal ticket, it wasn't long before my weight, jumped up to a fleshy 175 lbs. The meals got even better, when the basketball team started practice and was allowed to go on a "training table" at which point evening meals for the members of the team were upgraded to a well-stocked meat and potato menu in lieu of a lesser fare provided for the regular housed students and faculty. When football season ended, the basketball players moved to the "training table" and the football players had to step aside and take their places with the ordinary folk and their ordinary food.

Boyer and I, being of similar backgrounds made us well-suited roommates and we were happy with our new lodging arrangement. I guess it was somewhat analogous to being in the Army without the harsh regimentation that soldiers have to put up with, but, we too, had a fairly strict schedule to maintain, now that basketball practice had started. Our days started at 6:00 AM with a shower and a shave, breakfast at the cafeteria, classes starting at 8:00 AM and ending at 3:00 PM, basketball practice 3:30 PM til 5:30 PM, followed by showers, then dinner at 6:00 til 7:00PM. We were free to do whatever we pleased after the team at the training table had their fill and broke up from the last meal of the day. Routinely we went back to our room to study for a while before walking over to the canteen or strolling to downtown Moorhead where a pool hall and movie theater offered a splinter of entertainment if one could afford the costs. That was pretty much how our days went down on week days…then on weekends…Boyer and I would go home to get our laundry taken care of by our mothers. It was not a bad routine; in fact we enjoyed the break from parental oversight, although admittedly, oversight of a different nature took over as we were now under the directorship of Coach Jimmy, a bachelor who resided in the same athletic dorm as his young recruits. It was his job to enforce housekeeping rules and to make sure an 11:00 PM curfew was obeyed. He did his job with relish and he didn't cut us any slack. It was necessary for him to be authoritarian and he bore that responsibility with a definite self-assurance as evidenced by his frequent spontaneous room inspections. More than once, my bed making proficiency was challenged by the drillmaster and I had to redo the layers of sheets and covers from scratch. Likewise, Boyer suffered the same exposure from Coach Jimmy's unannounced shakedowns…I really think his housekeeping skills were worse than mine and he paid the price same as me.

It was really great to be out on our own away from family, although if one cared to fairly assess our self-sufficiency it would gather some doubt as to how truly free we were. Even though we reveled in the thought that we had flown the coop, in truth, it was a delusion. We were still reliant on family a lot more than we would admit. Living life on campus had its rewards but to maintain our scholarships, our class grades and averages had to be maintained at a passing level and quality. So that meant we had to hit the books every night but to be perfectly honest, we didn't do it with any eagerness and our education suffered. However at this juncture in our first semester, we were not far enough along in the school year to be worried about grades but at the end of the session in January, we certainly moved into a higher gear as far as putting in study hours to pull up our grades.

Our extracurricular activities were much more important…for example: Boyer had a steady girlfriend still in high school and even though I didn't confess to having a steady girl, I was making time with a little gal over at Greenwood. Because I didn't have a car, I was dependent on Thomas or Billy for letting me double date with them. Rarely did we go to

Greenwood on a week night, so my excuse for not hitting the books with any regularity because of a girl was a poor excuse. My problem was more related to indolence and lack of focus.

Part Eleven

The SJC gymnasium located between the canteen and football stadium was a big boxy building with seating on both sides of the basketball court. The seats were nothing more than elongated stair stepped box pews with no backrests. Below the eastside stands were located dressing rooms for the residing high school and junior college basketball players. Each player was assigned a chicken wire locker to store their one pair of Converse tennis shoes, white socks, practice jersey, a jockey strap and shorts. There were no individual locks for those lockers but the locker room's entrance door was locked at the end of each practice session. Although there was virtually no fear of someone pilfering our jockey straps and practice togs, we were very possessive of our canvas Converse shoes. If I recall the shoes were provided by the athletic dept. at no cost to the student athlete but if we lost them it was the responsibility of the individual to bear the cost of replacement. Thrown in the mix of freebies were game uniforms and warm-ups which were handed out by our team manager before each game. The athletic department also took care of keeping our practice gear washed and dried but not necessarily wrinkle free. It didn't matter since in practice we didn't care if our togs were wrinkled to start…it was just a temporary thing…because in a matter of minutes the apparel was sweat soaked and skin draped. Jockey Itch was an affliction that ran rampant in the humid and moldy locker rooms and a large bottle of salicylic acid was made available for dousing the player's offending and affected areas. I'll have to admit without getting too descriptive, the application of acid pierced the naked air with temporary groans of agony. In other words the pain was quite severe but the treatment was necessary to control the patches of dermatitis. Enough said about jockey itch.

Visiting teams were provided with similar temporary facilities on the opposite side of the gym. Besides ticket booths and concession stands on each side of the building, the Sunflower Junior College basketball arena as described, pretty much characterized the unpretentious compactness of the basketball arena. The little gym would be the venue for showcasing the basketball skills of SJC players and the rest of the junior college circuit in this year of 1958/1959. I would guess the seating capacity of the place didn't exceed 500 people. Although it was called Vandiver Gymnasium in honor of a former college president, the facility served both the college and high school teams for many years in the 1940s and 1950s.

Part Twelve

And in this 1930s vintage gym stood twelve young men assembled to start basketball practice in the fading days of October 1958. The word had gone out from Coach Bellipani that all the boys on scholarship were to be ready for the first practice session on this prescribed day and true to the timetable, we were dressed in our practice shorts raring to go. However, much to our displeasure, that practice session did not include a typical round of casual layups and shoot arounds. As a matter of record, I don't believe nary a basketball showed up on the court that day. Conditioning was Coach Jimmy's main objective that late afternoon and he had a series of exercises lined up to test his troop's physical shape and stamina.

First on the agenda, was a series of wind sprints from one end of the court and back? After about twenty of those tongue hangers, he made us run backwards for a like number, after that, all were made to run zigzag around and through chairs set up on the court. Then out came the old medicine ball, a large stuffed leather encased rounded footrest that weighed maybe ten lbs. Pairs of players were made to dart down the planks and back passing the medicine ball between them at neck breaking speed. At the conclusion of the medicine ball adventure, Coach had us doing a "reaction drill" based on his hand movements...away from his body meant retreat, close to chest meant charge, hands and arms to the left or right signaled us to move laterally with the body facing him and the feet shifting side by side.

Frictional damage to the feet was excruciating. It was all very fatiguing and painful for a bunch of out of shape 18 to 19 year old athletes. But to our mentor, there was logic to the madness he was heaping on us...yes; Coach was out to prove his contempt for our lack of training leading up to this day. In his farsighted judgment, and rightfully so, he thought his raw recruits would have enough sense to start a conditioning regimen on their own a couple of weeks preceding the start of practice. I don't know about the other fellows but I confess I didn't have the foggiest foresight to initiate such a prudent undertaking and I paid the price. Likewise, there were another six or so tenderfoots (no pun intended) who suffered as ignominiously as did this shortsighted chronicler. The cagy sophomores on the team made it ok owing to their toughened preconditioning and preparation. The moronic freshmen contingent thought they were in good enough shape to slide by but it was a given that ignorance seemed to pervade the young mind more than perceptiveness did. No doubt, that bit of wisdom displayed by the older guys obviously had escaped our absorption.

Hearing Coach Jimmy blow his whistle and announce "that's it for the day…you ballerinas be back tomorrow afternoon at the same time and we'll pick up where we left off today", I hobbled off the court and sat down in front of my locker, afraid to pull off my brand new Converse high top sneakers to see what my aching and bloody feet looked like. Taken aback by the sight of destructed skin on the underside of my bipedal locomotors, I thought to myself "somehow I've got to medicate these skinless stumps to counteract some of the soreness overnight to be ready for practice tomorrow." Otherwise, I won't be able to practice in 24 hours and of course Coach's take on the matter would not be pretty. He didn't put up with malingerers and the expected abuse from his windpipes would be deafening. Of course I was not faking it…my feet were mortally wounded and I would not be able to practice for a couple of days. Some of the other freshmen were in the same boat (sounds of puking could be heard from the commode area) but none of the others had their feet worn out like me. I chided myself for not applying *Tough Skin* to my feet before practice started that day but I thought my feet would stand up to the pounding but I had not anticipated all the slipping, sliding and pivoting especially in a brand new pair of rubberized shoes. By the way, *Tough Skin* was a product that could be applied to the skin to provide a resinous membrane that could prevent blistering.

I acknowledged the fact that my goose was cooked...but I was game to try an antidote and I applied a healthy coating of Iodine to my raw undersoles and after the stinging abated, I put on clean white socks. The next morning, I could hardly walk but I made all my classes. As practice time neared in the late evening, my apprehension was so palpable, that I broke out in a clammy sweat, knowing that Coach Jimmy would throw a tantrum and he did. I got a real bonafide ass chewing but after he looked at my feet, he became somewhat sympathetic to my condition and reluctantly conceded that I could skip the heavy frictional drills that 2nd day of practice. Despite his temporary restraint, his ire rose to a high level after he had time to think about my thoughtless disregard for my preseasonal unconditioned feet. He decided to make me a scapegoat before my teammates and he held me up as a good example of laziness and poor preparation. I felt belittled as my new teammates grinned knowingly that they had escaped his rage and that ole Billy Ray was the object of his dismay at the moment. There was no doubt... I was the pariah of the day but I knew Coach Jimmy very well and knew him to be a fair man...if I could only make it through this 2nd practice day, in short order he would be on somebody else's case and the headlights would be removed from the errant boy who was suffering from hashed bunions. With my ears ringing, I hobbled out on the court for that 2nd day of practice and made the best of a tarnished reputation that surely did not get me off to a good start with my college coach. In a couple of days I was good as new…the resiliency of youth is mind boggling…however my mentor and coach didn't soon forget my little peccadillo.

It was reassuring to know that those guys who were doing all that puking in the latrines at the end of that first practice would soon get their comeuppance. They would get their day in the limelight because I knew their mischievous predispositions would soon get the best of them and I also knew Coach Jimmy liked to distribute his cruelty over a broad spectrum of mostly freshman neophytes. Admittedly, he was not as harsh with the second year upperclassmen.

After two or three days of practice, it became obvious to the clueless bystander that the three sophomore transfers from Delta State College were destined to be first stringers and the other two open positions were up for grabs or so it seemed. Actually that was a misstatement because another sophomore, Tommie Edwards a holdover from the 1957 SJC team was almost certain to be our starting point guard. Although he was only about 5' 10", he was a seasoned ball handler and could hit the basket with a jump shot that had a 50% accuracy probability.

Speaking of the threesome from Delta State…the tallest of the group was Bo Vickers who stood 6' 6" and was our only legitimate center. The slim lad from Belzoni had a deadly left and right handed hook shot and was an excellent rebounder.

Buddy Jones from Ruleville was another left hander with a good shooting eye. If I remember correctly, he played forward and complemented Vickers and Franks, the other forward who possessed good rebounding fundamentals. Rounding out the three upper classmen was the aforementioned Donnie Franks from Gunnison, Mississippi who stood a slender 6'2" in height and had tremendously large hands. I don't remember him being a deadeye shooter but he mopped up the rebounds that Vickers missed or was not in position to make. Donnie's excellent rebounding ability was his strong suit and it was paramount for the team to have a well-schooled rebounder because overall the team was not blessed with much height. Of course in those days, none of the junior college teams had much height…on a given year in the 1950s…6'3" was an average height of the big boys in our league. Most of the back courtsmen were in the 5'8" – 5'10" range.

The fifth position on the 1958 SJC team, which was the "off guard" position remained unfixed and became a revolving door of different players for the entire season. A boy from Kentucky, Jim Helton, was the first pretender to settle into that position but oddly enough he decided to return home before the first semester ended. Lefty McDaniel, Gene Pope, Charles Boyer and Bill Callison took turns filling that position but after the dust had settled, I remember Lefty, whose home was Greenwood, Mississippi played the most due to his gritty athleticism and spunk. Coach Jimmy liked guys who hustled and Lefty always gave his all.

A Belzoni native, Pope had played with Vickers in high school but was a grade behind our tall center and was still green at the college level of play. Gene was a good enough basketball player but his playful antics, practical joking and less than serious attitude kept him in the Coach's doghouse. Remember, a while back I mentioned some mischievous teammates who puked their guts out after that first practice session...well, I won't mention any names but a particular freshman youngster from Belzoni was one of them.

Callison came down from Ohio at midyear and he and Pope hit it off from the start becoming immediate pals and a center of aggravation for our short and rotund mentor. They were pretty much bench warmers like Boyer and me but that didn't keep them from flirting with girls in the stands especially on our road trips where in some locations the bleacher seats came within a couple of feet of the visitors bench on the court sidelines. While our coach was engaged in trying to win a game, the miscreants on the bench were making eyes at the girls and passing notes. They had no idea what was going on with the game, but it didn't really matter because they had no expectations of entering the fray.

To round out the 1958 group, a lanky kid from Columbus, Georgia named Irwin Sanborn enjoyed some success on the team but aside from that, his fun laced wisecracking left a mark on me that made me remember him 53 years later. Unfortunately, he left SJC after the first semester and never returned to the Moorhead campus but his sense of humor being his most memorable feature stayed with me all those years.

Four months ago, when I started this storied undertaking, I referenced my old "1958 Retrospect" and ran across Sanborn's picture. It occurred to me that this long removed individual came from Columbus, Georgia which is not terribly far from my current residence in south Alabama. Proceeding with a hunch that perhaps in his career and life, Irwin didn't veer too far away from his roots I went to my computer resources and located his name and phone number in Hoover, Alabama, only a couple hundred miles up Interstate 65 from my home in Spanish Fort, Alabama. To make a long story short, we reconnected, met for lunch at a halfway point in Greenville, AL and are now sharing e-mails and ancient history. He goes by the name "Jay Sanborn" and I fully understand his preference for that sobriquet in place of "Irwin". I never was crazy about my given name, Billy Ray, either.

But back to the hazy days of 1958...after several weeks of practice, the team coalesced into five key players to form a core team. I am pained to admit, but fully understand why my inclusion was not in dispute. Aware that my talent was not ascribed to be of first team timbre, it didn't really bother me at that time for I knew the caliber of players on the first team far exceeded my physical stature, abilities and experience. The first team with the exception of one player was comprised of second year hoopsters and for that reason most of the freshman players didn't quibble about their secondary roles on the squad. We were for the most part happy to be on the team and happy to be chewing down on rubbery gravy steaks every night at the SJC training table.

In mid-November, all the golden foliage of the numerous trees on campus lay clustered on the ground beneath nuded tree limbs. After all… it was that time of year when frost was a nightly occurrence and frost bitten grass offered a crunchy feel to one's shoe soles as students crisscrossed the campus byways. All the students had now settled into fixed routines and the newness of the college experience had become somewhat relaxed and boring.

Although most of the monogrammed jacket wearing students at SJC felt the campus scene was "old hat" by now, the members of the basketball team were getting ready to enjoy the fruits of their labor by embarking on a trip to north Mississippi to take on some of their junior college rivals. We were very much looking forward to that trip because it meant we would experience some travel, some game activity and some views into the way the other junior colleges appeared in comparison to our collegiate setting in the Yazoo Delta.

The only thing that distinguished the Athletic Department bus from the prevalent yellow buses seen on all the elementary and high school campuses in 1958 were the school colors red, black and gray. A recently purchased bus, sporting the SJC colors had been painted at a body shop in Indianola and delivered to the Moorhead campus for use in the coming football season. Sporting a snazzy "**Sunflower Junior College Trojans**" logo on each side of the elongated vehicle, the football and basketball teams drew the attention of bystanders as it rolled through the little villages of Mississippi enroute to ballgames staged in the various small town communities that were home to the dozen or more junior colleges in the Magnolia state,

In mid to late November, I don't remember exactly...the boys of winter, filed into the red, black and gray bus with their little carry bags loaded with a couple changes of clothes. Coach Bellipanni sat up front in the bus next to the driver who was a student athlete...a football player from Inverness who was picking up a few dollars in compensation for transporting the basketball team to destinations north of Highway 82 up in the upper reaches of the State of Mississippi. In fact this first day out we were headed to Senatobia to play Northwest Mississippi Jr. College that very night....

In succession, like falling dominoes, we played games in Booneville (Northeast Mississippi J.C.), at Scooba (East Mississippi J.C.) and at Fulton (Itawamba J.C.) to complete a four game sweep on this particular outing. Of course, sweep is probably not the operative word in this case because a person reading this might misconstrue the team won all four games on that initial excursion. Nope...sorry to say but we lost all four games and I didn't play a lick. We really weren't that good. Our first stringers played hard in every game but if the truth were known, our team was patently outmanned in every encounter on that road trip. For example, Northeast JC had a heck of a player on their team named Vincent Del Negro, an All American junior college player. Upon graduation from the junior college ranks, he enrolled at Kentucky and played all-star hoops for Adolf Rupp for a couple of years. I believe he went on to play in the NBA.

A few weeks later, right before the Christmas Holidays excused the student body for a two week break from school, the SJC basketball team trekked up north again and decisively lost to the likes of the Ole Miss Freshman at Oxford. I don't remember much about the game but I can safely say I remember with great clarity the meal that Ole Miss fed the Delta boys that night. It was probably the most abundant and varied training table that any of the players on our scrawny team had ever set eyes on. On the same trip, the red, black and gray bus dropped down to Decatur and Ellisville, Mississippi and we played East Central and Jones Junior Colleges in their nice arenas. Without fail, all the facilities of our visitations were all superior to Sunflower J.C.'s little cracker box of a gym. If the reader is wondering…about the outcome of those games…once again…we lost those games too.

Our record at the Christmas break was something like 8 losses and 1 win…our single win coming at the expense of Holmes J.C. located in Goodman, Mississippi near Lexington.

I must say, the road trips were enjoyable…it gave us a break from school and the country boys on the team were treated to some venues and sights they had heretofore never seen. The group as a whole was very compatible and the boys enjoyed a camaraderie that laid down good memories for long range safekeeping. I believe the single most prominent element that brought us together was our playful attitudes. It seemed that everyone was a practical jokester and no one was averse to "doing as much mischief to others as one would expect to collect for themselves". I don't remember anyone ever resorting to anger from being a recipient of a joke.

Bill, Lefty McDaniel and Wayne Granbury, SJC campus, Early 1959

Returning from the Christmas Holidays in early January 1959 brought a resumption of play for the team that did not end until late February. We played most of the junior college teams in southern Mississippi which included Hinds JC, Co-Lin JC, Southwest JC, and Pearl River JC. But on second thought, maybe we didn't play Pearl River and Perkinston JC, two destinations located at the foremost southern tip of geographical Mississippi. That may have been too far to travel considering our meager budget.

However, one highlight of the second half of the season was our trip to Starkville to take on the highly touted Mississippi State freshman team. Our game was a warm-up preliminary to the varsity Mississippi State game with Southeastern Louisiana Institute.

After a crushing loss, the Delta roundballers were invited to watch the talented Mississippi State team maul the Division II SLI team. At that time in 1959, Mississippi State was a national power and Bailey Howell was their top drawing card. Coach Babe McCarthy, Mississippi State's highly regarded coach made an appearance and it was a great treat when he entered the visitors' locker room after the JC game and shook everyone's hand. He was known as the only SEC coach that could beat Adolph Rupp's Kentucky team on occasion. It was a rarity for an SEC team to beat Kentucky because they normally went undefeated in conference play and were perennial national championship contenders. Babe McCarthy was riding high at the time and I thought it was terribly impressive to shake his hand that night. Another highlight for the ole boy from Moorhead was my scoring four points at the end of the game (yes, Coach Jimmy sent in his scrubs after the starting five got behind by double digits with a few minutes to go in the game). I can in good faith make the claim that I swished in two jump shots in a legitimate SEC school arena without being called a liar. To tell the truth, I had forgotten about that bit of nostalgia until I started writing this part of the story. It was nothing to brag about but it was the highlight of my junior college basketball career.

And then as suddenly as it had started, the basketball season was over. Three of my teammates, Boyer, Sanborn and Helton, young men who had started practice with us in October had dropped out after the first semester ended in January 1959. The team, now down to nine members was a close knit aggregate and we departed the locker room scene that late February day with the satisfaction that those left standing retained a goodly stock of accreted memories, even though our season's won lost record was a disaster. But you know the old saying "it's not whether you win or lose, its how you play the game" was the only solace we could take away from the season of 1959 as far as winning was concerned. The nucleus of the team consisting of sophomores moved away the next school year to other small colleges, like Nichols State, Delta State and William Carey College. Vickers became an NAIA All American and in later years returned to Sunflower Junior College, by then renamed Mississippi Delta Junior College, to become Head Basketball coach. Donnie Franks went on to become a high school coach and administrator in south Alabama and the rest of the guys I'm not sure where they ended up. Wait a second, on second thought I do know that Tommie Edwards went on to Divinity school and became a minister. I'm not sure where Buddy Jones ended up but I think he went back to Delta State in Cleveland, Mississippi to finish his college education.

Owing to my half scholarship coupled with intentions of returning for a second year in the fall, I moved out of the athletic dorm, dejectedly surrendering my meal ticket and moved in with my Moore grandparents who lived out from Moorhead on a farm owned by my uncle Robert William Moore, a resident of Yazoo City. Once again just as I did in the early fall of 1958, I was riding the yellow county school bus to and from SJC every school day and my wonderful grandmother was plying my insatiable craving for food with good home cooking. Why would I be living with grandparents and not with my family who lived just three miles from Moorhead? Well, therein lies another digression that needs to be cleared up before the retelling of this history lesson unfolds into nothingness.

Part Thirteen

Although the event has been alluded to on several occasions in previous accountings, I need to go back in time to Early November, 1958.

The lives of the Troy Griffin family out on Sheffield Road had been inalterably disrupted by the failure of the 1958 cotton crop. Almost immediately... after the gathering of that pitiful crop had been quantified with predicted certainty the patriarch of the "B" boys (Bud, Bill, Ben and Bishop) left town in the old steer kissed 1952 Chevrolet and headed south in search of a paying job...his mantra being...any job will do...any exchange of labor that will provide a living wage for a family of six would certainly fill the bill.

He had his sights set on Baton Rouge, Louisiana, home of his brother-in-law Marvin Reeves who was married to his oldest sister, Zelma. Knowing my father's penchant for refusing to alert anyone of his comings and goings, it was seriously doubtful that he called Uncle Marvin to let him know of his plan to visit and the purpose of his mission.

As it so happens with most common decent folk like the Reeves family, they were happy to see him and gladly gave him room and board while he sought a job in Baton Rouge, a city of 100,000 people.

At this point, it was almost like Divine Providence had stepped into the breadline predicament. On the same day that my Dad arrived on Seneca Street in B.R. my gracious uncle sent him to **Jack's Cookie Company,** the factory where he worked as a nighttime security guard. As it turned out in what seemed to be perfect timing, the Company's personnel department, having just posted a job opening for a Grade I General Maintenance millwright and fitter, seized the opportunity to request the Mississippi job seeker fill out an application on the spot. Although he struggled with his writing he filled the app out to the best of his ability and signed it.

After returning to his brother-in-laws house, news of the maintenance job opening was casually mentioned to his Louisiana hosts. My uncle knew Troy was an all-around mechanical whiz, who possessed the knowledge and experience required to keep the cookie making equipment (pumps, mixers, conveyer belts, ovens, packagers, etc.) in the factory functioning without missing a beat. It certainly didn't hurt that the owner of the Willie Wonka assembly line was Uncle Marvin's good friend. In rapid succession, a telephone call to the owner from the uncle sealed the deal, sight unseen. Dad got the job and didn't have to take a physical examination. That's why I've always contended this miracle was a Godly intervention. Had that medical examination requirement been necessary, Dad's employment mission would have failed because of a six year old inguinal hernia.

Overjoyed and thankful, Troy Griffin returned to the Delta, loaded up a trailer with some odds of furniture, some clothes and cookware and returned to Baton Rouge with the wife and the two younger sons in tow.

To further establish the existence and probability of a divine intercession---let it be known that when Pete, one of Uncle Marvin's three sons, became aware of the Griffin's plight, he stepped forward to offer his home as a temporary living quarter for the displaced farm family. Blessed with Pete's and Edith's bigheartedness, the Griffins were welcomed to their home on Iroquois Street in north Baton Rouge. The arrangement gave Troy time to find and lease a rental house a few weeks later. Of course it was necessary for the new **Jack's Cookie** hiree to accumulate a couple of paychecks to bank enough money for a rental deposit. As luck would have it, Edith's mother owned a furnished two bedroom house on Duke Street, not far from Pete's house and it miraculously became vacant in early December of that year. That bit of good luck made for good timing. My folks now had a place to live and the brothers, Bud and Bill who were stranded in Moorhead now had a home to go to for the Christmas holidays. We were happy to have the opportunity to go the 350 miles to Baton Rouge and check out the sprawling city that sat along the banks of the Mississippi River. Furthermore, Pete and Edith, my parent's kindly hosts would be relieved of the imposition of two families residing in a one family dwelling. Their token of kindness during that period in 1958 will be remembered to the end of my being, without exception and forever more.

Back in Moorhead, Bud and I were suddenly scratching for enough loose change to pay our Greyhound bus fares from Kincade's Drug Store in Moorhead to the center of Downtown Baton Rouge come December 20th, 1958. Since I was no longer working at **Bill Collier's** gas station on Saturdays and Sundays due to my scholarship commitments and recurring road trips, I had to parlay a cash loan from Bud to fund my Christmas trip to Huey P. Long country. Making the trip even more interesting for the two college students was the complement of Bud's girl friend to the male travel party headed south. She in fact was going to New Iberia, Louisiana to spend Christmas with a sister who lived on the banks of Bayou Teche. The plan called for her sister to intercept her traveling sibling in Baton Rouge on the 21st and take her back to her home in the Bayou country.

That first trip to Louisiana was a blissful sendoff for the Griffin brothers. Never had I looked forward to an event so profoundly anticipated such as occurred on December 20th, 1958. That Greyhound bus trip was an all day affair that put the travel party in Baton Rouge around 7:00 PM a couple of hours after sundown. Our threesome was met by our cousin Pete and we were driven down Third Street (Baton Rouge's Main Street) for a bird's eye view of our new imposing hometown. Bud and I were overawed...the girl from Sunflower, Mississippi (population 200) I don't remember what she thought or what impressions she had of the Louisiana state capital. Pete gave us a touted overview of the downtown sights as we retreated to the Griffin's new home on north Baton

Rouge's Duke Street. Arriving at our home to be, we found it unpretentious, however, cozy and welcoming. Though she only had been in the house a bare few days, Mom had the place decorated in the colors of the holiday season with a nice fir tree shining as its centerpiece. Mom had displayed her normal beeline attention to having the place sharpened up for the travelers viewing pleasure. And she didn't disappoint.

It was a great Christmas. I had been homesick to see my family but before we could hardly unpack our cardboard suitcases, the vacation was over and we were back in the gray, frigid and rainy confines of the Yazoo Delta.

As sole occupant, Bud returned to the old modified shotgun house on Sheffield Road and I without a house to plant my feet returned to my modest co-habitated room at the SJC athletic dorm sans Boyer, my basketball playing roommate. After basking in all the family warmth and seasonal cheer for two weeks, it was a lonesome voyager entering a ghostly like dormitory building on that forlorn evening of my return to campus. There were only a few returnees present in the big almost vacant building that night and I must say my spirits were at low ebb.

But I got over it.

Back in fourth gear and as the first semester of my freshman year closed, my roommate, Charles Boyer packed up and left school, which in effect, was a revocation of his scholarship. His dropping out left me with a new roommate, a football player from Dublin, Mississippi named James Burchfield. He was a nice enough guy but he was very quiet and reserved. It was quite a contrast… from having a roommate as fun loving and undisciplined as Boyer to a room sharer as serious as James…it took some getting used to. But I must say, James was highly principled and worked hard at his studies. Makes me wonder where James is today and how his life turned out.

Part Fourteen

It was a time of reckoning, a time of thankfulness, and a time of tremendous change for the elder Griffins. Dad settled into his shift work job at the cookie factory and Mom placed the older boy in the nearest junior high school and the youngest child at an elementary school close to a thoroughfare that ran close to the new rent house.

Dad yearned for his rural way of life which was the only way his body and soul had drawn comfort from in his previous forty years of life. It was a new beginning in Baton Rouge for this reticent yet friendly man who struggled with the job regimens that were alien to his farm culture. Accustomed to rising at dawn to hit the fields with binding enthusiasm on hot summer days and the habitual milking of the cow on cold gray winter mornings, made the exchange for city life with the call for night work a tough walnut to crack and as might be expected he was not so captivated with his new job, but he knew his options were limited at this time in his life so he sucked it up and made the best of his temporary uprooting.

My mother adapted quickly to city life and promptly befriended the next door neighbors. She quickly settled into her housewifely duties which were devoid of farm chores…in fact, for her; it was a pleasure to be free of some of the unseemly farm drudgeries. She tried to humor her husband with tasty home cooked specialties before he trudged off to work in the middle of the night not happy with his circumstances but thankful for an income and a roof over his head.

Benny the oldest boy still at home enrolled at Istrouma Jr. High and immediately fell in with a group of young athletes who were just finishing up their football season. After participating in a few practices, the football coaches recognized his talent and started him on a weight lifting program. He loved it all and readily shed his homesickness for Moorhead. In short order, he joined the basketball team.

To keep me updated on his new life in Louisiana, Benny religiously wrote letters to me at my SJC address and to some of his ex-teammates on the Moorhead Grammar School team. The attention he was attracting from the Istrouma Junior High coaching staff was pleasing to his self-deprecating country boy ego but Benny was a well-grounded kid, and didn't, let his core sense of humility slip for a minute.

The youngest boy, Bishop, had soon cultivated a throng of seven year old friends at his school and from the neighborhood. Yes, the community in the vicinity of Duke St. and Acadian Thru-way was loaded with kids of all ages and it was a good place to raise a family in the innocent days of the 1950s. A majority of the families permanently encamped in north Baton Rouge were hewn from sturdy God fearing stock derived from transplanted forebears much like the Delta foursome just arrived in a single car and trailer. If one viewed a cross section of residents living in this area where the family chose to settle, it was clear that most of the heads of family had arrived in this industrialized city from rural areas located in Louisiana and Mississippi seeking employment opportunities in the petroleum, gas and chemical businesses and their offshoots. The people I had met on my Christmas break were super fine people and almost instantly I had felt a kinship to those warm and friendly neighbors because their backgrounds were so similar to my own. Most of them came from impoverished backgrounds but they were flourishing in their new circumstances provided by steady work and nominally paying jobs.

Luckily, the Griffins had settled into a good environment and it looked like the good steady job for Troy would be the start of a new prosperity for the family, an upgrade that could potentially and futuristically include home ownership and nest egg savings.

In the spring of 1959, Troy would lease his farm land to his brother in law, A.P. Brown and life would go on with the knowledge that his land was in good hands. It was comforting to know the land payments were being met as a result of the timely rental checks. In the meantime, city life for the Griffins in Baton Rouge chugged along routinely and the regular pay checks from **Jack's Cookie Co**. contributed greatly to an ease of mind that didn't exist before the fall of 1958. But after a steady dose of shift work and a substantial amount of overtime, there lurked in the mind of the household's breadwinner, a seed of an idea, if given only the slightest encouragement could and would foster a dream of the family's eventual return to the Yazoo Delta.

By now the reader must be mumbling to himself… "why all the mundane carrying on about family" fifty years ago. To be perfectly honest, I realize no one really cares about that stuff much less the reason for my being so expressive about this seminal event.

Furthermore, in retrospect, the event of the Baton Rouge migration and its year and a half duration became a major chapter in my life that changed my destiny away from my Mississippi Delta roots. Although I was not directly involved in the move per se, the crucial impact the family's relocation to Baton Rouge had on my future and the eventuation of my career path and marriage is somewhat engaging to contemplate at this late date in my life.

The indirect outcome of those events in 1958 and 1959 were pivotal in forcing me to flee to a different venue to seek my fortune. Even though I was ill prepared to obtain a decent job after I quit school, I knew I didn't have the wherewithal to stay in college subsequent to defaulting on my basketball scholarship in late 1959. Without regard to logic, I nonetheless, possessed a naiveté that emboldened me to go south in search of an entry level job in the Louisiana capital city of Baton Rouge. Despite a flawed notion that once in the door of a firm, I could work my way up the ladder to a good paying job, I never gave a second thought to the quality and self-satisfaction of a particular job …since it would be a job not necessarily of my own making. I was sensible enough to expect the apprenticeship years of any job would be boring. But that was ok --- I was used to boring jobs; I had faith in my limited abilities and I knew I would keep my nose clean and I knew for damn sure that my Delta attitude and work ethic was above reproach.

Unlike the well guided students who had set their sights on career goals and specific educational requirements, I, forever the farm boy, possessed of a perpetual optimism, thought a future realized through gainful employment and substantial elbow grease could in the long run yield a piece of the good life. I had always heard the axiom – "a college degree is a ticket to get one's foot in the door". Contrary to the certainty of that truism, I summoned the mistaken belief that I could get my foot in a door through other means of shorter duration.

Armed with that kind of rational thinking, this unwary upstart announced his intentions to Mr. Horton, college president, before taking leave of that place called Sunflower Junior College. After that encounter in the middle of the campus on that frigid early winter day, I confess, I never spoke to the stately Mr. Horton again in my "still counting" septuagenarian lifetime. My taking that proverbial "fork in the road of life" in late 1959 took some hitching up the pants but the writer, his mind firmly made up, never really looked back to assess the impact of that immature decision. I've always thought it futile and a waste of energy to ponder the "what might have beens" in my past. For me, there was no need for philosophical rear view mirror gazing.

As dumb as it seems, I was satisfied to move on after a multitude of those "so called" setbacks took place. Also, so as not to appear cocksure...during my life... more than a few "downers" did in fact intersect my orbit though seven decades, but nothing of significance that would knock me off stride. They turned out to be mere distractions and made me a better person in the pursuit of a fulfilled life.

Looking at a life in compendium without respect to the pitfalls that one would expect to encounter in a normal person's life, it can be said in 20/20 hindsight, the young sodbuster from Sunflower County did in fact take a reasonably correct fork in the road many years ago on a cold November day when he hitch-hiked his way to Baton Rouge, Louisiana. Yes…without hesitation it could well be an admission by any unbiased on-looker…that Billy Ray most likely took a dubious fork in the road that day. Had he stayed the course at Sunflower JC, who knows how his life would have turned out or where, his life path ……… would have led. Only God knows. But I have no remorse…my eventual journey turned out quite serendipitously everything considered.

To my…ubiquitous and omnipotent protector whose rectitude is still channeled to my earthly vessel as I enter my golden years, "I still have a desire to meet you in spirit one of these days…but I'm not done and I'm not impatient…I can wait a few more years for that meeting in the sunset, if you don't mind".

Hey…listen up…you nodding viewers of this written attempt to make some sense of a life spent in triteness, please excuse my impoliteness…it seems I've drifted away from the exact sequencing of this recollection…may I suggest that the clock of past remembrances be reset to March 1959?

Part Fifteen

The doldrums of a damp cold winter had gripped the Yazoo valley in a deadlock for too long. Its misery had had us by the nape of our necks for such an endless time; instilling its effects on the human mood in a negative way. An unlimited dosage of solar generated vitamin D was an antidote that was sorely needed by the natives of Yazoo, and a sliver of warmth and brightness thrown into the brew would make the advent of a change in seasons ever more welcome.

The landscape views of the SJC campus revealed Mother Nature was certainly making a gradual transition to springtime as evidenced by the sprouting of green clover, crocus, daffodil and Easter lily. A March blast of warm and humid weather moved in and took out some of the chill that had pervaded the Delta climes for a good four or five months. The buildings warmed up to the extent that the janitors turned off the steam boilers which supplied all the classroom radiators. It was a welcome cessation to an unbending monotony.

The downside to all that good news was an increased chance of Tornadoes which always threatened the flatland this time of year but we, the natives of the Delta lucked out once again as the weather system made its passage without undue turbulence. Since the weather front came from the west and not from the north, the unseasonably mild temperatures stuck around for a good week and blanketed the students of SJC with a fever of anticipation. Their spirits were juiced for they could see looming in the future, an end to the school year 1958/1959.

By then I was bedding down in my GrandMoore's house out in the country south of Moorhead and I was enjoying the attention Mama Moore was handing out, especially the home cooking. I was raking in groceries at such a prodigious clip; I became concerned that my Grandparents could ill afford my living with them.

Biding my time until the semester ended in early May, my scholastic progress being marginal at best, prompted me to accept the liability that I had to concentrate on my studies to post the grades necessary to satisfy my scholarship requirement. In other words, for me to keep my cashless stipend and return to SJC in the fall of 1959, I needed a "C" grade average and a critical number of quality points. It took some "cramming" on my part but my final grades fell in line with the requirement that put me in an acceptable stead to keep my scholarship.

As a consequence of the good news, I relaxed a bit and turned my sights to the basics of seeking summertime employment down in Baton Rouge country. I knew job possibilities would be greater there than in the Delta and of course my parent's home in the Bayou country was an interesting attraction, a place to plant my brogans for three months while I worked to accumulate some living funds and maybe check out some of those Cajun girls.

And so it went. I made my plans to go south on a Greyhound Bus as soon as school let out in early May 1959. I would depart Moorhead including my cadre of friends for a full three months until such time that I would return for my second year of college in that place "Where the Southern crosses the Yellow Dog" smack dab in the middle of the Yazoo Delta.

The time clock was racing…like a wheel horse in neutral gear rampaging down a bald hilled river bank. Days were being shed just like in the old movies where illustrated lapses of time were depicted as calendar pages being blown away in the wind. Or so it seemed in my recollection. Recapturing time is of no essence, but collated memories regardless of time are vastly important in reshaping one's images of cloudy bygones.

It was a Thursday. The calendar said it was the month of my birth and you already know the year. After wolfing down a breakfast of uncured ham and scrambled eggs prepared by my grandmother Moore, I grabbed my old red vinyl suitcase, hugged my maternal Grandparents and took leave of the house that had served as my home for a couple of months since leaving the SJC athletic dorm. Oh yes, and by the way that uncured ham that I spoke of was very good…without smoke and sugar cure, it tasted like a pork chop fried without hog lard. In these modern times I must say that particular meal is not seen as very healthy but it was tasty and it was a meal that would "stick to my ribs" because I had a formidable undertaking ahead of me that day whose outcome could possibly prevent me from taking a fork in hand later in the day.

In current time, 2012 AD, as my telomeres continue to shorten to a lethal length, I do remember that day quite vividly owing to the poignancy of having to leave my grandparents, yet I was hyped and anxious to start a new beginning at my parent's home base in south Louisiana.

As I left the little two bedroom farmhouse on this particular day, there would be no yellow school bus to ferry me to the town of my departure. Instead I caught a ride to Moorhead with my Uncle Bunk who owned the farm where the GrandMoores lived at that time. He dropped me at Kincade's Drugstore where I purchased a bus ticket to Baton Rouge and waited to hop a big Greyhound 60 seater. It was straight up 8:00 A.M. (at least the minute hand was straight up). With wetted shirt, it felt like summertime had arrived but I didn't notice my profuse sweating.

And so ended an epoch in my life, which in definition was a time that I consider as my 19 year Moorhead indoctrination. My weaning from the rich black earth was mostly over...but I was not harping nor was I forlorn.

With hands in pocket, I stood on the curb facing a large boxcar of a bus with its large entry door beckoning me to step aboard. By stepping up and in, I was entering the threshold of a notable embarkation. In a few short hours, Baton Rouge would appear in my view and my life would never be the same.

Made in the USA
Coppell, TX
21 September 2021